PRAISE FOR
Someone Else's Bucket List

"Somehow *Someone Else's Bucket List* is heart-wrenching and heartwarming at the same time. Although this richly layered story deals with grief over the loss of a much-loved sister, it is a story ultimately filled with hope; something we all need more of right now. Trust me, you want this novel on your 2024 must-read list!"
—Rachael Johns, bestselling author of *The Other Bridget*

"Guaranteed to tug on the heartstrings, *Someone Else's Bucket List* is a moving and bittersweet tale of embracing life after loss. Perfect for fans of Cecelia Ahern."
—Jessica Seaborn, author of *Perfect-ish*

"This book has my whole heart. Heart-wrenching yet so life-affirming and hopeful, this story pulsates with love and will completely sweep you away. You'll want to savor every word in this book and hug it tightly once you're done. A balm for the soul."
—Karina May, author of *Duck à l'Orange for Breakfast*, *Never Ever Forever*, and *That Island Feeling*

"*Someone Else's Bucket List* takes a poignant look at how the bonds of sisterhood can shape our lives."

—Namrata Patel, author of *The Curious Secrets of Yesterday*

"I loved *Someone Else's Bucket List*. It begins by breaking your heart then takes you by surprise by becoming uplifting and utterly galvanizing. Best of all, though, it's a stirring celebration of the power of sisterhood!"

—Matt Cain, author of *The Secret Life of Albert Entwistle*

"*Someone Else's Bucket List* is a moving story about Jodie and Bree, two devoted sisters who each take extraordinary measures to help the other. Author Amy Matthews's keen portrayal of grief and loss keeps the reader rooting for Jodie as she pushes out of her comfort zone to fulfill Bree's dying wish. This life-affirming tale reminds us that happiness is possible if we find the courage to reach for it."

—Jamie Beck, author of *The Beauty of Rain*

"Fans of Josie Silver and Cecelia Ahern will be taken by this story of joy after grief." —*Publishers Weekly*

PRAISE FOR

Best, First, and Last

"Matthews evokes the tangled legacy of mothers in this vibrant and addictively readable tale of heartbreak, desire, and adventure. With larger-than-life characters, the drama of multi-generational healing, a charming love story, and a dash of travel, *Best, First, and Last* is a colorful and thoroughly enjoyable read."

—Kim Lock, author of *The Fancies*

"Sharply observed, witty, and tangled, this is intergenerational adventure at its best."

—Emma Grey, author of *The Last Love Note* and *Pictures of You*

"I have a new icon for ageing: Bonnie is the irrepressible, irreverent grandma of my dreams with a past full of secrets and saucy lovers. Amy Matthews writes three generations of women with their own griefs and dreams, relatable struggles and loving messiness. Sweet, compelling, nostalgic, moving . . . I adored it."

—Clare Fletcher, author of *Love Match*

"One for the wanderlusters: a beautifully vivid, adventurous, and messy love story about love in all its forms . . . Amy Matthews is the queen of writing heartwarming family dynamics, and her complex, kick-ass female characters will stay with you long after you've reached your destination."

—Karina May, author of *Duck à l'Orange for Breakfast, Never Ever Forever,* and *That Island Feeling*

"Heartfelt, humorous, and heartbreaking. A novel that will make you feel it all."

—Michelle Upton, author of *Emergency Exit Only*

"*Best, First, and Last* took me on a JOURNEY. The lush setting is the perfect backdrop for this multi-generational story of the many ways love—romantic and familial—can shape our lives. At turns both funny and heart-wrenching, this is another gem from one of my must-read authors."

—Robin Lefler, author of *Not How I Pictured It*

"*Best, First, and Last* by Amy Matthews is equal parts witty and wise. The family members at the center of this warm-hearted novel might have their doubts about vacationing together, but I loved being along for the ride."

—Laura Hankin, author of *One-Star Romance*

BY AMY MATTHEWS

The Treasure House

Someone Else's Bucket List

Best, First, and Last

End of the Night Girl

THE TREASURE HOUSE

THE TREASURE HOUSE

A NOVEL

AMY MATTHEWS

DELL
NEW YORK

Dell
An imprint of Random House
A division of Penguin Random House LLC
1745 Broadway, New York, NY 10019
randomhousebooks.com
penguinrandomhouse.com

A Dell Trade Paperback Original

Published in Australia by Simon & Schuster Australia.

Published by arrangement with Simon & Schuster UK Ltd.

ISBN 979-8-217-37526-4
Ebook ISBN 979-8-217-37527-1

Printed in the United States of America

1st Printing

BOOK TEAM: Production editor: Cassie Gitkin • Managing editor: Saige Francis • Production manager: Chanler Harris • Copy editor: Michael Burke • Proofreaders: Rachael Clements, Julie Ehlers, Andrea Gordon, Barb Jatkola

Adobe Stock illustrations: Olesya Frolova (mug with leaves), Sham (chapter opener border), alimyakubov (space break ornament)

Book design by Alexis Flynn

The authorized representative in the EU for product safety and compliance is Penguin Random House Ireland, Morrison Chambers, 32 Nassau Street, Dublin D02 YH68, Ireland. https://eu-contact.penguin.ie

For
Team Better Than Average.
Solidly better than average since Paris 2014.

The home should be the treasure chest of living.

—LE CORBUSIER

The house had beauty and peace and the suggestion of a useful active life. . . . Five generations had lived in it, leaving behind them a comfortable aura of prosperity—not of wealth but of solid ease and plenty of good food and warmth and comfort. It was a house to love.

—KATHLEEN WINSOR

All things great are wound up with all things little.

—L. M. MONTGOMERY

THE TREASURE HOUSE

ATTIC BEDROOM
PARLOR
DINING ROOM
HALLWAY

BATHROOM
CUPBOARD
LANDING
ATTIC ROOM ONE
ATTIC ROOM TWO
KITCHEN
BACK DOOR TO PORCH AND LAUNDRY

ONE

Pittsburgh, Pennsylvania

Ordinary days change your life. They roll in like the tide, one after another, and you don't realize how far they carry you until you reach the shore. This particular ordinary day was a prosaic Thursday in early summer, just another monochrome workday, and I was killing time on my lunch break. I never thought opening an app would upend my life.

"Where shall we live today?" I asked my co-worker Eva, who was slumped at the end of the lunch table playing Candy Crush, her body as crumpled as her pinstriped work shirt. I was engaging in my favorite pastime of fantasy house hunting as I punched open one of my many real estate apps, eager to escape our colorless corporate break room that smelled of reheated lunches and burned coffee.

"Yesterday we were hunting in Fair Lawn, New Jersey," I reminded Eva, who barely looked up from her game. Fair Lawn looked like something out of a Disney movie—like the town in *Lady and the Tramp,* which my daughter Florence watched roughly nine hundred times when she was little. Flo had always spent her summer vacation being shuffled from babysitter to babysitter, often parked in front of the TV. I didn't have the money for summer camp, or even a day camp, and I could never afford to take time off work to hang out with her. The only thing summery about my own summer was that our boss had launched "popsicle days," where if it was over ninety-five degrees, she brought in boxes of popsicles for us. But it was hardly ever over ninety-five degrees in Pittsburgh, and the temperature didn't really register in the medical center anyway, with its industrial strength air-conditioning. The center was a satellite clinic to one of the big university complexes—a little brick bunker on the fringes of South Oakland. My section, which handled patient financial records, was right in the windowless center of the place. Surfacing at the end of the workday, I always felt like a deep-sea creature that had never seen light, blinking as I emerged.

In no way could my unglamorous job finance me buying a house—which is why I engaged in *fantasy* house hunting on my lunch break, rather than actual house hunting. Although I really did need to do some actual house hunting, because my landlord was raising my rent again and I couldn't afford another cent, particularly not for a run-down one-bed with erratic hot water and an overabundance of pests.

But who wanted to cruise rental listings for depressing little apartments during their lunch break? Fantasy house hunting was way more fun.

Yesterday's house had been a pristine white colonial in a lush green square of lawn, with a swing on the porch. It was the kind of house Hallmark movies are set in. Where you'd make patchwork quilts and bake apple pies and leave them to cool on the sill. And there'd probably be a (hot) gardener who'd come mow the lawn for you and let you hand him an icy glass of lemonade after. You know, wholesome, but with the possibility of fun.

It was the kind of home I used to imagine other kids lived in when I sat in school with my stomach rumbling, hiding behind the curtain of my uncut hair. It was the kind of house where laundry dried on the line in the sun, and there was always dinner on the table promptly at six.

It was the kind of home that belonged to people who weren't me.

For me, growing up, home wasn't even a place. It was a person. Christina Lynn Copeland. My mother, who most definitely never made an apple pie and left it to cool on a sill. And who wouldn't have been caught dead in Fair Lawn, New Jersey. *Stick with me, Angel Face,* Tina would say with a snap of her gum as she shoplifted a candy bar for me. *No one loves you like your mom*. She wore tight jeans and short skirts and dyed her hair bright colors. She had jangly jewelry that flashed in the sun. She swore and laughed and cried; she loved pop music, turned up loud, and dancing, which she'd do even on the subway. She lived off sweet drinks in cans, vodka from the freezer, and any pills she could get her hands on. Tina was a party waiting to happen, or the aftermath. There was no in-between.

I shifted in my chair, discomforted. Why was I thinking about Tina? She was more than 350 miles away in Hazelton Federal Correctional, and I hadn't seen her in years.

"Can we hunt for houses at the beach, Zoe?" Eva asked me. "We might as well pretend-enjoy the summer."

"Oh, pick Miami," said Caitlin, one of the clinic nurses, as she microwaved her leftovers. "I love Miami. And if you get a place, I can come visit."

"She's not getting a place," Eva said. "She's just *imagining* getting a place."

"So? Imagine getting one in Miami, and I can imagine staying with you."

Obediently, I searched properties for sale in Miami, pushing away thoughts of rent hikes and Tina. "Which suburb?" I hadn't hunted in Miami before.

"Nowhere too spring-breaky," Caitlin advised. "Somewhere classy."

I had to google classy neighborhoods. "Coconut Grove?"

"Sure, why not." The microwave beeped and Caitlin grabbed her lunch and joined us.

"Oh, look at this. A Mediterranean villa in South Coconut Grove. It has three beds and two and a half baths—"

"Who has *half* a bath?" Eva grumped. Sometimes fantasy house hunting put her out of sorts. Usually when her credit card payments were due.

"It has a pool!" I was more than a little mesmerized by the glitter of the blue water against the tropical gardens. I turned the phone so she could see the screen. Fantasy house hunting was like opening the pages of a book and imagining yourself into another life. Whether it was a Mediterranean-style villa in Miami or a midwestern bungalow in Minnesota, I could picture a fantasy life in all of them.

From a very young age, I'd known that all houses were different and that they hid different tastes and smells and colors and hopes and temperatures of feeling. I may never have had a home, but I'd seen a lot of houses in my life. Between the foster houses and all of Tina's apartments, I'd lived in more places than I could count.

Why was I thinking about Tina again? Nothing about a Mediterranean villa in South Coconut Grove should remind me of foster care or Tina. I pushed the thoughts away more forcibly and pretended I was about to buy the house in Miami, where I'd live a sun-splashed life with my daughter and never have to worry about my living arrangements ever again.

Despite her mood, Eva had been lured in by the villa. She'd lowered her Candy Crush and inched her chair closer. "How much is it?"

I looked. "Five-point-three million."

"Ouch." Caitlin winced.

"This is nothing." Eva gave her a pitying look. "Go on, Zoe, show her what you've got."

"Do you do this every lunchtime?" Caitlin asked, leaning in.

"Zoe does." Eva leaned her head on my shoulder affectionately. "She's what you'd call a pathological *nester.* She also has champagne taste on a beer budget."

"Not even a beer budget." I sighed as I swiped through glossy real estate photographs until I found what I was looking for. "I'm on a tap water budget." And I wasn't a nester, not in real life anyway. My actual home looked like temporary student accommodations. Every piece of furniture I owned was secondhand.

"Me too," Caitlin commiserated. "I should probably even be rationing tap water these days."

"Here." I stopped on a jewel-bright listing for a place in Palm Beach. "*This* is our house."

The listing had the heading *Your Once in a Lifetime Dream House*. Eva gave a low whistle at the sight of it. I laughed as I read the property description, because the word *fantasy* wasn't enough to cover this one. Delusion might be a better word for it.

"Thirteen-bed, fifteen-and-a-half-bath *single family house.*" I laughed in disbelief. "Which single family is this exactly?"

"One of those billionaires who has been divorced fifteen times and has summer custody of all his kids," Caitlin suggested as she reached over my shoulder to scroll through the photos.

The place had a saltwater fishpond, an infinity pool, *three* waterfalls in lush tropical surrounds, and a yacht at its own private mooring.

The three of us looked up from the phone to regard the pedestrian sight of Pittsburgh out of our lunchroom window. In unison we sighed.

"That's not a home, it's a resort," Caitlin said, straightening up and returning to her lunch with the air of someone resigned to reality.

I made an involuntary noise when I saw the listing price.

"That bad? How much? Fifteen million?"

"Thirty," Eva guessed.

"Uh . . ." I cleared my throat. "Try a hundred and thirty-six . . ."

"No way. Wait. You mean *million*?"

I tilted my phone so she could see. She swore.

"I need to win the Mega Millions." I sighed, putting my phone facedown on the table and reaching for my wilting salad. If I could win the lottery, I could move Flo out of our now unaffordable one-bedroom apartment. I didn't need three waterfalls and a mooring for a yacht. I just needed somewhere large enough for two people, maybe with a garden, and a good school nearby. Somewhere we could make a home.

But I knew a pipe dream when I saw it. I had just as much chance of buying a house as I had of winning the Kentucky Derby on foot.

Even so, I loved fantasy house hunting. I got a steady feeling when I imagined living in those houses, particularly the simpler places—little homes in flowering gardens, on quiet streets, in suburbs and small towns beyond the rippling wake of the cities. Ordinary homes.

Homes like the last foster home I went to.

I was thirteen the third and final time I went into foster care. When the announcement came over the school PA calling me to the office, I knew what I'd find there. Another caseworker with bags under her eyes and a practiced kindly smile on her face. I didn't need her to explain why she was there; I'd been expecting her. I don't remember this caseworker's name. She took me back to Mom's apartment to pack a bag, and then she drove me to a care home, where I waited for somewhere to go. The care home is a blurry still life in my memory: a bunk bed and the smell of cheap laundry detergent. I was so sick with guilt I couldn't sleep. I knew this time it was my fault I was there. There was a kid with a Pokémon pillowcase she used on her plasticky care home pillow, and she cried all through my sleepless nights. I don't think I cried. I think I was past crying by then.

When I left the care home a week later, I was driven to a ranch house in Bradford Woods, in the far north of Pittsburgh. I remember it was May, and the driveway we turned in to was lined with lilacs in full bloom. There were shade trees and a lawn so green and perfect it didn't seem real. Later I learned that Wayne Overbeck, my new foster parent, was obsessed with his lawn. His year was scheduled according to scarifying and seeding, mowing and fertilizing. His favorite summer pastime was pacing the lawn with his hose, beer in hand, listening to baseball on his headphones. Life was simple for Wayne. All he needed was his home, his family, and his lawn.

His wife, Suni, was a little more complicated, but not by much. She worked in student admissions at one of the colleges in town, and she never sat still. Suni always had some new hobby to keep her busy; sometimes she was scrapbooking, sometimes making mosaics out of little glass stones, sometimes foraging for wild foods, sometimes bird-watching.

The Overbecks had two kids of their own—Lance and Alison—but they also took in foster kids, because, as Suni said, "There was no reason to let two perfectly good bedrooms go to waste." Their house was balanced between order and chaos, full of people and noise: the sound of Wayne's baseball games on the TV; Lance's guitar and punk-pop music; Alison and her friends practicing for glee club; and their corgi Arthur's excited barking as he skidded back and forth between people's rooms. During my time there, which was all of my high school years, I occupied the eggshell-blue bedroom while a series of other foster kids were given the mauve bedroom: Thad, who was seven and stayed only a few months; Leanne, who was a year older than me and stayed for a year and a half; and finally Bethany, who was so shy she couldn't look people in the eye when she spoke to them. Suni and Wayne treated us all the same, like part of the family.

I liked life at the Overbecks'. But I still wished for Tina to get out of Muncy State Correctional, where she was locked up on possession charges. I wanted her to come get me, to feel her hug enveloping me in sunshine. Nothing is as good as your own mother, even when your own mother is a junkie. When I showed Flo *The Wizard of Oz* for the first time and Dorothy said, "There's no place like home," it was still Tina that I thought of. My feeling of home was a person, not a place. And it still is, only now that person is Flo.

As I ate my salad on that prosaic Thursday at work, I thought about all the places I had lived after the Overbecks'. Dorm rooms at college, a series of rented rooms in share houses. And then, after I got pregnant, there was a brief window of time when I'd lived with Tim. . . .

"Forget the billionaires in Florida," Eva said, disgusted. "Find us a house we can actually believe in." She pushed my phone toward me.

"I believe in the mansion," Caitlin said fervently.

Eva threw her balled-up napkin at her. "Well, I don't. I want a dream that might come true."

I tried to think of the most normal place I could, somewhere school buses stopped on suburban streets and kids rode their bikes through long summer afternoons. Ohio maybe? I scrolled through bungalows and split-levels in Cleveland, looking for lawns and a bedroom Flo would love. She'd spent her whole life sharing a room with me—wouldn't it be something to give her a room of her own?

Florence hadn't been planned. I'd been a naïve (dumb) twenty-one-year-old who was primed to fall in love the moment someone showed her a speck of affection. I was a mess of attachment and abandonment issues when I met Tim, and I fell hard and fast. I found myself knocked up in my junior year of college, to a guy I thought I loved, who was just as naïve (dumb) as I was.

He wanted me to keep the baby, and I was young enough to believe him when he said he'd always be there. I wanted to believe him so bad, and, as we assembled a flat-pack crib in the studio apartment we'd found, I really thought we might make it. Tim now lives with his fiancée, Alyssa, in Seattle, where he moved after graduate school. He calls Flo on Mondays, Thursdays, and Sundays, and sends her packages by courier. He pays child support. Mostly. It doesn't seem to bother him too much, living on the other side of the country from her. I, meanwhile, can hardly stand being away from her for a weekend when she goes to visit Tim. I would hike barefoot across the Rocky Mountains in the depths of winter to get to her. I would fight bears for that kid.

Or give up my education and work eight hours a day doing credit checks for a medical center.

I opened a listing for a pretty shiplap cottage, with a treehouse in a spreading oak out back, and a child's bedroom painted to resemble a fairy bower. I pretended we lived there and that I put Flo to bed each night in that candy-pink bunk bed, even though she was way too old for pink now. Or so she kept telling me. The unsettled feeling in my belly started to recede.

"How about this?" I turned the phone around to show them what I'd found.

Eva, who had kids of her own, sighed approvingly. "You think I could squeeze a third bed in there?"

Caitlin, who didn't have kids, wrinkled her nose. "That's not a fantasy house. It's too *real*."

I shook my head. "It's perfect."

No one tells you how hard parenting will be—the closest that seasoned parents ever get to spilling the secret to the uninitiated is a kind of wry look. Because how can you tell the untested that mother-love is a big blood-dark tumor of a feeling? It's nothing like a soft-focus Johnson & Johnson ad for baby powder. It's more like *Titanic*. You know the ship is going down, no matter what you do, but by God you're going to get that kid on a floating door (or in a candy-pink bunk bed) before you die.

Loving Florence scares me.

Until Florence, I never realized how sad I was, how alone. I didn't see how emotionally neglected I'd been. But when I looked at her, my life snapped into focus, and it was the opposite of pretty.

The thought of her living my childhood, alone in a cold apartment, reheating packet mac and cheese to the soundtrack of reruns, and constantly jumping to check the door was locked when the neighbors argued too loud? It just about broke me.

But how much better was I doing than Tina? Sure, I wasn't getting high or leaving Flo alone while I worked the streets, and I wasn't doing jail time, but we lived in a shabby rental with dodgy heating. A rental I wouldn't even be able to afford much longer.

"I *will* get a ticket for the Mega Millions," I blurted, as I stared down at the fairy bedroom that I couldn't afford.

And that was when Caitlin said something that changed my life forever.

"Forget the Mega Millions," she said as she rose to tip her uneaten leftovers into the trash. "You just need one of those treasure houses."

I had no idea what she was talking about. "Treasure houses?"

"You know, the ones on TikTok. The hoarder houses." Caitlin lit up as she pulled out her own phone. "Oh my God, you're going to love this. Here." And then she handed me my future.

TWO

Treasure houses, it turned out, were houses no one wanted. Filled to the brim with the detritus of messy lives, they were junk heaps. But you could see that once they'd been loved—you could tell by the remnants of patterned wallpaper that someone had obviously chosen with care; the old, rusted swing sets in overgrown gardens; dusty photos in tarnished frames.

I felt an immediate affinity with the treasure houses on TikTok.

The first reel I watched was of a teensy little house in Traverse City, Michigan. It was the size of a small mobile home and was surrounded by junk. There were old sinks, rusted-out wheelbarrows, ten-gallon drums tipped on their sides, and a general scattering of discarded objects. The couple who'd bought the house were a smiling, peppy pair in work boots, wielding hammers. The reels showed them clearing out their little house at double speed, their smiles never faltering. As I watched, the neglected house emerged from its gloom, turning into a cheerful buttercup-yellow cottage with sunny white interiors and views out of the front windows to freshly mulched garden beds.

And the kicker?

They paid $37,000 for the junk-filled place. And sold the buttercup-yellow dream for more than $200,000.

I mean, seriously . . .

$37,000 for a *house.*

The treasure houses were in far-flung parts of the country, in places that didn't specialize in McMansions and yacht moorings: Fort Flagg, Alabama; Quilty, Georgia; Nailsworth, Ohio. There were treasure houses in Minnesota, South Dakota, Indiana, and New Mexico, all in towns I'd never even heard of. The treasure house hashtag led me to people who were wrestling with mold, mildew, opossums and raccoons, salt damp, poison ivy and poison oak, asbestos and emotional overwhelm. But . . . every last one of them had a *house.* A home. On the kind of budget that seemed preposterous.

My kind of budget.

If those houses had been in more desirable places, they'd be sold for serious money, even as wrecks. But they were in nooks of the country where few wanted to live, and even fewer were prepared to take on the labor of clearing them out. I followed one woman who went by the tag HandyMom24—she was a single mother with three kids who had bought a treasure house in Washington state for $62,000. It was a farmhouse out of a picture book, only threadbare, with split window frames, a sagging chimney, and paint so faded and flaked it was hard to tell what color it had once been. The yard was a wasteland, with an ancient hemlock rising behind the house. My heart pinched at the sight of that farmhouse, crouching sadly under the hemlock like a homeless old dog.

But as the reels cycled, I saw HandyMom24 and her three kids unload dark new earth from a truck to cover the dusty yard. They splashed fresh whitewash on the house's exterior, turned the front door cherry red. While the house slowly transformed, a jack-o'-lantern appeared on the crooked top step in fall, Christmas lights twinkled in the hemlock in winter, and by summer little bursts of flowers had sprung up at its feet. The farmhouse was still old, but it was loved. Lived in.

I'm not ashamed to say that I watched those reels at least a dozen times after work and another dozen times later in bed, my headphones on so the sound of HandyMom24's narration wouldn't wake Flo. Our apartment was so small that you could hear everything the other person did from wherever you were in the apartment; from the kitchenette I could hear Flo's toothbrush, from the bedroom I could hear the hum of the refrigerator, from the shower I could hear the bedsprings as Flo sat down to put on her shoes in the morning. And our twin beds practically touched. That had done wonders for my love life, as you can imagine.

I often felt trapped, especially at night, trying not to wake my kid as I crept around the apartment, and the feeling only got worse as she grew. Her twelfth birthday was approaching. Twelve years of this life, creeping around. It had flown by, but also dragged. Twelve was the age I'd been when I'd gone to foster with Mr. and Mrs. Bracknell. They were deacons in some church or other and their house was very clean. The thought of Flo being packed up and taken to live with strangers filled me with a big, hot, hurting feeling. As I watched the reels of treasure houses into the night, I reached out and put a hand on her as she slept. I'd die before I let anyone take her away from me, the way I'd been taken away from Tina as a young child.

Flo snored softly, small puppy noises. She'd kicked off her covers, because it was a hot June and we didn't have air-conditioning. I heard drunken undergrads coming back from the bars, loudly shushing each other and giggling in the hall. I felt a million years old as I listened to them. Had I ever been that free? And would I still be living in this apartment when Flo was their age?

As I lay there in the darkness, I felt something break loose inside me. Hell, I was only thirty-two; I wasn't *that* much older than the undergrads in the hall. I should be ordering a cocktail in a sleek little bar, trying to catch a flirty bartender's eye, giggling with friends. I should be searching for the shimmers of possibility in every dawning day. I should be . . . doing anything but this.

As I lay watching people clear junk out of dilapidated houses, a wild idea took hold.

I could do that.

I could get out of this place. I could buy a house. Start over.

I could make the life I wanted, instead of living the one I'd inherited. Depending on the state of the place, and the town it was in, the prices of these treasure houses ranged from $30,000 to $100,000. For a whole house. A crappy one-bedroom apartment in my building had recently sold for $160,000 and it was only six hundred square feet. The treasure houses had multiple bedrooms, gardens, and sometimes even views of mountains, or rivers, or, magically, the ocean. Sure, they were wrecks, but I was young and strong. If other people could restore them, why couldn't I?

"What's that?" Florence asked the next morning at breakfast, pushing my phone down so she could see the screen.

"It's a treasure house."

"A what house?" She perked up, and I could tell she was thinking of pirates. I'd shown her *The Goonies* on our last movie night.

"Not that kind of treasure," I told her, heading off any talk of gold doubloons. "These are just houses full of junk that people are selling."

"They're selling the houses or the junk?" She bent over my phone, the tail of her braid curling on the kitchen bench. She swiped to the next reel.

"Both. You buy the house, but it comes with all the junk."

"Oh. Cool." She looked up at me, grinning.

Flo had big, hooded eyes and round cheeks and a tendency to chew the ends of her braids until they were like wet paintbrushes. She had inherited her father's thin, mobile mouth and his easy sportiness, but she'd got my darker hair and coloring and penchant for books. We were both on the tall side, with chins that were a little too wide, and since we both hated haircuts, we tended to have long, wild hair with too many split ends.

"Look, this one has a swimming pool." She pointed at the screen with her spoon.

"I don't think that's a pool. I think it's a pit."

"Why would someone have a pit in their yard?"

I'd listened to enough true crime podcasts to not want to know the answer to that question. I swiped on to the next video.

"How come you've replaced Harry Styles reels with junk houses?" Flo upended the cereal box and shook it until a mountain of Cheerios piled up in her bowl.

"Bite your tongue. Harry's irreplaceable." I took the box away from her.

"Vanda's mother lets her have Apple Jacks during summer vacation."

"Well, good for her."

"And Pop-Tarts."

"Pop-Tarts are dessert, not breakfast." I passed her the milk.

"They're sold in the breakfast aisle."

I ignored that.

"Don't you think it's depressing that I have to eat Cheerios instead of Apple Jacks while my mom phubs me?"

Sometimes it was like living with a junior prosecutor. "I'm not *phubbing* you, I'm house hunting." Flo had introduced me to the term "phubbing" with relish, as she liked to tell me off for snubbing her in favor of my phone.

Flo jerked and milk splashed all over the counter. "You're what now?"

"Oh my God, mop it up," I begged, scrambling for the dishcloth. "Don't just let it drip everywhere."

"Are you telling me we're getting a house with a *pool*?" Her eyes widened.

"No." I gently nudged her out of the way and swiped at the milk before it cascaded over the edge of the counter. "Look at all the milk you've wasted. And it wasn't a pool, it was a *pit*."

"A proto-pool!"

A proto-pool. Who even was this kid? "Where did you learn the word *proto*?"

She shrugged. "From a book?" She pulled the stool back up to the now-damp counter. "Tell me about this house. It better be close by because I'm not changing schools."

I hadn't even thought about that. My late-night dreams started to crack in the light of day. I had worked to keep Flo's life steady and predictable. It hadn't been easy staying in the same school district as rents went up. We'd moved twice already in Flo's short life, both times downgrading to be able to stay in Squirrel Hill South. I knew I couldn't keep it up. The new rent increase meant our next downsize would have to be to a studio. That was a soul-crushing thought. Flo would be a teen soon and no teen wanted to still be sharing a room with their mom.

No mom wanted to share a room with a teen either. . . .

"I can't afford anything close by," I admitted to her. "And you have to move schools for high school soon anyway. . . ."

"Mom. I'm *eleven.* I only just started middle school."

"Nearly twelve." I heard the phantom longing of Mrs. Bracknell's cello. "High school's not far off."

She rolled her eyes. "It's *forever* away."

But it wasn't. Those short years would slip by, like all the rest. My twenties had flown, along with Flo's childhood, and I was beginning to realize that no one was coming to rescue me. In another ten years I might still be sitting in this cramped kitchenette, or an even smaller one, if I didn't do something about it.

"The next move needs to be our long-term move," I told my kid, feeling a sense of resolve. Late Night Zoe had been right. We had an opportunity to be more than this. "We'll go somewhere that has good schools."

Flo eyed me. "I like my school."

"You'll like the next one." I hoped that wasn't a lie. I thrust my phone in front of her. "Help me pick a house?"

"Oh my *God.* You're serious?"

I nodded, waving the phone at her. "What about this one?"

"It's awful."

"You didn't even look."

"Where is it?"

I checked. "North Dakota."

"Definitely not."

"What have you got against North Dakota?" I asked, genuinely confused.

"I'm not living anywhere that can't decide on a name." Flo crossed her arms over her chest.

"North Dakota is a name."

"It's not. It's cheating off South Dakota."

"Fine, no Dakotas."

"Find somewhere here in Squirrel Hill," Flo ordered, leaning over to look at my screen.

I snorted. "We can't afford to buy a mailbox here, let alone a house."

Flo had somehow plowed through her mountain of Cheerios. She lifted the bowl and drank the dregs of the milk.

"Don't do that."

"If you can destroy my life by moving me to a junk house, I can drink from the bowl."

"Deal." I swooped in and scooped up her empty bowl. "I'm glad we've agreed on moving."

"Hey!" She caught up to what had just happened.

"No takebacks." I smiled at her. "But at least you get to drink out of the bowl for the rest of your life."

It was like a virus. I'd caught a bad case of treasure house. I kept my phone out on my desk and scrolled listings between calls at work. And then, feeling kind of feverish and itchy, I went online and checked out mortgage options. I wouldn't need *much* money . . .

but I would need a job to pay a mortgage and, if I moved, I'd have to find a new one. But surely everywhere had a medical center?

I had a small pot of savings too, squirreled away out of habit in case Tina needed bail money, or help getting set up when she got out of prison. Which wouldn't be happening anytime soon, since she'd been charged with trafficking across state lines the year before Flo was born, and was now locked up in Hazelton Federal Correctional Institution in West Virginia, where she'd be staying for the foreseeable future. But I'd been automatically paying into the "Tina" account. And it had been gaining interest for ten years. I had enough for a down payment on a treasure house—especially given the price ranges—and I knew Suni and Wayne would loan me the rest. They'd always said they'd be happy to help any of us out, should we need it. The thought of touching the "Tina" money for the down payment filled me with a momentary surge of terror. What would Tina do when she got out? How would she manage? All the old nightmares of childhood reared up at me. Hunger, homelessness, Tina's descent into despair and her inevitable relapse. Tina needed it. *I* needed it because I needed her to be okay.

But maybe Flo and I needed it too. And maybe we needed it *now*.

I escaped the medical center on my lunch break and walked to the park so I could be alone. I didn't think I could deal with rusted-out cars and mold, but I could do clutter. I was open to leaving Pittsburgh, but I didn't want to be too remote either. And I one hundred percent needed a good school district for Florence.

I googled the states with the best public schools. I wasn't sure whether the wild fluttering in my stomach was excitement or fear. It might have been both.

"I don't want to live anywhere hot," Flo announced when I got home. Suni was babysitting, and Flo had obviously been filling her in on my house hunting. I had a careful roster of sitters during summer vacation—it was stuck to the fridge and color coded. Flo went to her friend Vanda's house on Mondays, her friend Candy's house on Wednesdays and Thursdays, my neighbor Mrs. Selvaratnam watched her on Tuesdays, and Suni looked after her on Fridays, sometimes at their house in Bradford Woods, and sometimes at our apartment.

This was something else I'd lose if I moved. Babysitters.

My mind seesawed back and forth between wild spikes of excitement and cold reality checks.

"What's this about a treasure house?" Suni asked mildly. "And what exactly *is* a treasure house?"

"I already told her. She just wants *you* to tell her," Flo complained to me. "But we both agreed, you can't buy a house somewhere too hot."

"Not after this apartment," Suni said, still sounding mild even though she was giving me an evaluating look. "It's like a sauna in here." She took my bag from me and put it by the door. "Sit down. You look tired."

When I had lived with the Overbecks, Suni had been loving, if a little distant. But we'd recently lost my foster sister Bethany to an overdose, and now Wayne and Suni's daughter Alison was going through a frightening divorce from a covert lowlife who'd stalked and terrorized her after she left him. It had shaken Suni. She seemed less robust and more tender—with all of us.

"Did Flo show you any of the houses?" I asked, bracing myself for her response.

"She did." Suni joined me on the couch. "I can see why they're in your price range."

Even with the windows open and the fan huffing, the apartment was a sweatbox. The tired sound of the city winding down in the heat panted through the windows.

"I'm only going if my friends can come stay with us whenever I want," Flo announced. "And if I can have my own bedroom. And a dog," she added.

"Can you believe the prices?" I asked Suni, ignoring Flo's demands.

Suni's dark eyes gave a wry twinkle. "Yes." She pressed her lips together. "Have you seen what's inside them?"

I half groaned, half laughed. "I'm insane, right?"

She shrugged. Then she darted a glance at Flo. "Flo-bug, go have a cold shower and get your pajamas on while your mom and I talk."

"Are you trying to get rid of me?"

"Yes," we both said in unison.

"Fine, but just so you know, I can hear you from the shower."

We heard the bathroom door slap closed.

"Eleven seems like the new thirteen," Suni said, patting my arm.

"Are all of them like this, or just mine?"

"Yours is just a little smarter than most."

I sank back into the couch. Suni reached out and pushed my bangs off my forehead.

"I know it's crazy," I said, "but I could get a *house*." I looked around the apartment. "Except for your house, and a couple of brief stints in foster care, I've lived in places like this my whole life."

"I know," Suni said softly.

"I'm so tired of it."

She nodded and sagged back into the couch beside me.

I bit my lip. "I have enough for a down payment."

"Ah." She packed a lot into that one syllable.

"I was wondering . . ."

"About a loan?" she finished for me, giving me a sideways look.

"Yeah." I searched her face. "I mean . . . only if . . ."

"Of course," she interrupted my babbling. "You know we will." She reached out and took my hand and gave it a squeeze.

"Wayne will think it's crazy," I said nervously.

She laughed. "Wayne is a man who has lived in two houses his whole life: his mother's and then ours." She squeezed my hand again. It felt good, but it also made me want to cry. "You know what's crazy?" she said. "A hardworking woman not being able to afford somewhere better than this to live." She gave me an encouraging smile. "Show me the houses you're thinking about?"

"I haven't got any specific ones yet. I've just been scrolling. And, you know, thinking . . ."

"And wishing and hoping?"

"Yeah." I squeezed her hand back. Hard. "I'm scared nothing will ever change if I don't do something about it now," I said in a small voice.

Suni laughed. "Oh, Zoe, the only thing you can count on in life is change."

"For the better, I mean. I'm scared nothing will ever change for the *better.*"

"Well. You came to us, didn't you? That was a change for the better. Maybe this will be too."

Yes. I had been sent to them, and things had certainly gotten better in lots of ways. But part of me had hated it. Part of me still hated it. Part of me was stuck in my childhood, waiting for Tina to come home.

"You really don't think this is crazy?" It mattered to me what she thought. Suni and Wayne were the closest thing I had to family, aside from Flo.

"Depends on the house you pick."

Wayne collected pizza and joined us in the apartment for dinner. We scrolled through treasure houses and drafted a list in three columns: wants, musts, and absolutely nots. Flo explained her position on the Dakotas.

"I guess that rules out West Virginia too," Wayne said, unbuttoning the top button on his jeans so he could eat another slice of pizza.

"Oh, that reminds me!" Suni whispered to me, reaching for her bag. She pulled out an envelope and passed it to me under the table. It was postmarked West Virginia. From Hazelton FCI.

"It also rules out North and South Carolina," Wayne added. "But where do you stand on New Mexico?"

I tucked Tina's unopened letter into a book I'd left sitting on the counter. Flo still didn't know about her grandmother. Later, when she was brushing her teeth, I'd slip the letter into my underwear drawer, where it could nest with the other letters until I had enough time and privacy to read it in peace.

"Is New Mexico hot?" Flo cocked her head.

"So I hear," Wayne told her.

"Automatic no, then. Even before we worry about its name."

"You're running out of states."

"Am not." Flo fetched her atlas and opened it to a double-page spread of the country. "There's plenty left."

They pored over the map and I felt a burst of affection for them.

"Oh, good God," Suni squeaked, "was that a cockroach or a rat?" She pulled her feet up from the floor, staring in horror at the gap between the fridge and the wall.

"Cockroach," Flo said, without looking up from the map.

"Maybe." I craned my neck. "We do have a resident mouse."

"No, Angus McMouse lives in our bedroom," Flo said absently, "not the kitchen."

"He must come out to eat, though." I eyed the kitchen. I hated mice.

"A dog would keep the mice away," Flo told me brightly.

"Maybe a treasure house *would* be a step up. . . ." Suni kept her feet determinedly off the floor. "Although they probably all have mice too."

"The trick is to pick a house that's structurally sound," Wayne advised, mopping pizza grease off his face with a paper towel. "Mice can be dealt with."

"With a dog," Flo added.

Wayne benevolently ignored her. "Cosmetic damage is fine, but you want structural integrity."

"How do I do that? Make sure it's sound." I felt a wave of panic. Oh God. What if I bought a treasure house and it fell down on our heads while we slept? Some of these places looked like death traps.

"You get an inspection," Wayne said calmly. He really was taking this madness in his stride.

"I want seasons," Flo decided loudly, still considering her maps. "I don't want to live without snow days."

"Fair enough." Wayne nodded. "I like a good snow day too."

"Can we live near the beach?"

"Snow *and* beach?" Wayne looked dubious.

"Sure, like the Taylor Swift song." She started humming it.

"What's on *your* must list?" Suni asked me, cutting in.

"Good schools, a garden, and now structural integrity."

"And seasons and a beach," Wayne reminded me.

I added them to the list. "This might be getting ambitious."

"You'll just have to take a place with extra junk to afford it."

By the time we had polished off the pizza, we had a solid list of must-haves and a few absolutely nots. Including a list of states Flo refused to set foot in, not even for a dog. Florida was infested with alligators, Connecticut had sneaky spelling, which had made her lose a spelling bee once, and Arizona was riddled with cacti, which were too spiky to be acceptable garden plants. She was nothing if not firm in her opinions.

"I'm really not crazy?" I murmured to Suni, as I kissed her and Wayne goodbye.

"Everyone's a little crazy, honey," she said, rubbing my shoulder. "It's not a matter of how crazy you are, but how you use your crazy to be happy."

THREE

Oxeye, Maine

My crazy, it turned out, led me to a run-down town on the edge of a cliff. Flo and I had finally settled on a treasure house we were serious about and had come to Maine to see it in person. In the pictures it looked too good to be true, a wood-shingled cottage nestled in an overgrown garden. The property description said it had a glimpse of the ocean from its front windows. It was in an undeniable state of disrepair—but it wasn't the worst we'd seen. At least not according to the photos. It was like something out of a children's book, the kind of place infested by sprites, with a magical tree out back.

Oxeye. It was a dot of a town on the Maine coast, a few miles from the rich summer resort of Camden and the town of Rockport. I'd spent hours on Google Earth, zooming in on every corner of it. The place had a store, a gas station, a little library, a coffee shop, a couple of scenic bed-and-breakfasts, and a handful of summer vacation houses. Oxeye mostly seemed to exist to serve the campground to the south of it, which sat on a wooded spit that jutted into the bay. Our treasure house was on Tinker Street, one of two cottages at the head of a cul-de-sac, facing down the street to the cliffs and Penobscot Bay beyond. One side of Tinker Street was just woods, the other was summer houses with little rental signs out front, and there was a two-story hardware store on the corner, the first in a row of storefronts along the main road.

From what I could tell, Oxeye seemed kind of forgotten, abandoned by the side of the coastal road. But the house was in my price range, and the school district was excellent. There was a highly ranked middle school up the coast in Camden that Flo could attend now and a high school in Rockport for later. The school buses stopped in Oxeye, right at the end of Main Street. Even better, there was a small family medical practice in Rockport currently advertising for an office manager, and when I'd phoned about the job, they seemed overtly relieved that someone was interested in applying.

The realtor had also seemed relieved when I called about the house. "I . . . uh . . . can leave a key with the guy at the hardware store," she told me. "I have viewings all day in Camden or I'd meet you myself." She huffed a plastic little laugh. "But it's not like you'll need me to show you around. You've seen the photos, right?"

I assured her I had.

"Thank God." That awkward little laugh again. "Jake Abernathy is the guy at the hardware store. He can answer any questions you have."

But Jake Abernathy had questions of his own. "Gail told you it's full of culch, didn't she?" he had said dryly, when I'd called to arrange a time to collect the key.

I didn't know what *culch* was, but the way he said it sounded kind of charming. His raw concern for me and Flo was charming too. I pictured him with a fisherman's cap and a salt and pepper beard. A flannel shirt. He had a slow, careful way of talking, and his smoky voice and courteous manner led me to assume he was an older man. The gentlemanly type.

"It's really no place for a woman alone," he said, sounding more like somebody's grandpa now. "Let alone one with a kid. The realtor told you that too?"

I assured him that we knew full well what we were getting into.

Mr. Abernathy gave me directions to his hardware store, and I followed a road that curled off US 1 after Waldoboro and ran along the breathtaking coastline. Maine in midsummer was something to see. The sky shone a blue that didn't quite seem real, and everything was sharp edged and breezy fresh. The salty scent of the bay and the resin fragrance of the pines was intoxicating through the open windows as we wound north along the coast. We'd had a two-day journey from Pittsburgh in my little blue Honda Fit, staying overnight at a Days Inn in Hartford, Connecticut, and singing along to Disney soundtracks as we ate junk food from gas stations.

At last, we crested a hill to find ourselves abruptly in Oxeye, just as the directions had promised. Rusty cliffs dropped starkly at the edge of the road, down to the swells of the bay with its impossibly clear water marked only by the wakes of yachts, crisp white against aquamarine. Jake Abernathy's weatherbeaten store sat on the corner of Beach Road and Tinker Street.

Our street.

"Let's drive by the house before we get the keys," I suggested to Flo. I was already turning in to the street before she answered. I couldn't resist. I was dying to see the treasure house in person.

The woods on the south side of Tinker Street were thicker and wilder than they'd seemed on Google Maps, a dark mass of balsam fir, like a Christmas tree farm run wild. The perfume of resin was overwhelming. Google Maps sure hadn't conveyed the magic of the ocean gusts and the glitter of the seaside air. Instead of the hum of traffic, I could hear the restless soughing of the sea and the cry of gulls. Along the north side of Tinker Street, the shiplap-walled summer houses had their doors thrown open, and the faint sound of baseball commentary and music swirled out in lazy eddies. Beach towels were hung to dry along the picket fences like carnival bunting.

"I guess that's our junk house," Flo announced as we slid to the end of the cul-de-sac. Twin cottages stood at the head of the street, staring down to the cliffs, and it was obvious which one was ours because the left house was neat as a pin, a charming colonial with weathered wood shingles, bright white trim, and a lemon-drop-yellow front door. There was a cute little sign next to the door that read, "SYLVIE BY SEA." Lush hydrangeas bloomed pink and white on either side of the porch steps, and a pillowy green lawn that would have impressed Wayne ran all the way down to the curb.

The house on the right, though . . .

It was the witchy version of its twin, a gnarled crone of a cottage. Brambles exploded along the path, casting wickedly long canes into the sky. They bobbed threateningly in the sea breeze. Railings had fallen from the porch, leaving gaps like missing teeth, and the windows that weren't broken were so thick with dust they looked brown. The gutters were hanging down like sagging streamers, and someone had boarded up the front door with plywood. Keys would be no help to us there. How on earth would we even get in?

"I can't see any junk," Flo said, seemingly undaunted by the sight of our house.

"I think the whole place is the junk," I replied nervously. But what I was actually thinking was that this was too good to be true. A house like this one should be worth a fortune. Even run-down, it was right on the coast and only a stone's throw from the fancy tourist towns. So why was it so affordable and why weren't there people queuing up to buy it? Surely every investor on the East Coast should have been bidding on it?

"I like it," Flo announced. "It's got a vibe."

"We can't live there," I said, feeling numb at the scale of the house's disarray. It looked worse in person. An investor might just bulldoze the whole place and build something new. "It's not habitable."

"Wayne said it was."

It was true. Wayne had read the building reports the realtor had sent through. The building was structurally sound. Mr. Abernathy had been plain about that too.

"It's just culch," he'd said. "The place just needs some love."

Love is an understatement, I thought as I regarded the house on Tinker Street. This place didn't need love, it needed an intervention.

But we'd come all this way, and we might as well see inside while we were in town. And, I thought with a shivery thrill, imagine if we could live here, by the sea, in a place I shouldn't realistically be able to afford. . . .

Plus, Mr. Abernathy was waiting for us. So I turned us around and headed back down to the hardware store.

The Oxeye Hardware Store (and Lobster Shack) was one of those oddities that only exist in very small towns—it seemed to be a combined hardware store, souvenir outlet, camping supply shop, and food to go, judging by the various signs and cluttered window displays. There was a service window opening to a bunch of picnic tables that overlooked the cliffs, and a sign advertising lobster rolls and cans of Moxie. Along the side of the building were stacks of dented and well-used lobster traps.

When we pulled up, I couldn't help but notice the very hot, very half-naked man bussing the picnic tables. He was the picture of a coastal summer honey in cut-off jean shorts and not much else; he was stubbly and muscled, his hair a salty tousle. I felt a slow pulse at the sight of him, a slow pulse I'd not felt in a very long time. He was the kind of man who invited fantasies of summer flings, languid violet evenings, slow time wasting.

The kind of fantasies that didn't seem impossible, here in the sun-spangled sea light of Oxeye.

FOUR

"Can I stay in the car?" Flo asked, propping her feet up on the dashboard and opening her book.

"Sure." Fine by me. Surreptitiously, I pulled at the hem of my tank top and ran a hand through my messy hair. I'd spilled mustard all down my own shirt at lunch and had resorted to borrowing Flo's spare, cursing myself for packing light. Unfortunately, Flo's was a *Wicked* tank top with sparkling green and pink lettering, which was very short and very tight on me. Paired with my shorts, there was a lot more skin on display than usual. But maybe that wasn't such a bad thing. The hot guy clearing the picnic tables looked up as I slammed the car door, and the sun flashed off the lenses of his cheap plastic sunglasses. He had very expressive frowny eyebrows. And the most impressive shoulders . . .

My slow pulse became a throb.

But the coastal honey didn't seem pleased to see me. Those frowny eyebrows were just about touching over the bridge of his nose. "Lobster hour is over," he said shortly. "You missed it." He had a rumbling down-east accent—*lobsta owah is ovah.* Empty red plastic baskets teetered in his hands. There was no one at the picnic tables anymore, but judging by the number of serving baskets, lobster hour had been busy.

"That's okay," I said hastily. "I'm actually here to meet Jake Abernathy. He's expecting me." I gave him a bright smile, wondering if I even remembered how to flirt.

The hot guy looked even less pleased, if such a thing was possible. Maybe he was afraid Mr. Abernathy would make him serve us *lobsta.* He looked me up and down, his gaze lingering on the tank top. "I doubt it."

"I beg your pardon?" My smile faltered.

"I doubt it," he repeated irritably, dismissing me.

"Is he inside?" I wasn't about to be dismissed after coming all this way.

"No."

Wow. I mean, I'd heard Mainers could be taciturn, but this was just rude. Shame, because I didn't imagine a town this small had many men, let alone good-looking ones in my age range.

"He *is* expecting me," I said tightly, pulling my phone out and searching for Mr. Abernathy's texts.

"He's really not." He snorted. And then he headed for the store.

"Tell him Zoe Copeland is here," I snapped, following him, "and see what he says."

He stopped dead, and I almost broke my nose on his wall of a back. He was stupidly muscular. *Too muscular,* I decided, settling into disliking him. Clearly vain. Why were hot guys such *dicks*?

"Watch it," he growled, sidestepping me.

"You're the one who stopped short."

He gave me a very close inspection. "You can't be Zoe Copeland," he told me irritably when he was finished.

I flushed at his close attention and his refusal to believe me. "*Yes.*" I felt the need to reinforce it. "*I am.*"

"No, you're not." He shook his head definitively.

I frowned. This guy was impossible. "I think I know who I am."

"No. Zoe Copeland is a middle-aged mom. You're not a middle-aged mom."

"She is," Flo disagreed loudly through the open window of the car. The hot guy startled, noticing her for the first time. She'd put her book down and was leaning out the window. "And can I have a lobster roll? I've never had one before."

"I'm not *middle-aged.* And he said lobster hour is over," I snapped, heading her off. "Besides, you wouldn't like it." I turned back to the half-naked grump. "So, you *do* know who I am."

"I know Zoe Copeland is coming to pick up a key. And that she's a middle-aged mom." He was scowling in earnest now. "Not . . . *you.* I wouldn't let you order a beer without seeing some identification first."

"Oh my God. Is Mr. Abernathy inside?" I headed for the open door. I didn't want to talk to this pain in the ass anymore, no matter how hot he was.

"No." He exhaled irritably. "I mean, no, I'm here."

Now it was my turn to stop dead.

Wait. *What.* This guy was the gentlemanly fisherman from the phone?

"*You?*" I couldn't keep the disbelief from my voice.

"Yeah." He was scowling like the villain in a bad film. "Ah hell, come in and we'll sort this out."

"What's to sort out?" I said, confused. "I'm here to pick up the key and take a look at the house, like we agreed on the phone."

He ignored me and jerked his head at the car. "Does your kid want to come in and have a soda while we talk? It's hot out here." The red basket towers were wobbling in his hands. He readjusted his weight to steady them, and I could see the muscles of his stomach flex.

"Flo, come on," I called back to the car. "It looks like we might be longer than I thought."

The interior of Oxeye Hardware (and Lobster Shack) reminded me of an old-fashioned general store in a black-and-white movie. It smelled of linseed oil mixed with old woodsmoke. It had sash windows overlooking the porch, where the picnic tables had a prime view of the bay. Today, the windows were thrown open and the breeze caused the knickknacks that hung from the ceiling to jingle. There were framed photos of a golden retriever on every wall and a dog bed in the corner by the potbelly stove, but no sign of the dog.

Jake Abernathy looked like the very last kind of guy to be running a place like this. And now that I'd met him, he was definitely not the golden retriever type. His personality seemed more suited to a pit bull or rottweiler.

"Do you get your muscles from working, or from the gym?" Flo asked him casually, as we followed him to the rear of the store. She was completely unperturbed by his rottweiler vibe.

Jake missed a step and looked down at himself. "What . . . ?"

"You don't have to answer that," I said hurriedly. "Flo, don't be rude."

"Why not? *He* seems pretty rude. Besides, *is* it rude to ask about muscles?" Flo cocked her head. "He doesn't have a shirt on, so he must want people to look at his muscles."

I felt myself turning red because I *did* keep looking at his muscles. "Sorry," I grudgingly apologized to Jake, who was also turning red. "Flo, it's rude to comment on other people's bodies," I told her, secretly pleased that she'd unsettled him.

"Oh." She took that in. "Sorry I commented on your body," she told Jake, who had ducked through to a narrow kitchen and dumped his armful of red plastic baskets. We followed him as he hastily snatched a faded T-shirt from a hook and yanked it on. The T-shirt had a cartoon lobster on the front.

There was a huge pot on the stove, and the smell of cooked lobster and sharp green scallions was heavy in the air. Breadcrumbs littered the stainless-steel counter, and a bag of long white bread rolls sat half empty.

"That's okay," Jake told Flo, clearing his throat awkwardly. He crossed his arms and tried to rearrange his expression. He seemed chagrined. . . . What should have been a straightforward interaction—him giving me a key—had somehow turned into something really unwelcoming and weird. And I'd been expecting to meet such a *nice* man.

"You weren't what I was expecting," Jake admitted as he straightened his lobster shirt, echoing my thoughts.

"What *were* you expecting?" Flo demanded. She lit up, clearly hoping for an interesting response.

"Ah . . ." Jake was nonplussed.

"It's fine," said Flo encouragingly. "She won't be offended. Mom says it's in her constitution to take insults in stride after working in a call center."

"Flo," I warned.

My mouthy kid rolled her eyes and leaned in to confide in Jake. "She also has this thing about private conversations versus public conversations. But you can tell me if you thought we were criminals on the run or something."

"You want a soda?" Jake asked, looking slightly panicked. He didn't seem to know what else to say.

"Depends. What have you got?" Flo asked, following him to the refrigerator.

"Moxie, mostly." He opened the door and the light illuminated the bright orange cans. Flo shot him a dubious look.

"It's the official state drink of Maine," he told her, pulling a can from the fridge. "You'll probably hate it, it tastes like medicine." He handed it to her and glanced at me. "You want one?" He looked at me like I might bite. What on earth was it about me that he didn't like? He'd known me for all of two minutes.

I shook my head. "No, thank you. I'd just like the key."

He gave me a sour look. "I can't let you inside that house." He didn't sound regretful in the slightest. In fact, he sounded like he was a cop who'd caught me spitting on the sidewalk. "And Gail had no right telling me to give you the key." The sound of Flo popping the can punctuated his words.

"Are you kidding me?" I was bewildered. "We just drove twelve hours from Pittsburgh. *You* gave me the directions here."

"Yeah." He frowned. "But I didn't know you were *you*."

"What the hell does that mean?" What was wrong with *me*?

"Oh, this is seriously gross." Flo made a noise like a cat vomiting as she handed the orange can back to Jake. "Your state has problems."

"I warned you." He put it down and grabbed a lemonade from the fridge. "Here. Go drink it out on the picnic tables while I talk to your mom."

"*Please*," Flo scolded him. "Don't you have manners in Maine?"

"Please," he added tersely.

"Wait," I protested as I followed him back out of the kitchen. "I don't want to talk. I just want the key."

"Here, take a popsicle too." Jake slid open an ice chest and pulled a popsicle out for Flo. "You might see some whales if you look out to the bay. There were minkes out there yesterday."

"Thank you," Flo said pointedly, raising her eyebrows at him to illustrate that her manners were better than his. "And what's a minke? Is it like a mermaid?"

"It's a whale."

"Oh. Cool." She headed eagerly for the porch.

"Don't settle in," I warned her. "We're about to go." Because I was seeing this house come hell or high water. On principle. All my nerves about the state of it had evaporated.

"Look, Mrs. Copeland—" the impossible man began.

"*Ms.*," I corrected him, seething. A sexist aging fisherman was one thing, this surfer dude with a superiority complex was another. This man had zero charm. "And you called me Zoe on the phone."

"Right." He ran a hand through his salt-tousled hair and pulled the cheap sunglasses off. His eyes were the clear, pale blue-green of marble glass. Faint lines radiated beside his eyes, making it seem for a moment like he was smiling, even though he clearly wasn't. "Zoe. You don't want that house."

"What?" My voice came out louder than I expected. "Excuse me? What is going on here? I'm seriously confused." I crossed my arms.

"Ah . . ." He drew a deep breath. "Look. The house is a mess."

"I know. I saw the photos." This guy was playing some kind of game, and I wasn't having it. I wasn't letting him win.

"Sure. You saw photos. But . . . in real life, it's . . . worse."

I considered him, trying to control my temper. "I know. That's why I can afford it," I said bluntly. "Even then, I don't understand why there aren't developers lined up."

"It's just . . ." He made an inarticulate noise. "The realtor didn't tell me you were this young. I thought you were *middle-aged,* with a teen. Not, like, a first-time home buyer with a *kid.* I would have . . ."

"What? You would have what?"

"It's a lot," he said helplessly. "The house. And you're—"

"Excuse me," I cut him off. "I don't see how this is your business. It isn't even your house."

He swallowed and turned his head to look up at the ceiling. Eventually, he nodded. "You're right. I'm sorry." Jake cleared his throat. "I'm just the key guy. I'll lock up and throw some shoes on and then we'll go."

"*We'll* go? I thought you were just giving me the key."

But he'd gone already, padding barefoot off to the kitchen to close up shop.

"What was all that about?" Flo leaned through the open sash window, her mouth red from her popsicle, the open lemonade can in her other hand. She was gleeful with sugar.

"God knows." I shook my head. "Maybe he's been out in the sun too long."

"Did you like all those muscles, though?"

"Eat your popsicle."

"Why doesn't he want us to live on his street?"

I didn't know. And I didn't care. All I wanted now was to get inside that house.

FIVE

It turned out *culch* meant junk. And when Jake said the house was full of culch, he meant it.

"Watch where you step," he warned us as he took us around the back of the house. "Elton from next door keeps this side cut back and mown," Jake told me. "Which is good of him. He doesn't have to."

Flo trotted along behind Jake, taking the whole place in and looking like she was at Disneyland. "Mom, look, there's attic rooms!" She pointed up at the shingled roof behind the brick chimney. "I call an attic bedroom!"

"It might be a while before you're sleeping up there," Jake warned her.

"Why? Are there ghosts? Do we have to get an exorcist?"

"There's no room for ghosts, what with all the junk. And how do you know about exorcists at your age?"

"You don't know what my age is. I could just be a very short teenager," Flo rebuked him.

"Fair enough, kid."

"Why *is* it full of junk?" I asked, jumping in before Flo could really start in on him. I tried to peer in the side windows, which were whimsically round, like portholes, but they were too dirty to see through. I got a funny little twist in my stomach at the sight of those round windows. They were like something out of a fairy tale.

"It's kind of a long story." Jake sighed.

"Give me the short version," I suggested.

"There was a lady who lived here, she was a hoarder, she doesn't live here anymore." We'd reached the end of the neatly clipped and mown pathway and found ourselves blocked by overgrown bushes. Jake held back branches covered in splashy red berries. "Through you go."

Flo slipped through easily, but the space between Jake and the house was narrow and I was forced to all but rub myself against him as I followed. He was warm against my back and a slow shiver ran through me. I felt him tense at my touch. I guess I rubbed him the wrong way.

The backyard was a wall of green. It was as though the woods had spilled all the way to the back porch. Once there might have been a garden under there but now it was a wildwood, with tangles of saplings around the old trees. The wind soughed through them, causing the leaves to snap and ruffle. Where flower beds and vegetable gardens once might have grown, there was waist-high grass dotted with wildflowers. The overwhelming green tangle breathed the perfume of sap and summer.

"It's a little wild," Jake told us dryly.

"It's *great*." Flo's eyes were shining. "Are there any magic trees or tunnels or anything?"

"Are there snakes?" I added, eyeing the tall grass.

"Probably."

"Probably!" I scanned the ground for signs of movement.

"Don't crash out, Mom. There aren't venomous snakes in Maine, I looked it up." Flo was completely unfazed.

"Getting bitten by a nonvenomous snake would still hurt," I

snapped at her. I had visions of her ankles covered in puncture wounds. "You're *not* to touch them."

"It's good to have snakes. They keep the rats and mice away, right, Mr. Abernathy? That's what my reptile book said."

"Jake," he corrected her. "No one calls me Mr. Abernathy."

"Can I keep a snake for a pet if I find one? The book said snakes make good pets."

"Absolutely not." This kid was going to be the death of me. "You're not so much to *look* at one if you see one."

Flo rolled her eyes. "That doesn't even make sense."

Jake cleared his throat. "If you take the place, which I doubt you will once you've seen inside, you can hire someone to come mow the grass and cut things back. I know a guy."

I tried to imagine what that would cost, given the scale of the job. The yard looked huge.

"It's got the bones of a decent garden under all the overgrowth," he said, staring at the impenetrable greenery. "Somewhere back there is an old vegetable patch, and a well, and a bunch of crab apples. You could make crab-apple jelly if you're the jelly-making type." He gave me a sideways look and rubbed his nose. It was probably clear I wasn't the jelly-making type.

But maybe I would be, if I had an orchard of crab apples?

"There are some outbuildings too. But they're also full of culch." He seemed demoralized on my behalf as he considered the yard. His hair tumbled back from his furrowed brow. "Anyway, we'd best get in."

Get in? *How?* As far as I could see, there was no way to even reach the back stairs that led to the porch.

"These push back easily enough," he said, pushing more red-berried limbs away as he inched along the rusty corrugated iron that formed the right half of the porch. "This here is the laundry," he called over his shoulder to me, tapping the iron sheeting. "It's in original condition, you might say."

I could feel the bushes scratching at my bare arms and legs and wished I'd worn jeans and a long-sleeved shirt, instead of a tank and shorts. Especially given the threat of snakes. I noticed Jake's hand drift down to brush Flo's shoulder, just to make sure she was safe and following close.

"Down the other end there's a screened porch. It used to be quite nice, back in its day." He paused. "But the screens all need replacing."

Everything needed replacing. The back stairs looked rotted through.

"They're not as bad as they look," Jake said, when he saw my horror. He stood on them to show me, then jumped up and down on the middle step. "Safe enough."

"Why couldn't we go in through the front door?" I asked as I watched Flo follow him up the rotted-looking stairs.

"It's boarded up."

I'd seen that much. "But why?"

"The glass is smashed. Like most of the windows."

Right. This place might be on the market for a song, but how would I ever afford the cleanup? New glass for the front door and windows, new stairs and screens for the back porch, a complete cutting back of the backyard . . . The costs were adding up and we hadn't even set foot inside the house yet.

Flo wriggled past Jake as he opened the back door. "Mom, look at this place! It's a *museum.*" She disappeared to the right.

"Be careful!"

Jake stepped back to let me by, but the space was narrow and once again I ended up rubbing against him. Once again, I felt that slow shiver flow through me.

"She'll be okay. I went at it with the bug spray a few days ago," he assured me, his voice oddly tight. "There's no spiders or anything."

Oh, good God, I thought as I took in the interior. Spiders or no spiders, it was horrifying. The place wasn't a museum, it was a junkyard. It was far worse than the photos had shown. The "laundry" on the right was nothing but a lean-to made of corrugated iron; it looked like it was being held together by rust. It was filled to the brim with antique appliances, chief among which was a laundry mangle that must have been more than a century old. It was a tall cast-iron contraption with two big wooden rollers, which were turning now, thanks to Flo, who was gleeful with her discovery.

"Watch your hands with that thing," Jake warned her. "It's wicked painful if you get them caught in the rollers." He was standing close behind me and I could smell the salty, woody scent of him. Like driftwood warming in the sun.

"What is it? A torture device?"

"A mangle," he said calmly. "It's how people used to squeeze the water out of their clothes and sheets."

"Cool! Mom, we're keeping this." Flo gave the rollers a cheerful slap with her hand, like she was smacking the rump of a horse she'd bought at auction.

There was a stack of discolored copper tubs in the back corner of the lean-to, and a water pump over a concrete trough. And then there was the proper junk: an old stroller and a couple of rusty bicycles, both missing wheels; parts of a baby's crib and a brass bed; old tin cans with faded or missing labels; even an ancient surfboard that must have been nine feet long.

"There's a bathroom through that door at the end there," Jake told me, pointing to a door. "The toilet still works. Kind of."

"Kind of?"

"It's nothing a plumber couldn't easily fix." He didn't meet my eye.

"Mom! Look!" Flo was off again, diving out of the laundry and toward the screened porch. The back "room" was one long space, half iron-clad laundry and half screened porch. "It's a swing!"

"Don't!" I leapt after her and managed to keep her from sailing straight onto the dusty swing, which was hanging from the rafters. I had a chilling vision of the whole thing crashing down, bringing the ceiling with it.

"It's okay." Jake was calm. "I checked it the other day." He lowered himself into the slatted wooden swing. It creaked but held. "The place is safe enough. It's just . . ."

". . . full of culch?" I finished.

I thought I caught a flicker of humor at that. I wondered what he'd look like if he smiled. Annoyingly, he looked pretty good grumpy, but I bet he'd look spectacular with a smile.

"I mean," he said, clearing his throat, the humor disappearing back into gruffness, "I wouldn't go playing with the broken screens. They're sharp. And the mangle will hurt you if you stick your hand in it. It's not *totally* safe. But safe enough, so long as you're careful."

Flo hopped up onto the swing next to him. "How good is this? A swing in your living room!"

"This isn't the living room," Jake corrected her. He lifted his feet from the floor as she kicked the swing into motion. "This is just the porch. For summertime. So you can relax and enjoy the garden without getting eaten alive by the bugs." He cleared his throat awkwardly as we all looked at the rents and holes in the screens.

I took in the "garden" through the disintegrating screens. I couldn't say that the thought of staring at that jungle, with the looming mess of the laundry at my side, was relaxing, bugs or no bugs.

"How come there's so much furniture in here?" Flo asked. She pointed to the pile of furniture down the side of the porch. Three sofas and a bunch of wooden chairs, all in a stack. And then some end tables, piled higgledy-piggledy.

"It had to go somewhere," Jake said with a shrug.

"What's that thing?" I heard Flo ask as I inched my way through the furniture to examine the posts of the back porch. I pushed on them, wincing, half expecting the whole thing to come down on my head. But it seemed sturdy enough.

"What thing? Oh, that. It's a wireless cabinet. A radio. I figure it's from before the war."

"What war?" Flo bounded over to examine the big walnut cupboard.

"The Second World War." Jake watched her closely. "Pull open that front panel. Use the little brass tassel, that's a handle," Jake instructed. He stayed on the swing, swaying gently back and forth as he watched Flo open up the front of the cupboard.

"There's a record player in here!" Flo was as delighted as she'd been with the mangle. "My dad has one of these. Only his is all flat and silver and I'm not supposed to touch it because once I did and I scratched a record. He said it was a collector's item and couldn't be replaced."

Jake made a grumbling noise. "In my experience, most everything can be replaced. Except for people."

The furniture stacked up on the porch was a mix of styles. There were wicker chairs with faded green cushions that looked like they were from the 1960s or '70s, and a big, overstuffed couch in moth-eaten velvet that looked much older; there were two pretty bentwood rocking chairs, their cane seats punctured, and a wooden cushioned sofa that looked like a church pew. There was so much of it. Who needed this much furniture?

"What are all these knobs for?" Flo was playing with the dials on the old wireless radio. Distantly, I heard Jake trying to explain it to her as I ran my hand over a rolled-up rug, which sagged over a tapestry-upholstered armchair.

"Is the rest of the house like this too?" I blurted, cutting across their conversation.

Jake's green-blue eyes met mine again. They were full of unsettled sympathy. And a dash of annoyance. Like he was irritated that I was putting him through this.

"Worse," he told me bluntly. "Some rooms you can barely get in for all the culch."

He wasn't exaggerating. When he wrestled the back door open, we found the kitchen was as much of a junkyard as the laundry.

I felt like I'd stepped back in time by at least a century. A wood-fired iron stove crouched on the far wall like a sleeping animal; there was no sign of a modern stovetop, or even a microwave. The room itself ran the full width of the building, the size of the laundry and screened porch combined. There was a big wooden kitchen table covered in clutter, and a chipped white sink with exposed pipes underneath. A series of very pretty china plates hung on display on the walls, with teacups dangling from little brass hooks beneath them. Large sash windows bracketed the fireplace, but they were shuttered. It was a dim, sad kitchen, a relic from a time long fallen into ruin.

And yet . . . something about it gave me that twisty feeling, the same way those round porthole windows had given me a twisty feeling. It was like stepping into a story, but I couldn't decide if it was a story about to begin, or one long concluded.

Gently, I touched a bouquet of wooden spoons sprouting from a clay jug. If this kitchen had been uncluttered and clean and in order, it would be the kind of kitchen Marilla Cuthbert would keep in *Anne of Green Gables*. The big black teapot would be boiling away on the stove, and the pretty china teacups would be set out for company. And this scrubbed kitchen table would be the perfect place for Anne Shirley to sit, learning her lessons, chattering about bridal veils of cherry blossom. . . .

"It's a bit dark," Jake said, cramming his hands into the pockets of his cut-off shorts and squinting up at two bare lightbulbs that hung from the ceiling. "Used to be milk glass shades over those bulbs. They were mottled pink, really pretty. But they got broken a while ago. You could probably find replacements online."

I let go of my breath. I hadn't even realized I'd been holding it. For a moment my vision of the scrubbed and cozy Green Gables–style kitchen had been so strong that it stayed superimposed over the junk and the grimness of the room.

"People like everything new these days," Jake continued. "No one wants those kinds of old light shades—they sell for cheap. But they suited the place—you could find something similar."

"You seem to know a lot about this place." I looked up at the bulbs on their dusty cords. The light shades were the least of my problems with this room. The wallpaper was so old it was difficult to tell what color it might have been; I could barely make out the floral print through the murky stains. "How come you're so familiar with it?"

"It's a small town." He shrugged. "Everyone knows a lot about everyone. Light shades and all."

"Who was the lady who lived here?" I touched my toe to the rag rug. Beneath it, the floor was peeling black-and-white-checked linoleum.

"Did she die here too?" Flo interrupted eagerly, looking up from an old flour sifter she was playing with. "Is she one of the ghosts?"

Jake flinched.

"Flo! You're talking about his neighbor."

"Oh." She was chagrined. "That's right. I'm sorry for your loss."

"There are decent floorboards under the linoleum too," Jake told me. "And the walls are fine under all that paper. You could make it real nice." He cleared his throat and shot me and Flo a darting glance. "Maybe she does haunt this place a little." He glanced around. "She certainly hated to leave all her things."

The *stuff* in that kitchen was suffocating. Everything from plastic milk crates of tableware to jugs crammed full of random utensils to a pyramid of empty vases. There were pots and pans of every era—old cast-iron frying pans and 1970s beige saucepans with brown flowers splattered on their sides. There were at least four old blenders and two coffeemakers. There was also a stack of newspapers in one corner, all yellowed with age. I wouldn't have been surprised to pick one up and find news of the Civil War. Then there was the non-kitchen stuff: paintbrushes, a big sewing basket with patchwork quilt squares spilling out, and, randomly, a wine bottle stuffed with a Kewpie doll on a stick, the kind of doll that you buy at local carnivals. It was a complete assault on the senses.

Flo found a big frilled-edge glass candy dish full of colored buttons. She was running her hands through them, and they made a cascading clatter as they fell back into the dish. Somehow the same things that I found overwhelming filled her with joy.

"How old is this place?" I realized I should probably have asked the real estate agent this question. The shingled frontage hinted at age, and age meant problems.

"It was built in the 1870s, I think." Jake cocked his head. "Maybe it was the 1880s. But it's old. You could ask Elton next door—he'd probably know, given his is the same vintage."

"Awesome!" Flo held up an octagonal crystal button. "We get to live in history." Then she flinched, as though something had just occurred to her. "Wait. Does this place have wi-fi?"

"Not yet," Jake replied.

"Mom." Flo's tone was dire. "We can't live without wi-fi. You'd better put that at the top of the to-do list."

Forget wi-fi, how was I going to cook on a stove that looked straight out of *Downton Abbey*? I had no interest in mangling our washing every week either.

"I'm sure Elton would let you tap into his wi-fi next door until you get yours set up," Jake told us, running a hand through his hair. He looked as overwhelmed as I felt, and he wasn't even the one buying the place.

"How did anyone live here without internet?" Flo was bewildered.

"It was mostly a summer holiday place, from before the internet was even an idea."

"Shame. I bet she would have loved eBay," Flo said cheerfully.

"Is there heating?" I looked around for radiators. The thick old walls kept the place cool, even on a sticky-hot summer's day. I could only imagine how cold it would get in the winter.

"There's a furnace in the basement—I'll show you down there before we finish up."

I breathed out. Okay. So at least it had heat.

"There's no cooling, but it's designed for all the windows to be thrown open in the summer to catch the coastal breezes."

I doubted we could even find enough windows to open, given all this trash.

"Seen enough?" Jake asked, giving me a knowing look.

I didn't want to give him the satisfaction, even though my dreams were crumbling in the face of all the junk.

"Are you kidding?" Flo exclaimed. "We haven't even seen my attic room yet!"

Jake's blue-green eyes held mine. "You sure you want to keep going? It gets worse."

Worse? How could it get worse? I swallowed. "We want to see it all," I insisted, tearing my gaze away, so he wouldn't be able to see how freaked out I was.

"Fine." He sighed. Jake edged his way through the clutter and opened the door to the hall. Or rather to another wall of clutter.

I had to step around an old telephone table, which held a small cut glass vase of fake plastic flowers and an old rotary phone. There was a notepad with a pencil attached by a little gold chain, for taking messages. It was an odd little oasis of order in a hallway that was littered with plastic bags and washing baskets and even a beheaded garden gnome.

It's in good condition, the real estate agent had assured me over and over again. *It just needs a clean-out.*

"There are two rooms down the front here, a parlor and a dining room." Jake pointed to the open archways.

"You really know your way around the place," I said dryly, watching as he picked his way through the field of debris.

"I used to help her out," he said.

"What did you do, clean?" Flo sounded amused. "Because I wouldn't quit your day job."

He didn't reply to that, merely stepped aside and gestured us ahead. The wooden arches led to two rooms of similar proportions, each with a fireplace of brick, ornamented with lush tiles of green and amber. Those big porthole windows I'd seen from outside bracketed the fireplaces. Golden light poured through, mellowed by the filter of dust. If I cleaned the dirt from the glass, that light would be clear and bright, perfect for someone sitting in the overstuffed armchair next to the fireplace to read by.

Something loosened in my chest as I imagined sitting there through the long cold Maine winters. The parlor had the potential to be a beautiful room. The vintage tiles in the fireplace, the hardwood floorboards I could see between the rug and the piles of junk—it all sang of heritage and elegance and a life of ease.

"A chandelier!" Flo exclaimed in delight, twirling underneath the light fixture. It was a modest egg-shaped net of crystals.

"I don't know that it's a chandelier," Jake disagreed.

"It's fancy," Flo told him.

"Is it?" He squinted at it.

Flo rolled her eyes at his pickiness. "*I* think it's fancy." She was annoyed.

I let them argue—I was more interested in whether the overhead light worked. The switch was an aged toggle, but the light went on and off just fine. "How come the electricity is still connected?" I asked Jake. "If no one's been living here."

He shrugged. "The family thought they might need it to sort through all this culch." He gave the room a rueful look. "But then it got too overwhelming."

"They don't want any of this stuff?"

"I guess not."

I checked the ceiling for water damage and the cornices for cracks while I was craning my neck. There were small hairlines here and there, but nothing too ominous.

At least I didn't think so.

I tried to look for outlets, but there was too much junk to see the baseboards. I did my best to edge behind some of the garbage.

"Oh." I stopped, startled, as I glimpsed colored glass. There was a lamp tilting precariously on the corner of a big crate. It was like something from an art gallery. The base was brass, shaped like a sinewy tree trunk, leading to a stained-glass shade that was a detailed drip of tiny pink blossoms and green leaves. I'd never seen anything so perfect. "Is that *Tiffany* glass?" I asked, awed. I was too scared to touch it.

"Maybe." Jake shrugged. "Some of this stuff is worth a lot of money, and some of it's just junk. There are bags of Happy Meal toys out there in the hall, but also tableware that could be actual silver."

"It's a treasure chest," Flo said, looking around like she might find gold. "Like in *The Goonies.*"

"It's more like a dumpster," Jake warned her. "Whoever buys this place will essentially be dumpster diving, and for a good long while."

"Is there a proto-pool out back by any chance?" Flo asked him as I moved the Tiffany lamp somewhere safer, where it wouldn't be knocked over and smashed.

"A what?"

"You know, a pit that we could turn into a pool."

"You don't need a pit," I told her, turning away from the stained-glass lamp. "If we move here, you'll have the whole ocean." I tapped her on the head as I picked my way to the sash windows. "Do these open?"

"Uh, yeah, they should." Jake joined me and flipped the latches on the sashes. The cracked windows opened with a shudder and a squeal, and the ocean breeze gusted in, a relief after the mustiness of the house.

I inhaled deeply. The scent of salt and pine and the heady perfume of overgrown lilac was intoxicating.

"I can't see any ocean; all I can see is more jungle." Flo leaned through the window.

It was true. The view was obscured by the tangle of vines and bushes.

"Oh look, there's a porch swing out here too!" Flo pointed at the wooden swing, which had flaked off most of its white paint.

"When the garden's cut back, there's a real nice view from that swing down to the bay," Jake said, trying to tie back a heavy tasseled curtain that was sagging off its rail.

"How can you tell?" I leaned through the window too, trying to catch the glitter of the water through the tangle of greenery. "The agent said there was a glimpse of the ocean from upstairs, but she didn't say anything about a view from down here."

"I grew up on this street. I've seen it. Gail probably didn't realize, because of, uh, the jungle." Jake gave up on the curtain and it sagged back over the window. "We'd best get moving. The day's getting on." He shut the windows, and the mustiness closed back in on us.

We could barely get into the dining room for all the junk, but I could see it was a mirror image of the parlor, only there was also an old wooden serving hatch that opened to the kitchen. Flo thought that was the best thing about the place. "You can slide my cereal in here to me in the morning," she told me, as she leaned through the hatch. "And I can talk to you while you cook."

I ignored that.

"Are any of these valuable, do you think?" I eyed a stack of paintings near the fireplace.

Again, Jake shrugged. "My guess would be that some are and some aren't. Some probably just had sentimental value."

"Are there any precious gemstones in this place?" Flo asked curiously. "Gold coins or doubloons or anything?"

"I think I saw some costume jewelry and a penny collection upstairs," said Jake. "And there's a framed map of colonial Maine around somewhere—that's kind of interesting."

"Does it have a guide to buried treasure?"

"I've never looked."

"You didn't notice an *X* on it or anything?"

Jake humored Flo all the way up the staircase, grunting in acknowledgment as she chattered about pirates and secret stashes of buried treasure.

"But you know if you found pirate treasure it probably wouldn't be what you expect," she told him sagely. "It would be things like cocoa and spices and stuff. They used to be worth more than gold, you know."

"How do you know so much about this stuff? Were you a pirate in a past life?"

"Maybe. But in this life, I know because I read books."

There was another round leaded window at the head of the landing. Light fell through it, ruddy with dust, down to the hall below. I paused, trying to imagine the hall without the junk. The boarded-up front door was framed by two thin windows to either side and a window above. The house would swim in light with all these windows cleaned.

The hall ceiling soared up to the landing of the second story, so even though the space was small it felt expansive. I felt a quivery feeling in my stomach as the hall swam before me, and I could see it as it once had been: the front door open to catch the flirtatious eddies of breeze, sun warming the wood floor, the walls bright with lovingly chosen wallpaper, the air scented with sea salt and garden flowers and the smell of something baking in the kitchen.

I could learn to bake. I imagined Flo and me in that kitchen, sifting flour and dancing along to her latest playlist.

My heart pinched at the thought.

Never in a million years did I think that I could live in a house like this, with sea views and gardens on every side. That I could sit on my porch and watch the seasons pass in my garden and see the mood of the ocean shift with the scudding weather. Flo could climb trees and swim in the ocean and do her homework while I read by the fire. Disconcerted, I realized I was tearing up. I swallowed and suppressed the visions. I was getting ahead of myself.

"The master bedroom is at the front of the house." Jake's voice pulled me back to the task at hand—and to the oppressive sight of all the junk choking the stairs. I joined Jake and Flo on the modest landing, which was as cluttered as the stairs and hallway below. "There's a bathroom here on the left, and a linen cupboard on the right. Then two attic bedrooms at the rear, overlooking the back garden." Jake pointed.

"Cool!" Flo climbed over plastic bags to get to the back rooms. "I call the best one of the attic rooms."

I followed Flo. The attic rooms had steeply sloped roofs and dormer windows. The shiplap walls might once have been white but were now grayish brown. We opened the door to the room on the left first but couldn't get past the threshold because there were clothes racks filling every inch of the room. It was like trying to climb into an overstuffed wardrobe. The clothes seemed to be from every era imaginable: minidresses in lurid seventies colors, puffy skirts, peacoats and ratty fur stoles and cotton sundresses. There was even a yellowing wedding dress hanging on the end of a rack, with a little cap and veil perched on the top.

"Can I have these to play dress-up?" Flo asked, reaching for the veil.

"Not until we check for vermin." I rethought that. "And no. Because if we keep it all, you'll have nowhere to sleep."

"I'll sleep in the other room. Or is that one full of clothes too?"

Jake had stayed out on the landing, at the head of the stairs. He seemed like he needed to be close to an exit, as though he felt like the junk was closing in on him. He was holding on to the banister and looking tense.

"You're really still thinking about taking the place?" he asked me quietly while Flo examined the second attic room, which was filled with books, toys, snow globes, and other random detritus. "Even now that you've seen it?"

It was a good question.

In most respects, the house was a total nightmare. And a money pit. The windows up here were weather damaged, and I thought I'd seen water stains on the ceilings; the walls needed repainting and the floorboards resurfacing. . . .

None of it would be cheap. And how long would it take me to clear out the junk to even get to the real work? I'd be sorting bags and boxes and garbage for months.

And yet . . .

It would be a house of my very own. A place no one could take away from me. I could wake up knowing I'd be here at the end of the day, the week, the year. I felt my throat get tight at the thought. To have a place that was ours, somewhere safe and sure, where Flo and I could live our lives without worrying about our home being taken away from us . . . It made me shaky with feelings I couldn't even name.

The little attic room Flo was poking around in looked directly into the branches of the oak tree, and the light was tinged a hushed green. I could hear birdsong through the broken window and see the woods behind the wild backyard. I tried to imagine the room without the junk. It was small but cozy, an attic room that belonged to another age. From here, Flo could see the fall leaves blaze and the winter snow swirl; she could sleep to the lullaby of the sea. Maybe we could refurbish one of those brass bed frames in the laundry for her.

All this place required of me was courage and hard work.

A lot of hard work, I thought, as I took in the landing full of junk. Which I'd have to do while working full time and raising a kid. And then there was the issue of money. Could I actually afford to fix this place up?

But surely living in a place I *owned* that I couldn't afford to fix up was better than paying exorbitant rent on a place that would never be mine.

"*Mom!*" Flo's excited shriek rang through the small attic room.

"Look!" She brandished an old magazine. "It's that lady you like from the old movies. The one who was splashing about in the rain, singing."

I took the old magazine from her. It was from summer 1952, the colors lurid bright and plasticky. "No, that was Debbie Reynolds. This is Jane Powell."

"Huh." Flo held up another magazine. "You know these people too?"

"Sure, that's Doris Day and Rock Hudson."

"How do you know?"

"We didn't have cable when I was a kid. I watched a lot of old movies." I opened the magazine she'd handed me. The fragrance of dusty newsprint wafted up.

"The people who lived here must have liked old movies too. There's a whole stack of them." Flo wrinkled her nose as she looked down at Doris and Rock. She hadn't taken to musicals.

"You want to see more?" Jake grumbled impatiently. "Or do you want me to stand here watching you read magazines all day?"

"You need a snack," Flo scolded him. "I think you're hangry." She handed me the other magazine and joined Jake on the landing, where he was still holding the banister and looking like he wanted out of here as fast as possible.

"I'm not . . . *hangry,* I just don't want to stand in all this culch all day."

"No one asked you to show us around," I reminded him, tossing the magazines back into the attic room.

SIX

Oxeye, Maine, 1953

Marly Orcutt was sick of being the baby of the family. She was fourteen (almost fifteen) this summer, but everyone still treated her like a little kid. Her cousins Priscilla and Sylvie were their usual stuck-up, snotty selves, acting like they were all grown up while Marly was just a pip-squeak. Which she wasn't. She was almost as tall as Sylvie already, for Pete's sake. And she'd recently bought a *bra*.

Marly had spent every summer at Oxeye since she could remember. Her grandparents had left the house to her mom and her Aunt Betty. Every June, as soon as school was over, Mom packed Marly and her three older brothers into the station wagon, along with Happy and Yappy, their two irritable old terriers, and they headed for Maine. Aunt Betty was usually there already, since Priscilla and Sylvie's private school let out early, and Marly's cousins always claimed the twin beds in the attic room under the white oak. Mom and Aunt Bet slept together in the big room up front when their husbands stayed in town for work, and the boys got the second attic room, piled in like dogs in a kennel. When Marly's father and Uncle Don came for the weekends, Marly's brothers were moved to the porch and Mom and Dad slept in their attic room. Marly was always relegated to a folding cot in with the girls—who always made it clear they didn't want her there.

Marly was what her mother called "a late child" and her brothers called "an accident." But Marly had decided "afterthought" would be the most appropriate term, given that's how she got treated. Once they even forgot her entirely in all the chaos of packing up the house and left her behind in Oxeye. She'd had to go down to the general store and use the pay phone to call someone to come back and get her. Old Mr. Laughton had lent her the money for the call, and she'd called her dad's work number, knowing that Mom and the boys would still be on the road. Her dad had been busy, but his secretary had said to sit tight at the house and someone would come get her—Marly's mom would surely realize and turn around before she finished the nearly four-hour trip to Boston. It had taken two hours: one to notice Marly was missing and another to drive back. The year after that, Marly noticed they'd installed a phone in the house on Tinker Street.

This year, they were rolling into Oxeye on the nineteenth of June, Marly crammed in the back with the dogs, her brothers Bobby and Virgil taking over the entire backseat, and her eldest brother Paul driving like he was in a bumper car at the fair. Mom kept letting out noises of distress and grabbing at the steering wheel. Doris Day was on the radio, singing some sappy song about starlight and love. Mom loved Doris Day and Patti Page and all kinds of squares. Marly preferred it when her brother Bobby took over the radio. She liked it when Johnnie Ray was sobbing away, and she really liked the Orioles and the Du Droppers. But Mom didn't let Bobby at the radio dial if she could help it; she said all that wailing gave her a headache. Mom got a headache a lot. Eighteen-year-old Bobby was what Mom called a "handful," even though Marly thought sixteen-year-old Virgil was the real troublemaker. He was just so good at it that Mom never caught on.

Marly wished her father would come away with them for the summer, and not just for the occasional weekend, because he was a pushover compared to Mom. Bobby in particular could always get around him. Mostly because Dad liked keeping the peace, and if there was one thing Bobby could do, it was upset people.

Marly shuffled the dogs out of the way and pressed herself to the window as they reached the coast. She loved the first glimpse of the bay, the foaming cobalt flashes through the trees and the yachts flying toward the horizon. She held her breath as she looked for all the familiar landmarks: the roadside stalls with their turnip greens and asparagus, rhubarb and bunches of blue flag iris; the fishing tackle shack; and the elegant sweep of the Saint-Cyr resort on the spit just before they crested the hill into Oxeye.

Sometimes Marly imagined they were rich and were actually on their way to stay at Saint-Cyr, with its wide porches and its black-and-white-striped awnings. The resort was a white temptation in the woods, with unmatched views of Penobscot Bay. In summer it was full to the brim with families, and in fall with romantic couples having illicit rendezvous. Or so her brothers said—but they'd never spent fall in Oxeye and so how would they even know? Aunt Betty said Saint-Cyr had fleets of waiters in little jackets with shiny buttons, and bathrooms stocked with French soaps. From the car Marly could see the tennis courts as they drove past, and lawns leading down to the water, and there was a lifeguard's chair set up by the stone stairs that led into the bay. From the Oxeye cliffs you could get a clear view of the little yachts and canoes that sailed out from Saint-Cyr's private pier. It was like a place in one of those movies Mom dragged Marly to, where lazy beautiful people led lazy beautiful lives. Marly bet they served shrimp cocktail and ice cream at every meal at Saint-Cyr, and slept in beds with canopies, and quaffed cocktails on the veranda. Cary Grant probably even stayed there.

Maybe now that Marly was almost fifteen, she could convince Mom and Aunt Bet to take her there for a visit. Sometimes they took pity on her when the older kids ditched her, and they'd take her to the movie theater or the ice cream parlor in Rockport. Maybe now that she was almost fifteen they'd feel even sorrier for her? Because it was desperate to be fourteen-almost-fifteen and all alone for summer.

And she really *was* all alone this summer. Because her wretched brothers had decided to pack their damn tent. They said they'd pitch it just on the fringes of the woods, behind the wild little orchard of crap apples, and fend for themselves. Mom seriously thought all of their Boy Scout expeditions were paying off, but Marly knew it was because they planned to sneak off every night to Rockport, where there was a bar that didn't ask for ID. She couldn't *believe* Mom let them camp on their own.

"I don't see what the problem is," Mom argued, flapping Marly out of the way as she tried to wrestle the dogs out of the wagon. "I thought you'd be *happy* to have your own room."

"My own . . ." Marly was crestfallen. Which was stupid, because having your own room should be great, but she couldn't deny the deep sting she felt that the girls were finally ditching her for good. "What do you mean my own room? Where are Sylvie and Cilla going?"

"They want the boys' room. Aunt Bet fancied it up this spring. She said she needed something to keep her busy while Uncle Don was on that work trip, remember? So she came up and did a bit of decorating. I'm sure I told you," Mom said absently. "She thought the girls would enjoy a nice new nest."

Marly was sure her mother *hadn't* told her. Mom never remembered to tell Marly *anything*.

"Yoo-hoo!" her mother called as she opened the front door. "We're here!"

There was the sound of big band music drifting through the house. The warblyness told Marly it was coming from the old wireless, which Aunt Bet kept in the kitchen so she and Mom could listen to it while they "cooked." Their cooking looked a lot like sitting around yapping.

"Aunt Lori!" Sylvie came crashing down the stairs. For a skinny girl she crashed around a lot, Marly thought sourly. Sylvie was what Mom called "pert and perfect," a five-foot-three natural blonde who looked like she belonged in an advertisement for Coca-Cola. She was sporty and suntanned and always seemed about to burst into a cheer.

Marly secretly committed to memory all Sylvie's little gestures and movements, wishing she could be half as pretty and peppy. Although she would have died if anyone had guessed.

Marly's mom adored Sylvie. And Sylvie adored Mom. The two of them were mad for movie stars and swapped magazines all summer long: *Modern Screen, Screen Stories, Silver Screen, Filmland.* Sometimes they took Marly along to a double feature and occasionally they forced her to sit through the same film multiple times. The previous summer Marly had seen *Singin' in the Rain* at least half a dozen times—she knew the dialogue by heart.

"Please tell me you brought your copy of *Confidential,* Aunt Lori!" Sylvie exploded as she reached the bottom of the stairs, her ponytail swinging vigorously. "Mom says I can only read it if *you* think it's okay. Please say it's okay or I'll *die.* I'm the only girl in my class who hasn't read it yet!" Sylvie was seventeen and prone to exaggeration.

Marly watched as her mom pursed her lips and gave the kitchen door a surreptitious look, just to check Aunt Bet wasn't listening in. "If I lend it to you, you *can't* let your mother see," she whispered. "It's very . . . *adult.*"

Normally that would have pricked Marly's ears, but she knew that in this case "adult" just meant some old gossip was telling tales about Rita Hayworth or Frank Sinatra.

Sylvie didn't deign to say hello to Marly; she was too busy conning Mom out of her magazines. She and Mom disappeared upstairs, Happy and Yappy scrambling along after them, leaving Marly all alone in the hall.

Marly went looking for Aunt Bet, who at least knew how to say hello to a girl. She found her aunt out on the back porch, watching the boys wrestling their tent as she sipped a glass of iced tea from the comfort of the swing. Sun streamed through the porch screens, golden and dusty. Aunt Betty was in her fifties, fleshy in a firm way, strong looking, with a square forehead and jaw, and bright blue eyes the color of a gas flame. She was wearing a billowy blue-and-white-striped sundress that made her look a bit like a beach ball.

"Hi," Marly said, squinting out at her brothers, who weren't winning their battle with the tent. So much for being Scouts.

"Hey, Peach. Oh, look at that, you've grown." Aunt Bet's gaze was fixed on Marly's chest.

Marly flushed.

"Well, good for you. Did your mom get you a brassiere?"

Marly scowled at the memory and Aunt Betty laughed.

"My girls felt the same way." She patted the swing next to her. "Come watch these boys for a while. It's better than Abbott and Costello."

Marly flopped down beside her and the swing arced forward.

"I made iced tea." Bet gestured at the jugs on the coffee table. "But make sure you drink from the jug with the sailing boats on it, not the one with the seashells."

"What's in the one with the seashells?"

"Just a dash of vacation cheer." Aunt Bet winked. "But don't go telling Uncle Don—"

"—or he'll drink it all." Marly filled in the punch line. "Good thing he's not here, then."

Aunt Bet laughed when the boys' tent collapsed on their heads. "Won't it be nice to have the whole house just for us girls?" she said, bumping her shoulder against Marly's. "Although I guess we'll still have to share the bathroom."

"Dad and Uncle Don will still be here on weekends," Marly reminded her.

When Aunt Bet headed outside to rescue the boys from themselves, Marly shuffled upstairs. She found her mom and Sylvie ensconced in the main bedroom, their excited chatter drifting through the open door as they discussed rumors that Debbie Reynolds was dating Eddie Fisher. Marly rolled her eyes. The two attic bedroom doors were wide open but there was no sign of Priscilla. Marly took the opportunity to snoop in her cousins' new bedroom and discovered Aunt Bet really *had* done some decorating. The walls were painted a dreamy shade of palest pink, and the twin beds had been moved in from next door and covered with the flounciest of coverlets in dusky rose. There were gauzy mint-green curtains at the dormer window and fussy little pink lampshades with tassels on the brass lamps next to the beds. And there were pillows *everywhere,* all of them in rosebud prints with pink frills. It looked like something from a TV show.

Marly could just imagine Priscilla and Sylvie in here. Aunt Bet had probably bought them matching rosebud nightgowns too. Marly could smell their cold cream and talcum powder, as though they'd been here for weeks. But this year there was another scent too, brand-new. Fancy. *Adult.* Aunt Bet had always forbidden the girls from wearing perfume, saying they were too young, but things had clearly changed. Priscilla was nineteen and had just finished her freshman year at Smith, and Marly could definitely smell real perfume. It was cloying and floral, like sticking your face in a dish of potpourri.

Marly was glad she didn't have to sleep in that stink.

Or so she told herself. But in truth she was feeling painfully discarded. Secretly, she liked rooming with her cousins, even if she did have to sleep on a cot. She liked listening to them gossip about their friends and boys and cheerleading and what made a good husband and what they'd do after graduation. Now she'd be stuck on her own.

Marly was feeling sour and surly as she stepped into the other attic bedroom, the one she'd have all to herself now that the girls had a *boudoir*. The attic room under the oak tree had a cane double bed in the center of the room, sitting adrift on the circular blue rag rug. That was new. Marly opened the dormer window to clear out the odor of Cilla's dead-flower perfume, which had followed her in. The oak leaves outside snapped in the sea breeze like they were waving hello. Down in the garden, Marly could see Aunt Betty bossing the boys around. The roses were in full bloom, a riot of color planted by Marly's grandmother decades before, and the lupines were thickly crowded spikes of purple.

Marly unpacked her things, which took all of two minutes, and then flopped on the bed, which was far comfier than the old folding cot. She stared at the sloping ceiling. The last couple of summers had been boring. There weren't any kids her age in Oxeye. The place next door belonged to an older couple, Mr. and Mrs. Stafford, who basically napped all the time. When they weren't napping, they were complaining about the noise Marly and the others made. The rest of the houses on Tinker Street were owned by families with babies and toddlers. Other than that, the town was full of locals, none of them interested in a kid from Boston. Marly's brothers didn't want her around, and now neither did her cousins. She scowled at the ceiling.

Of all of them, Priscilla had always been the nicest to Marly. When Marly was little, Cilla had played with her, dressing her up and carrying her around, babying her. She'd gotten standoffish the last couple of years, though, not wanting to be hanging around with a kid all summer. Cilla thought of herself as grown-up and tended to join Mom and Aunt Bet downstairs, pretending she was interested in their boring grown-up chat. Still, even talking to stuck-up Cilla was bound to be more fun than lying here, staring at the ceiling.

"Where's Priscilla?" Marly demanded, barging into her mom's

room. Sylvie was curled up on the loveseat, bent over the forbidden magazine.

The mention of Priscilla got Sylvie's attention, though. Her head snapped up, her blue-gray eyes wide and gleeful. "Oh, didn't my mom tell you? Cilla's at luncheon at *Saint-Cyr*."

"What?" Marly's mother jerked as though she'd been kicked. She was unpacking her bags, folding her things into painfully neat rows in the drawers. Marly didn't think she'd heard Mom say *what* so energetically since Frank Sinatra had an affair with Ava Gardner. Except maybe when Frank divorced his wife to *marry* Ava Gardner.

"I know!" Sylvie put aside her magazine to stress how momentous it all was. "And she was invited there by a *boy*."

Mom joined Sylvie on the loveseat. "A boy!"

Marly collapsed into one of the overstuffed armchairs, giving up all hope of fun.

"She met him through her college roommate," Sylvie said, lowering her voice dramatically. "He's at Harvard. His family is staying at Saint-Cyr for the summer—or at least they are *now*. I wouldn't be surprised if he had them change their vacation plans just so he could be close to Cilla." Sylvie's eyes were shining just like they did when she talked about celebrities.

"No! Surely not . . ." But Mom's tone suggested it could be entirely possible. "Has your mother met him?"

Sylvie nodded so vigorously that it looked like her head might bounce right off. "Just this morning, when he came to collect her. He was driving a Chevy Bel Air in the most elegant gray, with—"

"Slow down, Sylvie. What did your mom think of him?"

"Oh, you know Mom. She thinks we should die old maids."

Marly's mom shook her head at that. "I think she just wants you to be safe and careful. You don't know what boys can be like, honey."

"Well, I think Mom liked him as best as she was able. He was *so* charming. Really, Aunt Lori, you'll *die* when you meet him. He looks just like Montgomery Clift."

Mom made a little sighing noise at that.

Marly kicked her heels against the floorboards. Was this what they were going to do all day?

Mom leaned forward. "What's his name? What's he studying? Tell me who his folks are! Are they from Boston or Philadelphia?"

"His name is Freddie de Marche and he's at law school. That's *all* I know. Cilla has been *so* close-mouthed, which is how I know it's serious."

"What do they eat for luncheon at Saint-Cyr?" Marly interrupted. "Prawn cocktail? And do they have one of those dessert carts, where they lift up the silver lids and you can pick what cake you want? Do you think Priscilla will have dessert, or will she say she's watching her figure?" If Marly was there, she'd eat dessert. She wondered if they had lemon chiffon pie. Marly loved lemon chiffon pie. But of course, no one bothered to answer her questions; they were too busy fussing over what Priscilla had chosen to wear.

"She had new white gloves, luckily, because her old ones were horribly worn," Sylvie explained. "And she wore her apricot dress with the full skirt, which looks awfully good on her, but I really thought she should have worn the green and white polka dot with the bow at the chin. It's much more elegant."

"If she's lunching with his folks, it must be serious!"

"Indeed," Sylvie said, satisfied with her aunt's enthusiasm.

Marly left, assuming they wouldn't notice, and they didn't. She headed out to the beach, where she tried skimming stones, but mostly just ended up pelting them into the water.

Being fourteen-almost-fifteen was a total drag.

SEVEN

The master bedroom ran along the entire front of the house, over the parlor and dining rooms, an ocean-facing sweep of coziness. And it was the only room in the house that wasn't full of junk—in fact it was immaculate. The far wall was dominated by three dormer windows, all of which looked out over the quiet little dead-end street, out to the cliffs and the bay below. From this high, the glitter of the water filled the view. As I stepped over the threshold, I could see the lazy gulls drifting on the sea breezes.

"The windows are clean," I said stupidly.

"Yeah." Jake leaned against the doorframe.

"And so is the room." I took in the long sprawling upstairs room at the front of the house, with its pale rugs and brass bed. A pink-and-white patchwork quilt sat folded neatly at the foot of the bare mattress. There were no plastic bags, no boxes, no milk crates. The floorboards were glossy and worn, honey colored where they weren't covered by the expensive-looking rugs.

Facing east, the bedroom would catch the dawn and full morning sun. There was a little sitting area with a squashy floral loveseat and a couple of matching armchairs. The wall sconces were pairs of upside-down frosted glass tulips and there was a scalloped mirror hanging on the wall above the loveseat, reflecting the sea and the sky.

It felt like home. Only no home I'd ever known.

"It's beautiful," I said, drawn across those honeyed floorboards to the windows. The sky was bluer than blue, and the ocean was sequined with jumping silver sunlight. From here I could see the bulk of the forest to the right, the shingled roofs of the summer cottages to the left, and Jake's store at the corner of the street.

My breath caught as a cloud of orange-and-black butterflies rose from the tangle of the front garden.

"Monarchs," Jake said. He'd followed me to the window. "They like the milkweed." He was sounding terser than ever. "Look, Ms. Copeland. You don't want this house." He was firm.

"I don't?" Wasn't the fact I'd made it through the entire house tour enough to prove to him that I was serious? And I knew they were monarch butterflies; I didn't need him to tell me. There'd been plenty of butterflies in Suni and Wayne's garden.

"This place is a wreck," he said forcefully.

"I thought you said it was just culch?" I kept my eyes on the butterflies as they spiraled across the green wilds. I wondered if I'd be able to make this garden as pretty as Suni and Wayne's. Maybe Wayne could teach me a thing or two about lawns. . . .

"A *lot* of culch," Jake snapped. "And plumbing and screens and lightshades and all the rest of it."

"You said a plumber would make short work of that toilet and that I could find lightshades cheap online." Annoyed, I turned away from the butterflies and the bright day and turned back to Jake Abernathy. He was standing with one hand braced against the sloping shiplap ceiling; his silly cartoon *lobsta* T-shirt had ridden up, showing his bronzed stomach. I tried not to look.

"You're not the type for this," he told me firmly. "This place needs serious time and money spent on it."

"How do you know what type I am?" I wasn't even sure *I* knew which type I was, but I didn't appreciate him mansplaining me to myself.

"You ever renovated a house before?"

"I've never had the chance to own a house before."

"Mom, come see this!" Flo's shrill excitement cut through the quiet house.

"It's work," Jake told me flatly. "Owning a house like this is work. Nothing but. This place needs someone who can restore it, not let it fall apart even more."

Oh. My. God. Was this guy serious? Did he think I couldn't see with my own eyes how much work this was going to be?

"Mom!" Flo interrupted, her voice echoing from the bathroom down the hall. "You have to come check out the tub!"

Pointedly, I turned my back on Jake and his disapproval and went to see the tub.

The bathroom was another time warp, this time to the 1930s or '40s. Flo was enamored with the clawfoot tub and floral wallpaper. The same upside-down glass tulip lights that were in the master bedroom hung on the walls. Whoever had decorated this place sure had a thing for fancy light fixtures.

"We're keeping this bath," Flo declared. "It's got feet. It looks like it might walk around while you sit in it."

"Don't get ahead of yourself. Your mother hasn't bought the place yet," Jake said from the doorway. "And she should think about it carefully, because this place—"

"—is a lot of work, I know," I finished his sentence for him. I wished he'd go wait outside and let us look around by ourselves. Maybe he could make friends with a snake or two while he was at it.

"Mom's good at work," Flo told him. "How do you think she got the money to buy a place like this?" She climbed into the tub.

"Don't." I reached for her but wasn't fast enough. She was already reclining in the tub.

"This thing is huge!"

Too excited to sit still, she soon hopped back out again and tore off toward the bedroom, leaving me alone with Jake. He was very still and watchful. "You seriously want this place? Even after seeing it?" he asked.

"Thanks to you showing me its potential." I gave him a fake smile.

"Right. Fine. Well, so long as you know what you're in for." He seemed to mentally shake himself. "Who am I to tell you how to live your life? Especially if the family has decided you can take a look at the place."

"Indeed," I said dryly.

"You'll want to see the furnace and the utilities, then."

When we walked back into the main bedroom, Flo was in one of the squashy armchairs by the window, flipping through a book. "Look, Mom. It's the same copy you have." She held up, of all things, *Anne of Green Gables.* It was a green cloth hardback with faded gold lettering and a little silhouette of a house under the title. I got that twisty feeling again. I'd gotten my copy at a library sale when I was a kid. This copy had probably been in this house since the year it was printed.

I'd been thinking about Green Gables in the kitchen earlier, and how much this house reminded me of Anne and Marilla, and now here was the book. In my new bedroom.

It was a sign.

Tina had always believed in signs. She used to say if we saw a yellow car it was going to be a good day (it usually wasn't). If the radio played "I Wanna Dance with Somebody" by Whitney Houston, her favorite song, it meant that she was about to meet the man of her dreams (she never did). If a cat looked you in the eye, someone unexpected would drop into your life (that happened all the time, but more because of Tina's nature than because of any cat).

I took the book gently from Flo. It was familiar in my hands as

I opened it. The same marbled flyleaf, the same yellowed pages. The same smell of aging paper.

"She loves that book," Flo told Jake. "I don't really get it. I tried to read it a couple of times, but nothing really happens. It's just a bunch of people going to school and walking about and talking and doing chores."

"A lot happens," I corrected her, appalled by her indifference to the folk of Avonlea. I put the book down gently on the little wooden table. There was a neat pile of hardbacks there, including one that looked like a bodice ripper, judging by the image on the dust jacket.

"*Anne of Green Gables* has no magic schools or Hunger Games or anything," Flo told Jake as she followed him down the stairs. "It's boring."

I paused at the threshold of the bedroom before I closed the door. The sun was a sharp sparkle on the ocean and the room shivered with light, even though it faced east and the day was leaning to a close.

This could be mine.

I imagined watching daybreak over the ocean from the brass bed; curling up on the loveseat on lazy weekends, listening to the call of the gulls and the restless whisper of the waves. The house was a promise of a life I'd never thought I could have. It gave me a buoyant, giddy, gusting feeling, like I was one of those gulls lifted on currents of marine air.

I knew I was buying this place.

I was a little unsteady as I followed Jake and Flo downstairs. I'd never been in debt before—the thought of taking a loan from Suni and Wayne was intimidating. I didn't want to let them down. I remembered the Tiffany lamp and the paintings stacked in the dining room. Maybe I'd find a treasure or two that could help me fund the renovations . . . and pay them back.

"There *is* a secret tunnel!" Flo all but squealed when Jake swung open the narrow wooden door under the stairs. "I knew Narnia would be here somewhere!"

"It's just the door to the basement," Jake told her calmly.

"But it's a *secret* door. How cool is that?"

Behind the secret door in question was a steep flight of stairs leading down into the dark.

Jake yanked on a tattered cord that hung down the wall to turn on the basement light.

"That's really weird." Flo couldn't resist trying it herself, pulling on the cord a few times to turn the light off, on, off, and on again.

"Not weird, just old-fashioned," Jake said. The two of them had fallen into a pattern of amiably disagreeing with each other.

They creaked carefully down the stairs into a dank-smelling basement, and I followed. The musty space was full of old furniture and garden tools. There also seemed to be enough empty pickle jars to start a small pickling business.

I jumped as the shadows moved. "Oh God!" There was a low, frightened yowl as something bolted over the tumble of junk.

"It's a cat!" Flo was delighted.

Jake hurried to close the basement window behind the departing animal.

Flo scrambled up onto a box and rubbed the dusty windowpane with her hand, but I could tell by her crestfallen posture that there was no trace of the cat. If it *had* been a cat. It could have been an opossum or a raccoon. Oh God, what if I had raccoons? How on earth did you get rid of raccoons in your basement?

"It's just a stray," Jake assured me, reading my mind.

"A stray *cat*." Flo shot me a sly look. "Maybe it's good we don't have a dog. It would only scare all the stray cats away."

"There's only one stray cat," Jake said. "And see, it's gone." He made sure the window was latched, as if the cat would be able to open it. "Just keep this closed and you'll be fine."

"Or we could open it and keep the cat?" Flo suggested. "Since Mom won't let me get a dog."

"We're not getting a stray cat. What if it has rabies?"

"I don't think cats get rabies."

"They do," Jake told her. "So don't go petting any stray cats."

"We can get the cat checked by a vet before we keep it." Flo gave me a pleading look.

"We're not keeping it, Flo. Besides, you heard Jake, it's gone."

"Is that the furnace?" Flo quite cheerfully changed the topic, pointing to the squat black furnace in the corner.

"Yeah, although if you're living here full time, you'll want to change to a heat pump. They're more efficient."

My heart sank as Jake explained why I might want to spend a heap of money updating the heating and getting the plumbing checked out. Not to mention the ancient electrical mains. By the time we got out of the house, he'd told me another half dozen things that were going to drain my bank account. I sure hoped one of the paintings in the dining room was a Picasso.

As Jake held back the red-berried bushes to escort us back to the street, an older man climbed out of a white Lexus that was parked in the driveway of the neat little house next door.

"Well, hey, Jake. What's going on here? Don't tell me you've found someone interested in the old place?" He was a lean old man with shining brown eyes and close-cropped silver hair. He wore a crisp checkered blue shirt and neatly pressed jeans.

"Heya, Elton. Ayuh, these ladies are taking a look."

"How come everyone around here says *ayuh* all the time?" Flo asked. "And I'm not a lady. Ladies are fancy people who wear stupid shoes." Flo tramped through the wild edge of the garden and out onto the sidewalk. She squinted at the man next door. "Are you our new neighbor? And what does *ayuh* mean?"

"Manners," I warned her, but the old guy didn't seem to be offended. He was already introducing himself.

"If this is your new house, then *ayuh,* I'm your neighbor. Elton Coutts at your service." He held out a hand for Flo to shake. "And *ayuh* is Maine for yes."

"Why don't you just say yes?" Flo seemed put out.

I adjusted my clothes, which had snagged on the bushes as we'd fought our way down the side of the house. I retied my ponytail and tried to look like I hadn't been in a fight with the garden. Some first impression I was making.

"Why should we?" Jake grumbled.

"I'm Florence Copeland." Flo shook Elton's hand, ignoring Jake. "It should be Snee really, because my dad's last name is Snee, but Mom wanted me to have her name, probably because she's the one raising me. And, also, why *don't* babies take their mom's names? Seems to me moms do all the painful stuff to *get* the baby. But also, Snee is a horrible name. Imagine being called *Flo Snee.*"

Mr. Coutts nodded along. "Yes, well, I can imagine, given I got landed with Coutts. I didn't have the option of taking my mother's name, though—not back in my time—but I can't say I would have wanted to, anyway."

"Why not?"

"Her name was Sidebottom."

Flo snort-laughed, which made Mr. Coutts grin, a big easy smile that made him seem like the world's kindest grandpa. His gaze drifted to me.

"Hi," I said, feeling absurdly shy. "I'm Zoe Copeland. Flo's mom."

"So, you're moving in?"

"I think so."

"Well, nothing's been decided yet," Jake broke in with his usual dourness.

"You must be close at least," Elton told me. "You're the first person the family approved to even see the place." Elton looked up at the house. "Well, I can't deny she's a darling old girl and worth protecting from blood-sucking developers. You should have seen her back in her day. . . ." He pointed to his own house, with its lemon-drop-yellow door. "She was as pretty as my place back then."

"Who?" Flo demanded.

"Your house," he told her affably. "She wasn't always like this."

"How do you know it's a girl?"

"Houses are always girls. Houses and ships."

"How come?" Flo considered the house.

I hurried to interrupt, knowing from experience that Flo's curious questions could spiral into chaos very quickly. "Have you lived here on Tinker Street a long time, Mr. Coutts?"

"Oh, well, that depends on what you mean by *lived.* This place was our summer house, the wife and I, for close on thirty years—but I would consider that vacationing, rather than living. Most of the year we lived in Boston."

"Don't you live while you're on vacation?" Flo asked. "And you had a whole house just for summers?" She let out a low whistle, something she'd recently learned how to do. "You must be rich. This is our first and only house, and we can only afford it because it looks like a trash heap."

"Flo!"

"What? It's true."

"Two houses is more than is strictly necessary, I agree," Mr. Coutts—Elton—said genially. "But this is my only house now. When my wife passed away, I moved here full time. What did I need with a big house in Boston, when there was just me? And it's nice to be here, where we made all our best memories." His gaze drifted back to our witchy house in its tangle of green. "There's lots of memories in old houses, good and bad, but your new home holds some golden ones."

I followed his gaze to where the shingled treasure house sat buried in overgrowth.

"Well, the day's getting on," Jake said abruptly. "We don't want to hold Ms. Copeland up much longer; she's got a long drive home."

I bristled. I had no plans to drive home yet. "It's Zoe," I reminded him sourly.

"You seem pretty set on getting rid of us," Flo told Jake as he propelled us to our car. She turned to wave to Mr. Coutts. "Is it because you want to buy the house yourself? Is this a plot? Are you trying to steal our house off us?"

Jake looked genuinely horrified. "I can't think of anything worse than owning that place."

"Good. Because it's ours. Right, Mom?"

"Yes," I said, stopping when we reached the hardware store. "I'm going to call the agent now." My heart was pounding. Oh my God, I was about to buy a house. A *junk* house. At least I was if the family would sell it to me. It sounded like they were pretty picky.

"This is really what you want?" Jake looked concerned, like I'd told him I was about to jump in the bay and swim across the Atlantic.

"It's what we came for," I reminded him, feeling snappy over his relentless interfering.

Jake shook his head in disbelief, his tousled hair falling across his sunglasses. "You must be half crazy."

I remembered the other houses I'd sifted through online. "This house is a find," I told him fervently. "You should see some of the others out there."

"Yeah, well, don't tell Gail that or she'll ratchet the price up." He smiled but still didn't look happy. "You might want to start a tab at my store," he suggested dryly. "I can order in the things you need as you need them. You're going to be renovating for a long time." He gave Flo a rueful look. "And you better get used to Moxie, kid, if you're going to be a Mainer." *Mainah.*

"You better keep stocking lemonade," Flo scoffed.

He shook his head, as though disappointed, but there was a glimmer of humor in his expression. "You got any idea when you'll be moving?" he asked me. "And are you sure you don't want another look at the place before you make your mind up?"

"We'll be here before school starts in the fall." I ignored his suggestion about seeing the house again. Maybe I was worried it would look worse on a second viewing. Right now I was clinging to memories of that long attic bedroom and its sea views—it was proof of what the house *could* be.

"Okay." He sighed. "Well, welcome to the neighborhood, I guess."

Jake watched us as we climbed back into the car.

"He didn't sound too pleased about us moving in," Flo said.

"I think that's just how he sounds."

Flo waved at him as we pulled out. Jake was standing by the front door of the hardware store, hands in the pockets of his cutoffs, looking like someone had just run over his dog. But dejection looked good on him. He was the kind of handsome that could carry anything off, even cheap plastic sunglasses and a hangdog expression.

After we left the house on Tinker Street, we drove up the coast, passing through Rockport to Camden. I felt euphoric as we cruised the coastal road, each little town so charming it hurt. Camden itself was stupidly pretty, a fairytale town with thickly wooded hills and a fishhook harbor where yachts bobbed like champagne corks. By comparison, Oxeye looked like a ramshackle afterthought. The only thing Oxeye and Camden had in common was the cobalt bay.

Flo and I found a quaint red shingled diner by the water, and I quieted her with a burger and fries and told her to amuse herself watching the tourists while I called the agent and then the bank.

It turned out buying a house could be shockingly easy and shockingly fast.

When the calls had been made, I dropped my phone on the table, feeling weak. "Flo? I think we just bought a house."

"Good." Flo jabbed a salty fry in my direction. "I was worried Jake was going to put in a bid while you were blathering away. Didn't you notice how he kept trying to talk you out of buying it? It was sus."

But I could barely hear what she was saying. I was having an out-of-body sensation. Just like I had when Tina got arrested. It was like I was watching myself from a great distance.

I'd bought a house.

A *house.* In a state I'd never been to before. In a town I'd only visited today. And I was about to quit my job. . . .

Oh my God. I was insane. How could I quit my job now that I'd taken on a house and a loan? What if I couldn't get another one? What if nobody was hiring? My heart was thundering. What if Flo and I ended up homeless because of my recklessness?

I never did crazy things. I was responsible. Boring. And yet here I was, leaping into the unknown of a new life. A junkheap of a new life . . .

"We should celebrate with a sundae!" Flo insisted. "How often do we buy a *house*?"

And because I was shaky from spending a truly scary amount of money, I gave in. She took full advantage of the situation and got a double banana split with chocolate syrup, whipped cream, and peanuts. A glistening, fat maraschino cherry sat right on top. Flo immediately handed me the cherry. She hated them—she said they tasted like cough syrup.

"I think you've had more sugar today than you've had in your whole life," I said weakly, taking the cherry.

She pulled the sundae closer, suspicious I'd take it away. "Can we turn one attic room into a spare room? Then we can have people come stay. Like Candy. Or Suni and Wayne."

Suni and Wayne. I should call to tell them the news, I thought numbly. But telling people would make it real. . . .

I nibbled on the sticky glazed cherry as I sat with the weight of my decision, vacantly watching Flo plow through the ice cream sundae. I'd just bought a house full of junk in a place I knew next to nothing about. We hadn't even driven by the schools. I hadn't checked out anything except the house and the hardware store.

"Flo-bug," I said abruptly, "I don't think I'm up for driving home tonight."

"Cool. Let's go stay in our house. We can find out if it's haunted or not."

The memories of bare bulbs and plastic bags and torn screens flashed before me.

"We can't," I told her, unable to hide my relief. "Not until closing. We don't technically own it yet."

"What's closing?"

"When the money changes hands."

"Oh. Okay. Let's stay here then. This town's cute." She spooned up a huge glop of melting ice cream. "Can we stay on one of those boats? That would be cool." She pointed to the yachts in the harbor.

"I doubt it." What on earth would it cost to stay on a yacht? "We can't afford anything around here," I warned Flo as I hunted for a motel. "Oh. How about this?" I asked, showing her the photos of the Oxeye campground with its little log cabins. The photos had been taken in fall when the woods were brassy with color. The cabins sat sleepily in drifts of red and gold leaves.

"Back *home* in Oxeye," Flo drawled, trying it on for size. "That sounds weird, doesn't it?" She pulled a face. "What happens if we hate the house once we're living there?"

I had a squirmy cold feeling in my stomach at the thought. "We can always sell it, I guess." I was reassuring myself as much as I was her. "And move back to Pittsburgh. But then we'll have to move out of Squirrel Hill and into a studio."

"What's a studio?"

"One room."

"The whole apartment is one room?" She pulled another face, this one more extreme than the last. "I'm not going to hate Oxeye that much." She reached for my phone. "Can we have a campfire tonight, at the campground?"

"I don't know what the laws are about fires in the summer. You might need a permit."

"Why?"

"Because it's wildfire season," I said as I booked the cabin. At least we'd still be on the coast, and only a stone's throw from our new home. It was only after I booked that I learned I'd have to pick the key up from one Jake Abernathy at Oxeye Hardware (and Lobster Shack). Great.

"Do you have the keys to *everything* around here?" I asked when I returned to Oxeye to meet him at the store. He was sitting out front at one of the picnic tables, watching the light fall rosy on the choppy bay as the day waned. He had a beer in one hand and a book open in front of him. The salty breeze eddied around us, riffling the pages of his novel. He was still stupidly good-looking.

"Pretty much, yeah," he admitted, reluctantly closing his book and leading me into his hodgepodge of a store. "It's a convenient location."

The windows at the hardware store were closed, and the place now had a hushed, sleepy feel. Jake reached behind the counter for a key, which was hanging on a little hook on the wall. The key was attached to a toy-sized orange and white plastic buoy. "So it doesn't sink if you're out on the water," he said, when he saw me looking at it. "If you're boating or whatever. It floats." He handed it over and my arm tingled as his fingers brushed mine. "Where's the kid?"

"In the car. She says she's overstimulated and needs some downtime."

His lips twitched at that, and a flicker of double dimples appeared. "Her and me both. I'll give you a map so you can find your cabin. You're in number five."

"No need to show us around this one," I said quickly, worried he was about to volunteer to give us a tour. One tour with Jake Abernathy was enough for today. "I'm sure I can manage to look around a one-room cabin on my own."

Jake gave me a reproving look with those marble-glass blue-green eyes as he slid a photocopied map toward me. "I was only trying to help." He took a pen and used it to trace the path from his store to the campground. "Here's the bay, and this is Beach Road here. You're going to drive down this road—"

I stopped listening about then, because I got distracted by his hands. He had working hands, suntanned, with gilded hair on his knuckles and a freckle on the back of his right index finger. His fingers had little nicks and scars, and there were specks of paint on his square nails. Also, he was leaning so close that I was enveloped in his scent, which was a blend of sea salt and wood shavings, sunscreen and beer. It was a summery smell that made my heart skip like it was the first day of vacation. "Got it?" he asked as his pen circled cabin number five on the map.

"Yep," I lied.

"Each cabin is off on its own in the woods, so be careful. The campground isn't staffed but you've got my number—call me if you run into any trouble. And if you're looking for breakfast tomorrow, the café two doors down from this place opens at seven; show them your key and they'll give you a fifteen percent discount. Colleen will look after you."

"Okay, thanks." I took the map.

"You know, you should probably spend some time in the town before you move here," he said gruffly. "Stay a couple of days. Meet a few people. Make sure you're not making a mistake."

"Thanks for the unsolicited advice," I said. The man was impossible. Although he wasn't wrong. "But my bid on the house has already been accepted. So you can stop warning me off now."

He was silent. He looked sorry for me.

"And thanks for your heartfelt welcome to town," I said dryly.

He didn't follow me out when I left. His beer and book sat forgotten on the picnic table as we drove off.

The campground was only a couple of minutes down the road from Oxeye, on a wooded spit of land that curled into the bay. The rusty cliffs grew lower and gentler as we drove, and there was a glimpse of a secluded sandy beach as we turned onto the spit. The photos hadn't done the campground justice. They'd made it seem low-rent and sad but in reality it was peaceful and secluded, everything you could want from a camping retreat. It felt like we were winding out of everyday life and into the wilds. The dirt road led through a woodland of spruce and oak, pine, maple, and hemlock.

When we passed a faded sign with curly writing on it, Flo squinted out the window to read it. "*Welcome to Saint-Cyr*," she said. "I thought this was still Oxeye?"

"It is," I said absently, focused on navigating the narrow track.

We drove by a sweet wooden playground of swings and monkey bars and a busy barbecue area. There were children squealing as they hung upside down on the bars while their parents cooked hot dogs and hamburgers on the grill in the fading evening. The campsites were discreetly scattered through the woods, just in sight of one another but far enough apart to feel private. Our cabin was in its own stand of trees, close to the water. It wasn't new, and it wasn't fancy, but it was full of charm. It was a proper old-fashioned one-room log cabin with a raw timber porch, complete with a couple of rustic, weatherbeaten rocking chairs. There was a cold firepit directly in front of our front door, but I'd forgotten to ask Jake if we'd need a permit, so I didn't let Flo have her fire. I made up for it by letting her use my phone for a while.

"Culch doesn't just mean junk," Flo called to me across the

cabin as I washed my face in the bathroom, which I was relieved to find was clean and serviceable.

I stared at myself in the small, fly-specked mirror. I looked pinched and stressed. I'd just spent so much money. . . .

"Culch means *usable* junk," Flo told me, sounding pleased. "The word *culch* comes from oysters." Flo looked up from the phone, frowning. She was draped over her cot upside down, her head over the edge and her braid dangling on the floor. "Is an oyster a fish, or a shell, or what?"

"I think it's kind of both. It's a shellfish." I'd never stopped to think about oysters and didn't really care to think about them now. I dried my face and hands.

I moved to the windows, glad to see they were screened to keep the bugs out. I opened them all, letting the woodsy sea air in, leaning into the sound of the bay murmuring and sighing. The wind made the trees shiver and rustle. I took a deep breath. At the very least, there were no more decisions to make today.

Flo rolled over. "Apparently oyster spawn—I'll look that up later, I bet it's gross—sucker onto culch and live there. And the culch is a bunch of junk that's settled on the seabed. Like shells and rocks 'n' stuff. So culch is *useful* junk. At least to the oyster spawn."

"I don't know how much of the culch in our house is useful." I sighed. "Our culch might just be junk."

She flopped back onto the bed, happily scrolling spawn pics. "Can I watch Netflix on your phone?"

"Sure." I felt a wave of relief at the thought of a moment's peace. I closed my eyes and let the sound of the sea fill me. The summer evening was a song of cicadas and waves and the wind in the leaves.

I heard the *da-dum* of Netflix booting up.

"You mind if I wander down to the water?" I asked abruptly. I needed to be alone. It was a keen feeling, sharp as nicking a finger on a kitchen knife. It was hard sharing a room with your kid—you didn't have space to feel your feelings. At least not openly. "I'll lock the door behind me," I said as I covered myself liberally in the cabin's complimentary bug spray. "And I'll stay close—you just need to yell if you need me." I felt guilty leaving her, but I needed a moment alone.

"Where's your charger?" Flo didn't care if I was in the cabin or not.

"In my bag."

Sometimes she seemed on the verge of being a teenager, and I didn't feel ready. I wasn't sure I'd be able to parent her. Even now, I felt I was failing her because I needed to be alone. I thought of myself in those cold walk-up apartments, abandoned by Tina. . . .

"If you see anyone, ask them if we can have a campfire," Flo instructed me cheerfully.

She wasn't me, I reminded myself. And I wasn't Tina. We were okay.

"I will. And don't forget, yell if you need me."

She didn't even reply. She just flopped onto the bed, curled over my phone.

I stepped out into the lush blue evening and inhaled shakily. I could feel the tension in my shoulders and neck as I locked the door. I slipped down to the water's edge, feeling the emotion of the day rise up, now that Flo wasn't watching me.

Oh God. I'd bought a house full of junk.

I was going to be the owner of that witchy cottage with its broken windows and bramble canes and *culch.* I had a loan on that junkheap.

I was going to cry, I could feel it coming.

I hid behind a maple and gave in to it.

The dark bay swam before my eyes, and I felt desperately alone as I sank down to the ground, my back against the maple, and pulled my knees up under my chin, hugging myself into a ball. How on earth was I going to do this? I was just one person. That house had accumulated lifetimes of garbage—what could one person do in the face of all that?

And I was one person who had to raise a kid and earn money. How could I possibly take on that house? How could I uproot us from Pittsburgh and the only people who cared if we lived or died? I wished Suni and Wayne were here. I needed someone to tell me I was doing the right thing. But deeper than that, there was a feeling I hadn't consciously felt for a very long time. . . .

I wanted my mom.

The thought of packing everything up, of hurling us into the unknown, stirred up deep old feelings. Sitting on the edge of the bay in the woods of Oxeye, I felt like I was falling back through time. I was a little kid again; the world was a big scary place, and my mom was nowhere to be found. Mixed in with the wild howling scary feelings was a bright cut of rage.

The first time I was put in foster care it was because Tina had overdosed. I was three. The only memory I have of that time is of a yellow bedroom and a woman who smoked a lot of cigarettes. I can remember looking up through a striated cloud of smoke to her face. Ever since that time, cigarettes have always smelled yellow to me.

The second time I was put in foster care was because Tina was picked up working the streets; she also had a stash on her. I was nine. Just a couple of years younger than Flo. I was at home in our little walk-up when an officer and a caseworker came for me. I remember that *Friends* was on TV; I remember the way the caseworker's eyes swept our poky little room as she gently asked me to pack a bag, to the accompaniment of the laugh track that followed Chandler's one-liners. I don't remember the caseworker's name, or what she was wearing, but I remember she had bags under her eyes, and she kept calling me *Zo,* like my name didn't have an *e* on the end. "Zo-*e*," I corrected her politely each time, but she kept doing it.

As I sat there in the Oxeye campground, I felt the way I had that night. The cold heaviness in my belly, like I'd swallowed a frozen stone; the tightness in my chest and throat; the hot pull behind my eyes. The feral panic that made me clench my fists until my fingernails cut red, grimacing smiles into the palms of my hands.

And what about Flo? Every ripple I made dictated the course of her life. What if this was the wrong choice for *her*?

What if the school was terrible? What if she couldn't make friends? What if she got bullied for being the freak who lived in the hoarder house her mom was incapable of cleaning up?

Jake Abernathy was right. I wasn't the type. I didn't know a nail from a screw. I'd never even painted a room before. I didn't know the first thing about weatherizing a house, or about furnaces and heat pumps; I didn't know how to keep a garden or clean out gutters or repair stairs or fix plumbing. I was so far out of my depth that the shore wasn't even in sight.

My throat hurt like I'd swallowed something hard. And in a wordless, hot, hungry burst, I wanted my mom so badly. It was a late-night wailing feeling, like the one I used to feel when Tina didn't come home. When everything seemed to press in on me, when all I wanted was to hear her voice outside the door, to feel her presence. To feel like someone had come to hold me and tell me everything was going to be okay. I buried my face in my bare knees, trying to cry quietly, so Flo wouldn't hear.

Eventually I shuddered to a wet halt and lifted my face. A pale pink shimmery moon was rising, almost full, swimming in the lavender night above the bay. Its unstable reflection swirled in the rolling waters below. Tina used to tell me the moon followed me. She said no one in the world knew the moon was mine, but it was tethered to me like a helium balloon on an invisible string, turning its face this way and that as it spun on its string. *It's yours, Angel. And no matter what happens, no one can take that moon away from you. You ever have a bad day, you can look up there and see your moon looking back at you, a gift from your mom.*

There would never be a day that I wouldn't miss her, I thought wretchedly. It didn't matter how old I got, or how many years it had been since I'd seen her, it still hurt like new. It was a deep feeling, full of grit, like a wound that had never been cleaned.

I wiped my face as best I could, given I didn't have any tissues, and crept close to the moon-splashed water, carefully navigating the rocky edge so I could go wash my hands and face. To my surprise I found an old set of stairs leading down to the water. They were steep, with a curved black wrought iron banister. There was another faded sign at the base, in the same curly writing as the Saint-Cyr sign back on the dirt road. *Private: Saint-Cyr guests only.* The salty bay water was cold, the shock of it pleasant on my skin after the hotness of all those feelings. I heard footsteps and hastily ran my cold wet hands over my face.

"Mom!" Flo's voice cracked through the hush of the woods.

I jumped. "Just wait there, honey," I called back hurriedly. I didn't want Flo to see me puffed with tears. "I'll be right up. . . ."

"Suni's on the phone! She says I need to get off Netflix and make sure you haven't been eaten by a bear. She read a Stephen King book once, set in Maine, where a kid got lost in the woods and eaten by a bear."

"I'm fine!" I called back, feeling the urge to laugh. I jogged back to the cabin.

"Hurry, I'm getting bitten by bugs!" She all but threw the phone at me and ducked back inside, safe behind the screens.

"Zoe?" Suni's tinny voice sounded from the phone in my hand.

"Oh, Suni. Sorry!" I put the phone to my ear and climbed the porch steps to one of the rocking chairs. I sat down shakily and tried to answer her rapid-fire questions about the house. "I was just getting some fresh air."

"Forget the fresh air, tell me about the house!" Suni demanded. The sound of her voice filled me with warmth. I sagged back against the rocking chair.

"It was what I expected," I admitted. "Only maybe worse. I put in a bid." I took a breath before I continued. "And they accepted."

"You *bought* the house? Already!" Suni's voice was a high-pitched squeal in my ear. "Wayne! Wayne! She bought the house!" I held the phone away from my ear as she yelled. Her enthusiasm eased the pressure in my chest, and I relaxed as I told her about the rooms full of junk, the Tiffany lamp, the kitchen, and the promise of that bedroom with its views of the sea.

"Wayne wants to know when you'll be closing. We'll come and help."

"You don't have to . . ." But the thought of them helping made everything feel less overwhelming.

"Alison might come too. She needs to get her mind off things. But I think Lance might be too busy with work to get away."

"Great," I said, even though I doubted Alison would be much help. She was in the depths of a pretty bleak depression with her divorce and I doubted she'd be up for a task as grueling as our treasure house.

By the time I managed to get off the phone, the pink moon had crested above the treetops, flooding the campground with light, and my new house felt less scary than it had when I was crying alone on the shore.

In fact, as I listened to Suni's energetic exclamations, it felt like an adventure. I thought about the house on Tinker Street, with its layers of time and secret history. Soon I'd step through the door and into its story, joining all the people who'd lived there before me.

EIGHT

Oxeye, Maine, 1953

Marly had been upstairs reading and missed Freddie de Marche bringing Cilla back from Saint-Cyr in his elegant gray Chevy Bel Air, but she heard plenty about it when she came down for supper. Even her brothers were interested—in the car at least—and Mom and Sylvie wouldn't shut up about the stupid boy. Cilla, who did look sweet in her apricot dress, was blushing and coy. Although she refused to answer Marly's questions about dessert carts.

Cilla looked a lot older this year. Maybe college did that to a person, Marly thought. A *girl* anyway, since Marly's brother Paul sure didn't look or act any older. He was just as puerile as he'd ever been. Cilla, however, had cut her hair in the poodle style everyone was crazing over, even though it suited hardly *anyone.* Cilla, however, could carry it off. Her wavy hair made it look effortless. She was wearing lipstick too, and a touch of rouge, and reeking of those dead flowers.

"Are his folks nice?" Aunt Bet demanded. She'd had a bunch of the iced tea from the seashell jug and was more relaxed about the whole thing than she might otherwise have been. "Are they good people?"

"I only met his mother and his sisters," said Cilla shyly. "His father is still in town working, of course. But his mother was perfectly lovely."

"And where's town?" Marly's mom asked.

"Boston."

There was relieved sighing at that.

"How lovely that you'll be close to home." Marly's mother sounded pleased.

"Oh, Aunt Lorraine, you talk like I'm *marrying* him!" But Cilla smiled a secret smile as she said it. "He *has* asked me to the Saturday dance at Saint-Cyr, though," she confessed, smiling a less secret smile as Sylvie almost fell over herself with envy.

"Oh, whatever will you wear?" Mom exclaimed. "You'll need something new."

"Don't be ridiculous, Lori." Aunt Betty scoffed. "She brought her pale blue tulle, that will serve well enough. She can't go buying a new dress every time a boy asks her to a dance."

"But it's *Saint-Cyr,* Betty."

"That blue tulle took me an age to make, and she's hardly worn it."

"Do you get to go to Saint-Cyr whenever you want now?" Marly asked, leaning over the back of Priscilla's chair. "Can I come too?"

"Stop bothering her, Marly." Mom gestured for Marly to give Cilla some space.

"It's fine, Aunt Lori. And no, you can't come. It's terribly exclusive."

Marly was offended. "What's that supposed to mean?"

"It's not for children," Priscilla told her, smooth as cream.

They ended up eating a late supper because everyone was so busy squirreling every detail out of Cilla, and when Mom and Bet finally remembered to feed everyone, they only managed cold cuts and a stupid green salad. After supper, Mom and Sylvie went upstairs with Cilla to advise on accessories to match the blue tulle. Marly sat on the porch watching the fireflies wink to life, listening to Aunt Betty boss the boys around as they did the dishes.

"Does anyone want to play Monopoly?" she asked hopefully when the dishes were done.

"Nah," Paul said, looking shifty. "We thought we'd go play cards in our tent."

Marly glared at him. She knew they were sneaking off to Rockport.

"We've already said goodnight to Mom," Marly's youngest brother Virge said, "so she doesn't have to tramp out in the dark."

"And don't wake us up in the morning, you little pip-squeak. We want to sleep in." Bobby gave her a dead arm as he passed.

Marly swore at him, but he only laughed.

"Goodnight, *Marilyn*."

"Don't call me that!" She hated her name.

Her brothers laughed as they disappeared into the firefly-speckled night, leaving her alone on the porch.

This was going to be the most boring summer *ever*. She didn't want to join in the fashion show upstairs, which Aunt Betty had now defected to, but she also didn't want to sit around downstairs by herself. It was empty and weird. Eventually she went up to her room, closing the door on the chatter about opera shoes versus pumps, and climbed into bed with a book she'd taken from the shelf in the hallway. Mom and Aunt Bet left their bodice-ripping summer reads on the shelf when they were done with them, but Marly was categorically forbidden from reading them. Mom said they weren't for kids because there was too much *intimacy*. That was her stupid word for it. She said it in a prissy, giggly, blushing way that made Marly cringe. But tonight Marly had taken the fattest one she could find, making sure it had a lurid cover. The dust jacket showed a woman with her dress just about falling off, and a man with a fencing sword. It was called *Forever Amber*. If no one was going to pay any attention to her, she might as well do something against the rules.

Marly stretched out on her new bed and sank into the seventeenth century. It was actually a decent book. Even though there was *intimacy,* in the form of a romp in the hay, in one of the first chapters. She took the dust jacket off and hid it under the pillows so her mom wouldn't know what she was reading when she came to say goodnight.

Only, Mom didn't come say goodnight.

Marly couldn't believe the nerve of her. She'd chattered away for hours with Cilla and Sylvie, and then the chatter migrated downstairs to the front porch. Marly was lost in her book and so didn't really register the running of water in the bathroom and the slow quieting of the house. But then, around the time Bruce abandoned Amber in the book, pregnant and alone, Marly realized everyone had gone to sleep. And *no one* had said goodnight to her.

It was like she wasn't even here.

The abandonment was a hot poison in her stomach. She could have been kidnapped for all they knew. She got up and dropped her book on the floor with a thud, hoping it would wake her mother up. But of course it didn't. No one cared if she was thumping around in here. No one cared at all.

As Marly stood there, fuming, she heard rustling in the oak tree outside. It was too much rustling for a squirrel. But just the right amount for her damn brothers. Of course they had come up with some plan to terrorize her, something they did all too regularly. Her blood was up and so she snatched up the book, prepared to rip them to shreds. She stuck her head out the window.

"Quit it, you chuckleheads, or I'll tell Mom you went to a bar!" she hissed.

The rustling stopped abruptly. And she saw it wasn't her brothers in the tree. It was someone she'd never seen before in her life. A young guy, about Paul's age. He was lit by the spill of light from

Marly's room but his face was mostly obscured by the leaves of the oak.

"I don't know you," Marly blurted. *Was* he a kidnapper?

"Hey, kid." The guy in the tree sounded sheepish. "Sorry. I . . . uh . . . I might have the wrong house."

"You might have the wrong house to *break into*? Why, because you got caught?" Marly wondered if she should throw the book at him—it was pretty heavy and would probably do some serious damage. But then she'd never find out what became of Amber.

"I'm not breaking in." He was indignant. And in his defense, he didn't look like a burglar. The guy was in shirtsleeves and a V-neck sweater vest. As he leaned forward into the light she saw he had an oval face and a high forehead, with close-cropped dark hair and thick eyebrows. His lower lip was a lot fuller than his upper lip and Marly could see a silvery scar on his chin. "I'm just *visiting*," he insisted. His eyes were pale blue, like shoal water, and they were somehow impish and chagrined all at once.

"You're visiting by sneaking up a tree?" He didn't seem dangerous, but you never knew, so Marly kept the book handy.

"Yeah. You wouldn't understand, you're just a kid. But it's meant to be romantic."

Marly rolled her eyes. "You're telling me it's *romantic* to bust into a girl's room in the middle of the night? Who did you think you were visiting?" But suddenly, Marly realized exactly who was in the tree outside her window. And Sylvie hadn't been wrong—he did look a lot like Montgomery Clift.

"Look, sorry I woke you, kid. I think I need the house next door." He started down.

"Stop! You go climbing into the Staffords' window and you're liable to get yourself shot. Mr. Stafford has hunting rifles, you know."

Montgomery Clift paused.

"You're here for Priscilla, I presume?" Marly drawled. "Freddie de Marche, right?"

"Well, sure. Who else would be visiting her like this?" His eyes narrowed.

"Priscilla's in another room." Marly rested her hands on the windowsill and considered him. "What were you planning to do when you got up here?"

He flushed. "Just say hi."

"Wow, my aunt will love to hear about this. A grown man creeping into her daughter's room to *just say hi.*"

"Now listen, half-pint, there's no need—"

"I think there's every need," Marly disagreed, deciding on the spot she didn't like him. "My cousin's a nice girl."

"She *is* a nice girl," Montgomery Clift said, trying to hide his anger behind a placating smile. "She didn't know I was coming, I promise. I just thought it would be romantic."

"You think if I scream and everyone comes running, they'll think it's romantic?"

"Kid, how about you just get Priscilla, and we'll clear this up. She'll vouch for me."

Marly wasn't about to get Priscilla. This was the most fun she'd had all day.

Marly considered the guy in front of her. The squirming, the flushing. He was caught off guard. She wondered what she could get out of this.

"What are your intentions toward my cousin?" Marly asked sternly.

"My intentions?" He was close enough that she could see the frown line forming between his eyebrows.

"Yeah. This doesn't look good for you, you know. It makes you seem like a molester."

He was outraged at that. "Now, hold it right there!"

"I mean, you didn't climb a tree to talk politics, did you?"

"I came to *see* her, not . . . *molest* her."

"You came to see her in her bedroom, in her nightclothes. Seems like you were hoping to see a *lot* of her."

"Your mind is in the gutter, kid. How do you even think like this at your age?"

Marly turned the book under her hand so he couldn't read the spine. "I have brothers."

"Listen . . . What's your name?"

"Marly."

"Listen, Marly. My intentions toward your cousin are only good. I like her. We have friends in common. I'm a decent guy—I'm not here to disgrace her."

Marly had an abrupt realization. "You're staying at Saint-Cyr, aren't you?"

He frowned. "Why?"

"Are you allowed to have guests? Can you invite people to play tennis or to eat dessert or whatever?"

He blinked, frowning. "I don't see what—"

"I'm open to bribery," she said honestly.

"Bribery?" He seemed totally taken aback.

"Sure. You get me into the resort for the day and I won't tell anyone I caught you coming to molest my cousin."

"Stop saying the word *molest*."

"Sure. If you let me into your resort."

"It's not *my* resort."

"Fine. I'll go get Aunt Bet and—"

"Stop!"

Marly stopped. In truth, she hadn't really moved in the first place.

"How old are you?" he asked tightly.

"Almost fifteen."

"Jesus. How did you become a hardened blackmailer at your age?"

"Natural talent."

He shook his head. "I can't let you loose at the resort unaccompanied; they've got a rule about kids under sixteen being under adult supervision."

"Fine. You can supervise me." Marly really wanted into that resort. It would sure beat sitting around here with a book.

Freddie de Marche didn't seem to know whether to laugh or wring her neck. "All right, enough is enough. Go get your cousin."

"No way. It would wake Sylvie too and she'd tell Aunt Bet on me for talking to you in my *bedroom* alone, even if it got Cilla into trouble too. Sylvie's a goody two-shoes." She narrowed her eyes at him. "I thought Cilla was one as well." Marly plucked an oak leaf from the tree and twirled it between her fingers. "And yet here she is, with a molester for a boyfriend."

"Stop saying *molest,*" he warned her through gritted teeth.

"Have we got a deal, pretty boy?"

He glared.

Marly shrugged. "It's no skin off my nose. I'll just scream and everyone will come running. And they won't get mad at me for screaming at a burglar, will they?"

He swore, but it was nothing she hadn't heard before.

"I want a whole day at Saint-Cyr," she told him firmly. "Breakfast through to supper. I want to play games on the lawn, maybe go out in a boat, and I want dessert."

"Your aunt seemed like a reasonable woman. She might understand a little romance," he mused. "Maybe I'll just risk it. . . ."

"She's not reasonable at all. Not when it comes to her daughters. And did you know my uncle fought in the war? Marines. You think he'll be happy about you creeping in to molest his baby girl?"

"Stop with that! Climbing a tree isn't molesting anyone! Haven't you ever seen *Romeo and Juliet* at the theater? It's *romantic.*"

"No, but I've read it, and there's plenty of molesting going on. That's what all the lark and the nightingale guff is about—he's in her bedroom when the sun comes up."

Freddie de Marche didn't appreciate her literary knowledge, she could tell. "That wasn't molestation. It was *love.*"

"I won't say anything if you let me spend one little day at your resort." Marly pretended to examine her fingernails. "Seems like a solid deal to me."

Freddie de Marche closed his eyes and sighed. "I must be insane. But sure. One day, in exchange for you never telling *anyone* about this."

"Don't you want Priscilla to know about your romantic plan to molest her?"

"Enough already. And no. I don't want her to know that I got blackmailed by a grade-schooler."

Marly scowled. "I'm in high school." She couldn't understand what Cilla saw in this guy. Other than his looks. "And I want to come to the dance too, so let's make my day at the resort this Saturday."

"Absolutely not. Kids don't attend dances."

"This one will. Don't worry, I can look older. I'll smack some lipstick on and pass for eighteen."

"I doubt that." He rubbed his face tiredly. "And how are you going to explain this to Priscilla? The fact that you're crashing our date at the dance? And why on earth would I choose to hang out with a little kid all day, anyway?"

"*I'm* not explaining this to Priscilla. You are. I'm sure you'll think of something." Marly gave him a jaunty grin. "Now excuse me while I lock my windows. You never know what kind of person might be lurking outside." She gave him a sarcastic wave. "See you Saturday, Freddie de Marche."

It didn't occur to Marly that meeting Freddie de Marche might be a defining moment in her life. It just seemed like a bizarre little incident in an otherwise boring summer. But what do you know about destiny when you're not even fifteen?

NINE

"Mom, there's another cat!"

My stomach fell at Flo's cry from upstairs, but fortunately she just meant another ornament. It was the last week of August and our first official day at the Tinker Street house. Although we weren't moving in just yet, because Suni had taken one look at the place and categorically forbidden us from sleeping there. Instead, she'd booked cabins at the campground and given us a week to get it habitable enough to live in.

"The priorities are bathroom, kitchen, and sleeping areas," Suni ordered. "By the time Wayne and I leave, I want to know you'll be able to live here hygienically."

Alison had joined us for the weekend, and she was pretty pessimistic about her mom's plan. "It'll take more than a week, surely," she'd said glumly, regarding the chaos of the kitchen. She was in sweats, her long dark hair pulled up into a messy bun, and she surveyed our house with a flat expression.

I understood her pessimism. Even though I'd known what to

expect, it had still been a shock to return to find the railings like broken teeth, the cracked windows and wild gardens, and all the *stuff*. . . .

It was hard to know where to start. We couldn't empty the porch or the kitchen junk out to the lawn, because there was no lawn, just the wild green tangle, threaded with brambles and thorns. And there was no space in the hall or the front. Where on earth could we put everything?

"I think we're going to have to tackle the garden first," Wayne finally said, as we tried to navigate the overstuffed house. He stared down the hallway, with its plastic bags and milk crates and boxes full of God knows what. "We'll clear a space outside and start emptying things out to sort."

"But what if it rains? I need to try and sell some of this stuff—I can't have it ruined by rain. . . ." I was feeling overwhelmed before we'd even started.

Wayne took his Pirates cap off and scratched his head. "Well, I just don't know what else you're going to do, honey."

"Maybe we can get some tarps?" Suni suggested. "Or can we use the outbuildings?"

"They're full of culch too." I groaned and sat on the stairs. "What have I got myself into?"

"*Culch?*" said Suni, raising an eyebrow. But I didn't have time to answer, because Ali was leaning over the banister looking frustrated.

"Zoe, Flo keeps disappearing," she complained. She'd been put on Flo duty but was wary of following her into the clutter. Ali resented having to come help, but her parents weren't leaving her alone in Bradford Woods, given that the restraining order she had against her ex didn't seem worth the paper it was written on.

"The person who lived here must have loved cats," Flo shouted down from one of the back rooms. She emerged and joined Alison at the banister with a porcelain cat in each hand. "That's two more up here. I found three in the kitchen, and another one in the laundry. How many do you think there are?"

"Flo-bug, I don't think porcelain cats are our first priority," Suni said.

"Ah, let the kid amuse herself." Wayne grinned up at Flo. "Honey, why don't you start a cat collection in your mom's new bedroom, where it's clean and safe?"

"All right. I'm going to start a button collection too. I'll get the button dish from the kitchen and bring it up here." She zipped down the stairs, patting me on the head as she passed.

"One of my new neighbors, the guy at the hardware store, said he could recommend someone to come help us cut back the garden," I told Wayne. "But I hate to think what it will cost."

"Needs must, kiddo." He jammed his cap back on. "Come on, we'll go talk to him and pick up some supplies."

"What supplies?" Suni asked. "You're bound to have everything you need here in the house . . . somewhere."

"I was thinking some heavy-duty gloves and face masks for the dust," Wayne said. "And we'll get some other bits and pieces too. I brought my tool kit but it's not quite up to a challenge like this."

"Okay, well, pick up the keys to the cabins while you're there," Suni called after us. "The booking confirmation says we have to get them from the man down at the hardware store anyway. I think his name's Jake."

"Yeah, we know him," Flo told her, as she dashed back up the stairs with the button dish. "Mom liked his muscles."

"Flo!"

"She did. She kept looking at them. Ali, you'd probably like him too. He's ripped."

"I've sworn off men," Ali was saying flatly as Wayne and I disappeared into the kitchen and out the back.

It was the dog days of summer and Tinker Street was somnolent in the morning heat. The summer houses were quiet and the sound of a motorboat was a low lazy undercurrent in the distance.

"Well, you picked a winner of a spot, no doubt about that," Wayne said admiringly. "Look at that view."

We gazed down to the glittering of Penobscot Bay and the hazy horizon beyond, where gulls wheeled against its vast canvas. This was where we lived now, I marveled. In this pine- and salt-scented town, with that view on our doorstep.

As we approached the hardware store, we could hear the Red Sox game on the radio, and the sound of excited barking followed by a low pleading whine.

Jake was standing by the picnic tables in front of the store, barefoot and without his shirt again, his body just as bronzed and just as muscled as I remembered. He was holding a red plastic basket full of bread and lobster bits. Tied to one of the porch posts was a speckled brown and white hound puppy, with long floppy ears and awkwardly large paws, whining as Jake threw lobster pieces and breadcrumbs to the gulls. "Dogs don't eat lobster," Jake told it irritably.

"Seems to me a Maine dog might eat lobster," Wayne observed amiably as we approached. He reached down and gave the dog a scratch.

"This is yesterday's lobster," Jake said shortly. "It's liable to make her sick." He threw another piece to the crowding, noisy gulls. "These guys, on the other hand, have iron constitutions." He nodded hello to me. "Saw you drive in this morning. I was going to pop over and say howdy, but I thought you might need some time to settle."

"Not much settling to be done for a while with the condition of that place." Wayne laughed. He was still pulling gently on the dog's ears. Wayne loved dogs. He'd been heartbroken when his corgi Arthur had died.

"Jake, this is Wayne." I never knew how to introduce Wayne

and Suni, so I kept it simple. I didn't like saying he was my foster father—it told people too much, and too little.

"I'd shake your hand but . . ." Jake held up his fishy hand.

"I'll consider it shook."

"I assume you've come for the cabin keys?"

"That and supplies," said Wayne, giving the dog a thorough cuddle. "What's this little guy's name?"

Jake watched him, disgruntled. "She doesn't have a name."

"She wasn't here last time we came," I said, keeping my eyes fixed on Wayne and the dog and not on Jake's naked torso. But from the corner of my eye, I could see his muscular arm flex as he upended the plastic basket of scraps. The gulls exploded in a hungry frenzy, fighting for the best of the lobster. The puppy also exploded, barking at the birds. Wayne laughed.

"You tell 'em, girl."

"Did you just get her?" I asked Jake.

He grunted. "Kind of." He headed into the store, leaving the puppy tied up, straining on her leash and barking at the birds. Wayne and I followed him in. "My sister gave her to me as a present. But I'm not keeping her." He sounded disgusted. "Who gives someone an animal as a gift?"

Wayne appeared to be very taken with Jake's store. He made a delighted noise and disappeared into the clutter.

"Let me just wash my hands and I'll get the cabin keys," Jake grumbled.

The sash windows were thrown open to the heat and I leaned against the counter, watching the shine of the bay and wishing I could be down there in the water, instead of up here facing a hot day full of culch.

Jake reemerged from the kitchen and snatched two cabin keys off the hooks before sliding them over the counter to me, along with another photocopied map. He circled cabins seven and eight and handed it over. His sea-glass-green gaze flicked up to mine as our hands brushed.

"Thanks," I said, trying to sound like my heart wasn't pounding a mile a minute.

"Your folks staying for the week, huh?"

I nodded. "Flo and I are staying in a cabin too, until they're happy with our cleanup," I admitted. "They seem to think we'll get buried in an avalanche of stuff if we try to sleep there now."

Jake didn't seem surprised.

The puppy set up a frenzied barking and was tangling herself up in her leash.

"Dog!" Jake called. "Be quiet!" He swore under his breath. "Hold on while I go untangle her."

I watched his broad back as he went to rescue his puppy.

"This place is great," Wayne said as he emerged from the aisles with an armful of stuff. He had face masks and gloves and what looked like a scythe. "It's like something the Grim Reaper would use, isn't it?" He was thrilled with it. "And check out the price—it's a bargain."

"People mostly use power tools these days, I guess," I said, amused.

"I should have brought my weed whacker from home, but this'll be more fun." Wayne looked as delighted with his old-fashioned scythe as Flo had been with her porcelain cats.

Jake came back in with his puppy, who was falling over her feet with joy at being by his side. He seemed irritated by her affection. "Sit," he ordered, taking her over to the dog bed by the cold pot-belly stove.

She didn't sit. She followed him, trailing her leash, her pink tongue lolling out of her mouth.

"That thing won't make a dent in your yard," Jake said dryly, nodding at the scythe.

"We came to ask who we should call to cut back the yard," I admitted. "You said you could recommend someone?"

"Oh yeah, I have a cousin in Rockport. He's pretty busy right now though, mowing lawns for all the summer folk. But I can give him a call. When do you want it done?" Jake pointedly ignored the puppy, who was looking up at him with adoring eyes.

"Ideally as soon as possible," Wayne said, dropping his purchases on the counter. "We can't really get moving with the place until we have somewhere to dump all the stuff."

"I probably should have organized this before we came," I mumbled. I felt completely out of my depth. But in my defense, I'd had a lot to do in the couple of weeks before the move.

"I'll message him, but I don't reckon he could get here today." Jake fished his phone out of his pocket. "I can give you a loan of some tools in the meantime, though, if you want, and you can have a go at it yourselves. You could at least clear the area by the back door."

Wayne thanked him. "We might need some tarps too. Zoe doesn't want anything ruined by rain." Wayne wandered back into the aisles.

The screen door slapped open. "Goddamn it, Jake. You got to stop feeding those gulls," a snappish voice rang out, announcing the arrival of a new visitor. "They're a menace. And they make a mess of the picnic area." An older woman with a bouffant hairstyle dyed carrot orange bustled into the store, carrying a rack full of bread rolls in clear plastic bags. A cloud of drugstore perfume came in with her.

"What do you care, Doris? You don't have to clean it up." Jake didn't look up from his phone.

"No, but I've got to walk through it. And those little bastards try and steal my bread. I feel like Tippi Hedren in *The Birds* out there." The orange-haired woman gave me a sharp look but kept going through to the kitchen. "I don't know how the boys next door put up with you," she complained loudly as she went.

"If anyone has to put up with anyone, I have to put up with them," Jake grumbled as he kept typing his message. "Alan practices those bagpipes at the crack of dawn. Who plays bagpipes?" he asked me. "You ever heard of anyone playing bagpipes?"

I shook my head.

"It's a wonder anyone comes back to their B&B with all that racket."

"People like it," Doris called crossly. "It's local flavor."

"Sure, if you're in Scotland," he called back, even more crossly.

"You haven't even started on lunch prep," Doris scolded him, reemerging with her empty rack, having delivered the bread rolls for lunch trade. "Why, you'll be overrun soon, and you haven't even chopped the scallions."

"I was waiting on the bread," Jake told her sourly. "Which is late."

"Giving you plenty of time to chop the scallions." Doris joined us at the counter, evaluating me. "And who's this little lady? New girlfriend? If you're getting involved," she told me, "you should know, love, that he *is* always this rude." Doris was a sturdy, broad-shouldered woman, barely five feet tall. She wore bright pink shorts and a shirt covered in yellow and orange polka dots. "People seem to think they'll thaw him, but this is as thawed as he gets. He was born frosty."

Jake shook his head at me, as though telling me to ignore her. "Doris, this is Zoe Copeland. She just bought the house on Tinker Street."

"You're the girl who bought Marly's place?"

"Marly's place? If you mean the house at the end of the street, then yes." I perked up. I'd been meaning to ask about the family who'd owned the house before me. The real estate agent had been thin on details, and Jake was downright cagey.

"I'm glad it's sold to a young'un." Doris gave me a bright look. "Welcome to town. Jake didn't tell me you were pretty." She gave him an unsubtle nudge with her elbow.

"Uh, thanks." I felt myself blushing.

"I'm Doris Laughton from Laughton General Store and Bakery." She looked me up and down.

"Nice to meet you." General Store *and* Bakery. Every store

around here seemed to do at least two things. When Flo and I had breakfasted at the café on the corner the last time we were here, we'd discovered it was a café *and* an art gallery, exhibiting paintings and sculptures made of found objects. It also stocked handmade jewelry crafted from driftwood, shells, and sea glass. And on Main Street, the library also took in dry cleaning, and the librarian, Josie, offered pet grooming on weekends from her home on the corner. The gas station was also a surf store.

"We don't do much baking anymore, though," Doris told me, lowering her voice as though this news was confidential. "Just the rolls for the lobster shack and the whoopie pies for the café. That's plenty to keep us going on with. Gary and I have earned our semi-retirement after all these years."

Jake's phone buzzed. He seemed relieved by the distraction.

"We stock bread and milk and the like," Doris told me cheerfully. "But for your fresh things, you'll be wanting the market in Rockport. They deliver too, if you need it. We're more your emergency kind of store. Like when you run out of sugar or need a stiff drink."

"We'll probably be in later," I told her. "To pick up some coffee and milk and basics."

"Righty-o." She pursed her lips, which were as orange as her hair. "Well, Jake. Those scallions won't chop themselves. Whenever you feel like getting off that phone and doing some actual work . . ."

"I'll keep that in mind, Doris," Jake said blandly, not looking up from his phone. "Thanks for the bread."

"It's a wonder he keeps this place afloat," Doris told me, in a pointedly loud voice. She looked down at the puppy, who was still staring up at Jake with big liquid brown eyes. "You named this dog yet?"

"I'm not keeping her," Jake said shortly.

Doris rolled her eyes and headed for the door. "Sure, you're not. Welcome to town, Zoe Copeland. Tell him to name his damn dog."

"Hud says he can come mow your place day after tomorrow," Jake told me, putting his phone back in his pocket.

The day after tomorrow . . . I winced, thinking of all the cleaning up Wayne and I would have to do to make a start on the house before then. "Thank you." I cleared my throat. "Any idea what it will cost?"

"Depends how much you want him to do, I guess," Jake said. "But he said he'd give you family rates, so it shouldn't be too bad."

"Look at this, Zoe!" Wayne had found some kind of old-fashioned contraption. "It's an old hand mower!"

"Suni will kill you if you try to take that back home to Pittsburgh," I warned him. But there was no stopping him. He was in his element.

"Oh, I forgot," Jake said, as soon as he'd rung up all Wayne's purchases and grabbed some tools for us to borrow. "I've got something for you."

"I'll start carrying stuff back," Wayne told me happily. "It'll take me a couple of trips." He gave a practice slash of his scythe as he headed out the door.

"Don't hurt anyone," I called after him.

"That thing's blunt as a wooden spoon," Jake told me. "I don't think he could hurt anyone if he tried." He scooped up his puppy's leash. "Come on through."

I followed him through the store, completely at a loss as to what he might want to show me. I couldn't help but notice the play of muscles in his back as he walked. His sweet little dog skipped alongside him, sometimes tripping over its own feet. Behind the Oxeye Hardware Store (and Lobster Shack) was a neat little yard with flourishing vegetable gardens in raised beds. A shade tree covered half the yard, a wooden doghouse with a red painted roof beneath it. There was a name painted over the doghouse door: *Ben*. I wondered how long Ben had been gone. I glanced at the new puppy. It might have some big paw prints to fill.

"Here." Jake walked me to a small shed at the back of the property. He let the puppy off her leash, and she went bounding to a water bowl next to the doghouse. I gingerly stepped into the little shed as Jake pulled a dustcloth off something leaning against the back wall.

It was a beat-up wooden door, with four panes of glass and a brass knocker shaped like a sleeping cat.

"It's your front door," Jake said. "I took it off and got the glass repaired for you."

"Oh," I said awkwardly, wondering how much the repair job was going to cost me. And why he'd thought he could interfere with my property like that. "Thanks."

"I figured you'd need a front door as soon as you got here. If you want, I can come put it on after the lunch rush is over."

"Thanks," I said again. I bit my lip, waiting for him to tell me the damage.

"It's on the house," he said hastily, reading my expression. "Sorry I took it without asking. I guess I got into overly familiar habits with that house." He sighed. "I've been its caretaker for a while."

Of course he had been. He seemed to do everything around here. I touched the cat-shaped door knocker. "This is very generous of you."

He grunted. "So . . . do you want me to come install the door later?" He seemed not quite able to meet my eye.

"I don't want to put you out."

"It's no trouble. Would only take a minute and your dad looks like he'll be busy clearing the yard."

I didn't correct him. It was easier for him to think Wayne was my dad than to explain my messy life. "Okay, thanks. If it's no trouble."

For the first time, I started thinking about the reality of living in a small town and having neighbors. Neighbors who did things for you, who knew your business. I didn't know if I wanted Jake, or anyone, knowing the details of my life.

By the time I got back to the house, Flo had found another cat. Only this time it was a real one. A big fluffy ginger with golden eyes. Which was lodged under the loveseat in my new bedroom.

"It was in the tub," Flo told me excitedly, "and then it ran in here." She was on her hands and knees, cooing at the recalcitrant cat. "It was drinking water from the dripping faucet. It was probably dying of thirst, poor thing."

The wretched cat didn't look like it was dying of anything to me. It looked big and fat and healthy. "How do you know if an animal has rabies?" I asked Ali, who was flopped across the bare mattress on my brass bed.

"Is it foaming at the mouth?"

"Is that a sign?" I couldn't see any foam.

Ali shrugged.

"We need to get it out of here," I ordered as Flo slid a saucer of water under the loveseat for the cat.

"Don't crash out, Mom, it's just a cat. Come on, kitty," Flo cooed to it. "I'm going to call it Marmalade."

"You're not keeping it."

"Zoe! You've got visitors!" Suni's voice came singing up the stairs.

Visitors? Who the hell would be visiting me?

"I want the cat out by the time I get back, Flo. Open up the windows so it can get out."

"It's all right, Marmalade," Flo soothed the still hiding cat. "I won't let her throw you out the window."

"I'm not throwing it out the window, Flo, I'm *encouraging* it out," I huffed. "And don't you dare touch that thing, it might have rabies. Ali!" I begged. "Watch her closely. I don't want a rabid kid."

Sighing, Ali got off the bed and came over to slump in an armchair instead.

I closed the door and jogged down the stairs and out to the

screened porch, where Suni stood chatting to two older men. One was tall and languid, in a linen shirt and tailored shorts and boat shoes; the other was short and frenetic, his gaze darting all over the clutter. The taller man was holding a basket and chatting easily to Suni.

"Zoe, these are your neighbors," Suni said as I joined them. "Roger and Alan. They run the bed-and-breakfast next to the hardware store."

"Ah, the lovely Zoe," the taller man said. He had a sweet smile and a twinkle in his soft brown eyes. "Doris said you were young and lovely, and she wasn't wrong. Which she sometimes is, isn't she, Alan?"

"Sometimes," Alan said dryly. He had salt and pepper hair that stood up in tufts at the back, as if in protest at the heat. His round cheeks were like ripe apples and he gave off an air of distracted but limitless energy. I assumed this was the famous Alan who upset Jake by playing the bagpipes at dawn.

"We thought we'd bring you a little something to welcome you to the neighborhood," Roger said warmly, offering the basket. He peeled back the checkered tea towel to reveal a mountain of golden, powdery rolls. "They're scones." He was clearly proud of them. "I got the recipe from an Englishman I romanced in my youth. It was the best thing about him." Roger laughed. "There are also some homemade preserves in there. We thought you'd need some sustenance on moving day. Especially given . . . well, you know." He waved his languid hand at the pile of furniture in the corner.

"Isn't that kind," Suni exclaimed as I took the basket.

"Thank you so much," I said. "I wish I could offer you a coffee or . . . anything. But . . . well, *you know,*" I echoed, also waving a hand at the room.

"We do know," they said in unison. They seemed delighted to be inside the house, knee-deep in my mess.

"There are some treasures in here, though, aren't there?" Alan said, peering around with curiosity.

"Oh, look at him." Roger grinned. "Desperate to go ferreting around for treasures. Loves his antiques, you know, and Jake would never let him go poking around."

"What do you plan to do with it all?" Alan asked, his gaze settling on the walnut wireless radio.

"Um, sort through it first, I suppose. And then sell anything valuable."

"Well, do keep me in mind if you're selling things," Alan said, his bright blue eyes darting back to me.

"Oh stop," Roger scolded him. "She'll think we're here with ulterior motives, and we only came to welcome her."

Alan's apple cheeks flushed even redder. "Of course. Welcome. But if you *do* need any assistance sorting the wheat from the chaff, or a place to start looking for buyers, I'd be only too happy to help."

"Thank you." I sighed. "I might take you up on that."

"Mom! I got it!" Flo came bursting in with her arms full of fluffy ginger cat.

"I told you not to touch it!" I didn't know whether to rip the possibly rabid cat out of her arms or not. What if it bit or scratched her? Wasn't that how you got rabies? It was probably best not to make any sudden moves.

"Ah, you found Debussy," Roger clucked. "Naughty boy, we've been looking for you!"

"He's yours?" Flo's face fell.

"Not exactly," Alan said, although he reached out to scratch the cat under the chin. The animal was dangling limply from Flo's grip, its yellow eyes unperturbed. "Debussy belongs to no one. He's his own man. He pops in for a visit now and then, though, usually after Jake's been throwing out those stinking lobster scraps. Marly used to feed him regularly, though, so he tends to be here more than anywhere."

That was the second time today I'd heard the name Marly. I wanted to know more about the woman who'd lived here, but at present I was distracted by getting the cat out of Flo's arms.

"He doesn't have rabies, does he? My mom is convinced all cats have rabies." Flo gave me a pitying look.

"Not as far as I know."

"There you go, Mom. You can chill." Flo hiked the cat up as it tried to slide out of her grasp. "I'm Florence," she told our visitors, and once they'd introduced themselves she began peppering them with questions about their clifftop hotel. "Do you actually have to cook people breakfast in a bed-and-breakfast, or is it just a name?"

"I'll go put these . . . somewhere," Suni said, taking the basket of scones off me. "Maybe I'll get Alison to go get some take-out coffees. . . ."

From outside there came a loud curse. Alan and Roger turned, concerned. "I think the man with the scythe may have run into trouble?"

Following the noise, I saw that Wayne had discovered that his new toy was nearly useless. Both he and the scythe had ended up tangled in thorny brambles.

"Maybe you should hire someone to do that?" Roger suggested mildly from behind me.

"Oh, I have. Wayne's just trying to make a start," I said, as I tried to pull Wayne out of the brambles.

"Is everything okay?" Mr. Coutts from next door appeared.

"We're just trying to clear a patch so we can empty some of the furniture out onto it," Wayne grumbled as he regarded his scratches.

"For the love of God, Wayne, just use the power tools from the hardware store," Suni exclaimed. "I told you that old thing was useless."

"Do you need extra hands?" Mr. Coutts asked me.

"No, I couldn't possibly ask you to help," I assured him.

"It's no trouble. That's what neighbors are for. And I've wielded a power tool or two in my time."

"Well, I haven't," Roger said lightly, "but I can certainly bring a delivery of coffees and sandwiches." He elbowed Alan. "And Al can put on his work clothes and get involved, can't you, hon?" He winked at me. "Anything for a chance to get a closer look at your clutter."

That was how I found my backyard full of helpers that first day. Between Elton Coutts from next door, Alan from the bed-and-breakfast, and Wayne, Suni, and me, we managed to clear a decent-sized patch of the garden by late afternoon. Roger brought a cooler of cold drinks and a ready supply of sandwiches and cookies. And late in the day he threw an embroidered tablecloth over a couple of milk crates and served us an afternoon tea of scones with preserves and cream.

That was how Jake found us when he ambled in after the lunch rush at the lobster shack. We were all sitting on the back porch, sticky with preserves and sweaty from cleaning up the yard.

"You found Debussy," he said, seeing the orange cat sprawled across Flo's lap. He didn't seem half as surprised to see the rest of them. If anything, he looked like he'd expected it.

"Is he yours?" Flo asked suspiciously, drawing the cat closer.

"God, no."

She relaxed. "Good."

"You never said our new neighbor was pretty," Roger rebuked him lightly.

I flushed, my gaze darting to Jake. He was in a powder-blue T-shirt that made his eyes glow like the morning sky.

"It didn't seem relevant." Jake shrugged.

Roger snorted. "That's why we despair for you, Jake."

"You left it to Doris to tell us too!" Alan complained. "You know we hate finding things out after Doris."

"I brought the door." Jake ignored them and addressed me. But he looked a touch pink and wouldn't meet my eye. "Okay if I put it up now?"

"Yes, thank you," I said, aware I was sounding oddly stiff and formal. I rose from the swing and rubbed my sticky hands on my jeans.

Jake's double dimples dented faintly. "All right then."

"Do you need me to help?" I asked.

"Sure." Jake shot Roger and Alan a look, as though they'd said something. Which they hadn't.

"Lead the way," I invited. I was feeling tired after a hot day's work in the yard. It was a bit demoralizing to pick our way through the maze of junk in my yard as we headed out and around the front. I felt like we were just moving junk from one place to another but not really making progress. Having a working front door would be something, at least.

"You want to hold the ply while I take the bolts out?" Jake bent over his toolbox once we'd reached the front porch.

I braced myself against the plywood that covered our missing front door, and with a short buzz of his tools, Jake soon had the thing off.

"Hop out the way," he said gently, as he carted the plywood out to the front porch.

"Oh," I exclaimed, shocked as the plywood came down and I moved to stand in the open doorway. I mean, I'd known the porch had a view of the ocean but knowing and seeing was something else. From the threshold of my house, I could see straight ahead to the bay, and it was glorious. The sky was bronzed from the heat, the clouds buttery in the late-afternoon light, the ocean a gilded mirror. Briny fresh air flooded into the hallway, swirling out the dry dustiness of neglect. "Wow," I said lamely, unable to find the words to do it justice. I drank it in. This was the view from my front door.

"Gives you a reason to keep on going, doesn't it?" Jake said, grunting as he lifted the heavy door and carried it to the doorway. I moved out of his way, hyper-aware of our bodies brushing as he passed me.

A branch of palest lilacs hung over the broken porch railing. I broke off a stem and held the blossom to my nose. I'd always loved lilacs, ever since the summer I'd been driven up Suni and Wayne's driveway, greeted by rows of the flowering bushes.

I tucked the stalk into my hair elastic so I could enjoy the perfume, and watched Jake make short work of the door.

It was incredible, the way this one little change—the addition of a front door with shiny clean new glass—made a world of difference. Rather than looking like a condemned building, the house looked like, well, a house. I felt myself stand straighter.

"You want me to fix up the horseshoe while I'm here?" Jake asked, as he finished with the door.

For the first time I noticed the horseshoe over the door. It was aged and thick with rust, askew on its single nail. "It needs fixing?"

"You need it up like this," Jake said as he fixed it with the ends facing up. "So you can gather up the luck. If you have it the other way, all the luck drains out." Jake stood back and admired his handiwork.

"You didn't strike me as the superstitious type," I said, surprised.

He shrugged. "I didn't say I believed it. It's just what people do."

"Thank you," I said. "This—the door, the horseshoe—actually makes me feel a lot better for some reason."

"Gotta have a door," he said as he packed his tools away.

"Hey, Jake!"

Jake squinted down the street to where a couple of kids and their tired parents were walking toward us along Tinker Street. The kids had towels strung over their shoulders like capes and were still full of energy. "Hey, Ted," Jake called as the taller of the two kids pelted toward us. The kid was all long limbs, with sharp elbows and big feet. He reminded me of Jake's puppy.

"That's the de Marches," Jake told me. "They have the summer place next to yours." He pointed at the little white cottage next door. "Ted and Lila are probably around your kid's age." He pulled a face. "Although, as she keeps reminding me, Flo could just be a short teenager."

I grinned. "She's eleven."

He nodded. "Ted's older, then. He's twelve. He's a Twitch celebrity or something. Streams himself playing video games."

"Jake!" Ted was tumbling up the cul-de-sac. "Dad says he'll drive us down south to surf tomorrow!" He stopped dead as he saw me. "Is this the lady who bought Marly's place?"

As their parents wandered up, looking hot and irritable, laden with beach bags and a cooler, Jake did the introductions. It turned out Ted's dad, Perry, was yet another of Jake's cousins.

"You've taken on quite a task there," Perry told me as he put the cooler down. He looked like a finance bro on summer vacation, with his polo shirt and expensive sunglasses. He also looked utterly defeated by the walk up the hill.

"This house is a task that seems to get bigger by the minute," I agreed.

"Colleen at the café said you have a kid," Ted said, craning his neck as though he might be able to see her through the windows in my new front door.

"Ted, don't pry," his mother scolded, pushing her hair out of her face. She was a lithe blonde who probably usually looked sleek and chic, but right now was pink and sweating.

"My daughter's name is Flo," I told Ted. "She'll be starting at the school in Camden next week. Do either of you go there?" I asked hopefully. It would be so much easier if Flo knew a couple of kids before she started.

"No, we're from Philly. We go home in a couple of days."

"And then school starts," his mother said, with measurable relief.

"No one much really lives in Oxeye outside of summer," Perry told me. "Except Jake here and the people who run the shops."

"Plenty of people live here," Jake told me, sounding annoyed.

"Right, kids, we're going to shower and take a nap. Barbecue at Great-Aunt Priscilla's at seven." Perry clapped his hands. "No arguments. Showers all around."

The two kids pulled faces and complained loudly as their parents rounded them up.

"See you there, Jake," Perry said with a wave. "And welcome to Oxeye, Zoe."

They flung their beach towels over their low front fence as they went, leaving them to dry. I could hear the kids chattering as they all disappeared inside. Their summer cottage was whitewashed and cheerful, with daisy bushes by the front porch and an immaculately clipped lawn. The shutters and front door were painted a soft sea-mist gray.

"So they're here every summer?"

"Just a few weeks of it. They share the cottage with the rest of Perry's siblings. Perry's always complaining he gets the dog days." He took his toolbox and headed down the steps. "Most of the summer homes in Oxeye are old family places. People who come from Boston or Philly but aren't fancy enough to have a place in Camden." He gave me a wry look. "We're not so fancy around here—sorry."

"That's okay. I'm not so fancy either."

The double dimple flickered for a second. "Got a fancy front door now, though."

"I do." I looked at it, clinging to the feeling it gave me—the feeling that we'd made headway with this hot mess of a house. "Thank you."

"Pleasure. I'd best get off now. Have to make sure things are in order at the campground before I wrap up for the day." He gave me a wave over his shoulder as he headed off.

"Mom!" Flo's voice came honking down the side of the house. "I lost the cat in the house!"

I sighed. Of course she had.

TEN

By the end of the week, Flo and I had met everyone in town. Or rather, everyone had met us. One by one they dropped by to evaluate us, and one by one they stayed, chipping in to help. Ted and Lila de Marche didn't spend the next day surfing with their father—instead their father spent the day watching the Pirates-Cubs game on an old color TV with Wayne as the two men pretended to sort through the detritus in the laundry. Perry de Marche seemed relieved not to be surfing, while Ted and Lila had taken a shine to the house and had spent hours combing through the rooms with Flo, who was in her element as she instructed them to collect any and all porcelain cats.

Colleen from the café came by with a plate of whoopie pies and ended up instructing me on how to recognize quality china; we also met Josie from the library, who dropped in to welcome us to Oxeye and was soon enthusiastically cataloguing the stacks of newspapers. Alan and Roger were frequent visitors too—Alan was as fascinating as an episode of *Antiques Roadshow,* assuring me my Tiffany lamp *was* genuine, and Roger kept up a steady supply of coffee and scones for everyone. Elton from next door arrived with a tent he'd borrowed from a friend of his in Camden—it was the kind people put up for weddings and was perfect for protecting our culch from the weather. He put himself in charge of organizing the collection that grew out there. By the end of the week, the kitchen had been entirely cleared out, as had the back porch and the laundry, and our upstairs landing and bathroom were spotless. Even Flo's little attic room had been emptied and made habitable. Every other room was now filled to the brim, but that was next week's problem.

As was my new job. I'd gone for an in-person interview on our third day in town, after a phone interview with one of the doctors. The medical practice was in Rockport and looked more like a church hall than a doctor's office. It sat between a pair of beech trees and had a gray shingled roof and blue-gray shiplap walls. The window frames and front door were jaunty white, and on each windowsill planter boxes exploded with geraniums.

I liked the look of it. I could imagine walking in that white door every morning, passing the funny little timber sign that read:

DR. MAUD GERRISH
Quality healthcare with a smile

&

DR. PARKER NOCK
Book an appointment with someone who knows what they're doing and stop googling your symptoms

There was a sign taped in the window: OFFICE MANAGER NEEDED. MUST BE ORGANIZED AND NOT TALK TOO MUCH. I'd gathered my courage and gone in, but I needn't have worried. A smiling and very kind Dr. Gerrish offered me the job before I even opened my mouth. I left with a stack of forms to fill out and

Dr. Gerrish's best wishes for our move. I hadn't even met Dr. Nock. But it felt meant to be. And any anxiety I might have about starting a new job could wait until we'd wrestled the Tinker Street house into a semi-livable state.

During that busy first week, Jake's cousin Hud had appeared, as promised, with a trailer full of equipment and a couple of helpers. He plowed his way through our front and back yards, his power tools a persistent whir through the hot afternoons.

"I'll try not to cut down anything worthwhile," he'd said when he'd arrived, eyeing the jungle. "But I can't promise anything." He was a weather-beaten, laconic guy, probably in his forties. He wore a faded and crumpled old Red Sox cap and a pair of plastic sunglasses that looked straight off Jake's rack at the lobster shack. I didn't see how he could tell what was worthwhile or not, but he seemed to know what he was doing. It took him three days, but by the time he left, the gardens had a shape, even if they still looked like they'd been neglected for a lifetime. Now we could see the stand of crap apples, and several other sturdy old trees.

"You've got a nice hornbeam there," he'd told me, pointing. "And mountain holly and moosewood." He'd managed to find the old vegetable beds that Jake had mentioned, which were marked by weathered wooden railroad ties, and a rose garden too—the roses running wild and witchy. "Give them a hard prune and they'll come good," Hud told me. He shook his head. "Marly never was one for gardening. Didn't have the patience for it."

I felt a stab of curiosity about the woman. Everyone kept mentioning Marly, but when I tried to ask questions, they clammed up. It seemed Mainers were a close-mouthed lot.

In my mind, I pictured Marly as a scruffy old woman, stuck in her ways, irritable. Isolated. It was the only way I *could* imagine a woman who'd buried herself alive in *stuff.*

"So Marly lived here?" I said to Hud, hoping he'd tell me more.

"Ayuh." Hud drawled the Maine slang for yes and shook his head and grinned. "Not a lady to suffer fools." He laughed and reached into his back pocket as he closed the topic. "Here you are." He handed me his card. "If you want me to come mow the lawns and keep things under control, just hit me up."

"I don't know if I'll have the budget for that," I admitted, but I took the card, disappointed that he wouldn't say more about Marly.

"I'll give you family rates." He took a last lingering look at the backyard. "I'm glad someone's doing the place up. It was a shame to think of it being sold, but if it has to pass out of the family, I'm glad it's gone to someone who'll love the place."

Family?

"You were related to Marly?" I said, surprised. "Oh." The penny dropped. "That means Jake is too?" That explained why he'd thought he could steal my front door without asking.

"Ayuh. But everyone's related to everyone around here. It's that kind of place." Hud headed for his truck. "Nice to meet you, Zoe. You take care of that garden, eh," he told me. "It deserves some love."

When he finally sent the bill, I assumed he'd made a mistake. But it turned out family rates were bargain basement rates, and I realized that maybe I would be able to afford him after all.

"You didn't tell me you were related to the woman who lived in my house!" I accused Jake when I went down to the hardware store to buy sealant to repair the kitchen sink.

"You didn't ask." He was untangling his dog from her leash. She was tied by the cold potbelly stove and had somehow knotted herself up. "Does it matter?"

"Sure," I said, hunting through the shelves. "It makes you seem less creepy, for a start."

"*Less* creepy?" He was disgruntled. He was actually wearing clothes today, for a change—a soft green and white striped cotton T-shirt and jeans. His hair was flopping over his forehead in its usual salt-sprayed tumble, and he looked sun-kissed, like he'd just come in from the beach. Which I knew he hadn't, because the mess of the lunch trade was still all over the picnic tables out front.

"Less creepy, but still creepy?" Jake prodded me.

His puppy barked, trying to get his attention. She licked at his neck as he struggled to unknot her leash.

"Have you named her yet?" I asked.

He scowled. "Only so she can be trained, not because I'm keeping her."

"Oh my God. You *have* named her. Doris said you would." I picked a sealant at random from the shelf. "Is this one any good?"

He scowled. "Depends. What are you using it for?" He had to unclip the puppy to get her out of the tangled leash. "And for your information, you can't train a puppy without naming her. And you can't *not* train a puppy when she chews on everything in sight," he muttered under his breath.

I told him what I needed the sealant for.

"Pick the yellow one, it'll be better. Wayne doing it, or you?"

"Me." I peered at the instructions. "Wayne's busy trying to fix the downstairs toilet." Which wasn't going well, judging by the amount of swearing that erupted regularly from the bathroom.

"How come you call your folks by their first names?" he asked curiously.

"They're not my biological parents," I told him, keeping the explanation as vague as I could. And then I changed the subject. "How hard is it to seal a pipe?"

"I'll come by after I close the store and show you." He sighed.

"No, I have to do it now. I'm sick of mopping up every time someone makes coffee." I put the yellow tube on the counter. "What did you call your dog in the end?"

"Hazel. And she's not my dog. She's leaving as soon as my sister gets here to collect her."

"*Hazel?*"

He shrugged. "She looks like a Hazel."

I considered her. She did look like a Hazel. It was something about her big brown eyes. I reached down to give her a scratch behind the ears, and she melted at my feet. "What breed is she?" I knew nothing about dogs.

"Springer spaniel," he said in disgust. "I mean, do I look like a spaniel guy?" His gaze drifted to the photos of the golden retriever on the wall, and he sighed again, this time like a balloon deflating.

"So, I assume if you're related to her, you know what happened to her?" I asked, watching as his puppy rolled onto his bare feet, wriggling happily.

"We're not talking about Hazel anymore, I assume?"

"No. The woman who owned my house." I paid him for the sealant.

"The woman who owned your house got sick and couldn't manage things." He passed me my yellow tube. "That's how life works." He grabbed a pair of plastic sunglasses off the rack. These ones were ombré neon green and yellow. He slid them on, like he was in a rush. "Now if you'll excuse me, I have to clear up after lunch."

Whoever Marly had been, she really hadn't been able to manage things. Nothing worked properly at Tinker Street. Every time we tried to fix something, it just made it worse. When I was messing around under the sink with the sealant, I wrapped my hand around the ancient metal pipe and the stupid thing cracked. It was brittle as old paper. Just when I was cursing it roundly, Wayne exploded from out back, cursing even louder.

"You can't be serious!" He swore black and blue, much to Flo's glee.

"Wayne broke the toilet!" she told me brightly, sticking her head through the kitchen door. "I mean, broke it even *more*. You should see it."

I didn't want to see it. I could *smell* it.

"Just call a plumber," Suni advised when she came downstairs to see what the commotion was. She was covered in dust.

"Oh my God, what's that *smell*?" Alison appeared too. "It smells like something died."

"My toilet just died," I groaned.

"Wayne killed it," Flo corrected cheerfully. "And there's all this black gunk everywhere."

"Plumber! Now." Suni snapped her fingers at me and went to collect Wayne. "You get away from that filth this instant and go shower! You're liable to get some horrible bacterial infection."

By the time I finally got through to a plumber, it was after hours. The emergency service rate was exorbitant, but I could hardly let the broken toilet keep oozing sludge into the house. I sent Flo back to the campground with Suni, Wayne, and Alison and waited for the plumber to arrive. I should get him to fix my kitchen sink too, I thought morosely, as I regarded the water leaking from the shattered pipe. This was going to cost me.

This was the first time I'd been alone in the house, I realized, as I sank into the silence of waiting. All week the place had been a commotion of people and activity. We'd hauled things around, cleaned things out, stacked things, tossed things, fixed things, sorted things. I hadn't stopped moving all week. Now that I was here alone, in the falling dark, feeling the abrupt absence of people, I was struck with the full import of moving. This was *my* house.

It was silly, but I felt like I'd barged in on someone and not introduced myself.

The kitchen had been cleared over the course of the week, stripped back to a bare black-and-white-checked linoleum floor, which was peeling and long overdue for replacement. We'd left the wooden table and the mismatched wooden chairs, and a single rocking chair by the fireplace, but otherwise the room was empty. It was a huge space, spanning the whole width of the house. The tall windows on either side let in the violet, velvety dusk. Suni and Alison had spent an afternoon scrubbing the old oven range—and the room still reeked of vinegar. I'd been tempted to remove the range entirely rather than clean it, but Doris told me not to be so ridiculous, it was worth its weight in gold.

"Once you get the hang of it, you'll never regret keeping it," she told me sharply. "People pay a fortune for these old things. And this one doesn't have so much as a speck of rust."

Tonight, the range sat good as new. I could have been standing in the same kitchen a century ago, it was so devoid of modern conveniences. The dusk gave everything an otherworldly feel, as though time had slackened its hold on the night.

Who had stoked that range on this night a century ago? Who had sat in the rocking chair? The twilight hush felt heavy with the presence of people unknown to me. Except for Marly. I knew her by name at least.

I drifted into the hall, which was more cluttered than ever now that we'd moved everything out of the kitchen. Through the glass panes of my new front door, I could see the deeply shadowed street outside, and the lights spilling out of the summer houses and the hardware store on the corner. The sky over the dark ocean was inky blue, the clouds pearly gray.

The house on Tinker Street didn't feel haunted exactly, just sleepy with memory. I headed upstairs, which was now mostly habitable, except for the attic room full of clothes. Between us, we'd managed to box up the stuff in Flo's room and clear it out completely. Suni and Ali had done an incredible job of washing the walls and ceiling, cleaning off years of dirt. Wayne had assembled Flo's bed, which we'd brought from home. It now sat under the eaves in the corner, already made up with her rainbow quilt, her stuffed unicorn, and the purple pillow with the frill that she loved. A cute little bookshelf sat empty, ready for Flo to fill, and an old-fashioned wooden desk had been pushed under the window for her. The room needed new paint, and a rug, and an awful lot more, but it was a start. And it was a room of her own—which she'd never had in her life before.

I felt shivery with emotion as I sat down on the chair, staring out at the thick-leafed oak branches outside the window. Flo would be happy here. I knew it, as sure as I'd ever known anything.

I sat there until the evening glow had faded completely, and then I went to my own bedroom to wait for the plumber.

It was as perfect as I remembered. More perfect, because Suni had made up the bed for me. I'd kept the brass bed frame, glad to say goodbye to the narrow single I'd used for years, and Suni had bought me queen-size sheets and new pillows as a housewarming present. The room was a haven, and I felt like I was stepping into its open arms.

Through the window, I could see the moon rising over the bay, not pink this time but shimmery silver, and thin, like the curve of a cheek. It cast nets of moonlight over the waves and chalked the street with a long platinum streak. I opened a window to let in the restless song of the sea.

Down below, I could see the de Marche kids as they tore around their backyard chasing fireflies, and the people at the next house over packing their car so they could leave in the morning; the lights at the back of Roger and Alan's bed-and-breakfast were buttery golden, and the slide of cars passing along Beach Road winked red and white. Above the hardware store, Jake had all his windows thrown open and through one I could see the faint blue flicker of a television and hear the sound of Hazel's excited barking.

The scent of lilacs was thick on the briny, piney air as I leaned against the windowsill. From here I could see the faint glitter of lights through the thick woods down on the spit, where the campground stood. And to my left, the curl of the shore sparkled, outlining Rockport's city limits. I'd wondered if I'd feel lonely here, in this tiny town, but tonight I felt anything but. From up here, I could see people wherever I looked. Even the dark mass of the firs on the right side of Tinker Street felt comforting—a presence at my side rather than a frightening absence.

"I like it here," I said to the house, sighing.

And I half imagined the creaking of the floorboards was the house sighing back. I wondered how many moonstruck summer nights Marly had spent here in Oxeye. And if she'd ever been happy here, before she'd buried herself in junk.

ELEVEN

Oxeye, Maine, 1953

Marly got her day at Saint-Cyr. But it wasn't quite what she expected. Firstly, because Freddie de Marche ended up inviting her entire family, which was not part of the plan. And secondly, because by the time the day was over, she had a red-hot crush on him.

"You invited *everyone*?" she complained when he dropped by with his stupidly wide-ranging invitation.

"You think people would believe I wanted just *you* along? It would be ridiculous to turn up and invite you out of the blue. As far as they know, we haven't even met yet."

Marly didn't like conceding a point, so she stayed silent.

"This way you get what you want, and they won't question it because they get to come too. Everyone's happy," he said smoothly.

"Except me."

The slick jerk. Marly could see he'd won Aunt Betty and Mom over instantly. And Marly's brothers were all chummy with him, keen to hit the water on the sailboats and to meet some of the girls they believed swanned about the resort in their bathing costumes.

"Well, lover boy, the deal was that *you* would escort me around." Marly sulked. "None of this bunch will play tennis with me or take me out in a canoe. I want someone to do things with."

"I'm sure your brothers will play tennis with you and take you out in a canoe." Freddie rolled his eyes at her scowl. "But if they don't, I promise I will, because a deal's a deal. But the deal is *one day,* and one day only. And if you step so much as a toe out of line, I'll tell them you're a nasty little blackmailer."

"And I'll tell them you're a midnight molester."

He ignored that. "But if you behave yourself like a perfect angel, you'll have a good day, and no one will know you're an extortionist. Or that I was a misguided romantic."

"You mean molester."

He gave her a spiky look. "One day only."

"Including the dance. You remember that when they try and leave me at home tonight."

"They're not going to leave you at home. You really are the sourest kid."

"I'm not. I'm just sick of being left out. If I'm included, I'm sweet as pie."

"Sure you are, pixie stick."

"Don't call me that."

"I'll stop calling you that when you stop calling me a molester."

The whole house was in a flutter in the lead-up to Saturday. Dresses were pressed, shoes were shined, hair was set. Even the boys fancied themselves up. Marly could barely get into the bathroom to wash her face.

Priscilla was acting like she was the First Lady or something. She was all haughty and hostessy, as if she owned the resort. For Pete's sake, she'd only ever been there once before.

"It's such a shame he doesn't have brothers." Sylvie sighed. She was wearing her pink gingham sundress and looking pretty as a picture. Marly caught Priscilla eyeing Sylvie with a touch of concern. But Cilla didn't need to worry, she was striking in her green and white polka dots.

Marly thought they were idiots wearing fancy dresses when there was canoeing and tennis on offer. Personally, she'd opted for pedal pushers and a striped boat-necked shirt. There was no way she was missing out on the fun just to look fancy.

"Oh, Marly, put a skirt on at least!" Mom scolded. "It's *Saint-Cyr*."

"I *know* it's Saint-Cyr. I want to go out in a canoe."

Mom didn't put up much of a fight. She was too excited, and who really cared what a kid wore? "Fine," she said, sighing, "but put your hair up, will you? You look like a scarecrow."

Mom herself had set her hair and was in her best suit, with its tight knee-length skirt, her white gloves immaculate and a silly little hat perched on her bouffant hair. Aunt Bet was also in a suit, looking hot and uncomfortable in her blazer and pumps.

They went in Mom's wagon, even though the resort was all of two minutes away, because all the women were wearing stupid shoes and couldn't walk down the hill. Marly was stuck between Sylvie's and Priscilla's poufy skirts while her brothers were crammed in the back of the station wagon, acting like a pack of wild dogs. Marly wished they could have just walked. It was a pretty walk down to the coast through the woods.

They passed the sign with its curly *Welcome to Saint-Cyr* greeting, and the gravel driveway crunched under the wheels as Mom nervously drove them down to where the valet waited. And he *was* wearing a little jacket with shiny buttons, just like Aunt Bet had promised. The buttons were as big as half-dollars and winked in the sun.

"What do you think I should tip him?" Mom whispered hurriedly to Aunt Betty.

Freddie de Marche was loitering on the porch of the hotel,

waiting for them. He was in loose cords and a short-sleeved knit shirt, nowhere near as dressed up as Marly's folks were, but far more elegant looking. His pale blue eyes were masked by a glamorous pair of tortoiseshell sunglasses, and he was smiling like a politician gearing up to kiss some babies.

"Good morning," he welcomed them lazily. Everything about him had a lazy air. Marly wondered if all rich people were that languid. Maybe they didn't drink enough coffee. Or they slept too much. Freddie had expensive-looking teeth, Marly thought, like he got them cleaned by a dentist every morning. "I've organized a table on the patio, if you'd like breakfast?"

"Oh, we've already had breakfast," Aunt Betty said in a weird, breathy kind of voice.

"Mother, he's organized a *table,*" Priscilla prodded.

"Perhaps coffee if no one's hungry?" Freddie suggested. "The coffee here is excellent."

"*I'm* hungry," Marly volunteered. She wanted to know what fancy people ate for breakfast. She doubted it was shredded wheat, like her mom forced her to eat.

"I'm sure the boys are hungry. They're always hungry," Mom twittered. They followed Freddie de Marche as he led them through the foyer, leaving Marly to bring up the rear.

Saint-Cyr itself was everything Marly could have hoped for. It was what Mom would call *perfectly exquisite.* That was what she said when things were rich-looking. The foyer was polished black-and-white tile, with a staircase that split in two like the one in *Gone with the Wind,* and there were tall palms everywhere in copper tubs, and a giant vase of red and white gladiolus on the desk. The place smelled like lemony furniture polish and the ocean. Marly's tennis shoes made a squeaking noise as she walked. That's what happened when you waxed your floors too much—things got squeaky.

They passed through the French doors out onto the back porch, which apparently was the "patio" even though it didn't look anything like a patio. It was actually just a deep veranda with white wicker furniture. Freddie led them to a long table under the awnings with a perfect view down to the bay.

Freddie pulled Cilla's chair out for her, and then did the same for Mom and Aunt Betty. Sylvie stayed standing until he pulled hers out too. Marly pointedly sat herself. Their waiter appeared in another one of those jackets with half-dollar buttons, and everyone ordered coffee and orange juice and not a single person let Marly get a word in edgewise. Freddie de Marche noticed, his stupid lips twitching with amusement.

"What about you, kid?" he drawled, right when the waiter went to walk off. "You fancy some waffles or something?"

"Marly's had her shredded wheat. She's fine," Mom said with a fake little laugh.

"No, she's hungry," Marly retorted. Marly hadn't eaten anything that morning, determined to make the most of her day out and to eat as much resort food as she could stomach.

"I recommend those waffles then," Freddie de Marche said, leaning back in his chair. "Get the Canadian bacon and syrup too. Trust me, it's a winner."

They all acted like he was a goddamn saint for letting her order waffles. Mom and Aunt Betty didn't order anything but coffee, and Sylvie and Cilla ordered *grapefruit,* for Pete's sake.

"Is your mother here?" Priscilla was asking Freddie when the food arrived. Her half grapefruit was topped with a shiny red cherry.

"I thought we could have tea with her later," Freddie said, acting as though he'd like nothing more in the world than to sit around with his mother and Cilla's folks on this sparkling June day. "She's excited to meet you all," he added, but Marly could tell he was lying, even if no one else could. "And boys," he said, giving Marly's brothers a polished grin, "I took the liberty of penciling in a sailing lesson for you, if you're interested." He checked his watch. "Starts in about fifteen minutes. I thought you might take your sister?"

"No," Mom said firmly. "Last time they took Marly out on the water, they almost drowned her."

"Mom, I was eight!" Marly couldn't believe her mom was screwing up sailing for her. She'd hoped for canoeing, but sailing was a million times better.

"To be fair, we'd probably still drown her," Bobby volunteered.

"She's very drownable," Virge agreed.

And that's how Marly found herself stuck at the table with the simpering women while her brothers went off sailing on this linen-fresh June morning. The bay was an outrageously beautiful shimmer at the end of the lawns, and yet here she was in front of an empty waffle plate, listening to Mom and Aunt Bet pump Freddie de Marche for information on his career plans. Freddie himself didn't look too thrilled about it either—that was something at least.

"Can we play tennis?" Marly blurted eventually, bored to death with all the talk of law and Harvard and blah blah blah. "Cilla, you and Freddie can play me and Sylvie."

"I didn't bring my tennis shoes," said Priscilla, the spoilsport. "And we can't just invite ourselves to play, sweetie." The "sweetie" was pointy and sharp.

"I didn't bring my shoes either." Sylvie sounded more regretful, but not regretful enough in Marly's opinion. "Didn't think tennis was in the cards. Shame, because I *love* tennis." She actually fluttered her eyelashes a little, which Priscilla noticed and didn't like.

"Tennis *isn't* in the cards," Cilla said tightly.

"Well, it can be," Freddie said, draining the last of his coffee and giving Marly a resigned look.

"Great." Marly was on her feet already. "You four can sit here and drink seltzer and watch the yachts while Freddie and I play tennis."

"Freddie doesn't want to play tennis with you, Marly dear," Cilla said in that same cloyingly sweet voice, which carried a lethal undercurrent.

"He's wearing tennis shoes," Marly observed. "I think that shows he's keen to play tennis." Honestly. Who wanted to just sit around all day?

"Marly," Mom said warningly.

"It's quite all right, Mrs. Orcutt. I'm nothing if not a gallant host," Freddie de Marche said in his lazy way. "And I'm awful fond of little kids."

Marly glared at him.

"You're most welcome to order more coffee or take a wander around the grounds. I'll give Marly here a game or two and we'll be back before you know it."

Cilla's face fell like he'd just said he was off to hike the Himalayas for a year. But Mom and Aunt Bet were melting at his graciousness.

"Isn't he just the most perfect gentleman!" Mom was saying as Freddie led Marly away.

"She's only saying that because she doesn't know about your tendency toward molestation."

"Drop it, short stuff, or I won't play with you."

Marly trotted to keep up with his long strides. "I should warn you that I'm better at tennis than I look. And *you* look like a guy who had tennis lessons growing up but lacks the killer instinct needed to win."

"You're a pain in the ass, you know that, kid?"

"Yeah." She did.

He laughed and shook his head. "Come on, then. Let's get you a racquet and you can show me your killer instinct."

Freddie de Marche was good at tennis, but he was also good at making it fun and not just beating the hell out of her like her brothers did. They had a few volleys that left Marly breathless and laughing.

"That was great," she said, deeply satisfied after three matches. He'd won all of them and seemed surprised she wasn't upset about it.

"I'm used to losing," she told him without rancor. "But only to brothers. When I play kids my own age, I wipe the court with them."

"Even though your technique is appalling."

"I've never had lessons," she told him as they returned their racquets and crossed the lush lawns. "I've just got—"

"Killer instinct, I know." He put his hands in his pockets and slowed his steps to match hers. "Sorry your brothers didn't take you out on the yacht."

"I told you they wouldn't." Marly glared at the sparkling bay.

"Well, in their defense, you *are* quite drownable."

"Can you take me out on a yacht? Or at least in one of those canoes?"

"It depends on what your cousin wants to do. I don't think she'll forgive me if I ditch her *all* day."

"But all they do is sit around," Marly moaned. "And *look* at all this." She swept an arm to the boats and the volleyball net and the croquet court. "There's so much fun to be had."

Freddie laughed. He seemed genuinely amused by her. "Patience, pixie stick. We've got all day."

"No, we don't." Marly dragged her feet. "Because they want to get back early to curl their hair or their eyelashes or whatever for the dance."

"Well, there you go. We can go for a sail while they do that. Then I'll drop you home. Unless you need time to curl your eyelashes or whatever too?"

"Seriously?" She was surprised he was volunteering to take her out for a sail.

"Sure. Despite being a pain in the ass, you're quite good company. I was a bit worried I'd be bored here this summer," he confessed, "and yet I've already been blackmailed by a criminal prodigy. And my sisters won't play tennis anymore—they don't like to perspire in public—and everyone else at this place seems roughly the age of Methuselah." He laughed. "Although don't expect this to continue after today. I don't make a habit of playing tennis with kids."

"Yeah, well, I don't make a habit of playing with molesters."

"Drop the m-word now, kid. I invited you here and played tennis. I've kept my side of the bargain."

"I'll downgrade the m-word to *potential* m-word, how about that?"

"And after the sail?"

"I'll drop it completely," she promised. "Provided you give me a dance tonight. Because no one else will and I want to try dancing at least once. Proper dancing I mean, not the kind you do at school. My mother says dancing is the closest thing to heaven and I'm determined to prove her wrong."

He snorted. "Cilla or Sylvie might dance with you?"

"Don't count on it."

"Fine. I'll dance with you if nobody else does." He stopped dead. "Oh God damn it."

"What?"

"It's my father."

Mr. Stanford de Marche looked like a man who'd be more comfortable in a uniform, Marly thought. He was a stiff sort of man, with a military haircut, a ramrod-straight back, and a complete inability to engage in small talk. Marly quite liked him. Freddie, on the other hand, couldn't cope with him at all. He went from being all lazy to being itchy and snappy and generally out of sorts.

Mr. de Marche wasn't pleased to find his son had guests. "I'd planned to relax this weekend," he'd growled at Freddie, not caring that Marly was standing right there. "Not entertain total strangers."

"So don't entertain them. Go drink a fifth and take a nap," Freddie said in a flat voice.

"And who is this Priscilla girl anyway? What happened to Birdie?"

Marly joined in. "Yes, what happened to Birdie?" What kind of girl was called *Birdie*? And what would Priscilla think about this!

"Birdie's in Capri for the summer with her parents," Freddie said tightly, ignoring Marly. "And Pris is a friend."

Pris? A *friend*?

"Wow," Marly said, once the terse little conversation was over. "You're such a gentleman."

"Oh, hush up," Freddy said, still glaring at his father's retreating back. "Birdie and I aren't serious, and neither are Pris and I."

"Cilla," Marly corrected. "She hates being called Pris."

"She never complains when I do it."

"No, well, she wouldn't, would she?" Marly griped. "But trust me, she secretly hates it."

Freddie de Marche of course made a point of calling Priscilla *Pris* all day after that. And Priscilla, the idiot, let him, even though Marly could have sworn she saw her eye twitch every time he did.

Mr. de Marche seemed to put everyone off as much as he put Freddie off, Marly noticed—even his own wife. Mrs. de Marche was elegant and very, very thin and looked like she'd just licked a lemon, especially when Mr. de Marche was around. They all had a rather stilted luncheon together in the dining room. Marly's lucky brothers missed the whole thing, still out on the bay in their yacht while Marly had to sit, bored as hell, at the end of the table next to a potted palm.

"He's a bit much, isn't he?" Mom murmured about Freddie's father to Aunt Betty as they got ready to leave.

"Almost as much as she is," Aunt Bet murmured back.

Cilla wasn't pleased when she learned Freddie planned to take Marly out on the water. "You don't have to," she said, a frown forming.

"I know, but the kid was pretty heartbroken when her brothers left her behind this morning."

Marly tried to look heartbroken.

"Maybe *I'm* heartbroken at not going out too," Cilla said, looking sulky but trying to do it prettily.

"Don't you need to curl your eyelash—" Freddie cleared his throat. "I mean, don't you need to get ready for the dance?"

"There's plenty of time," Cilla lied. "And we haven't been alone all day."

"That's settled, then," Mom said cheerily. "Priscilla and Freddie will go for a sail while we go home and get ready. Come on, Marly." She clicked her fingers at Marly like she was a dog.

"Sorry, kid, I tried," Freddie murmured as they waited for the valet to bring the car.

"You better dance with me tonight," she hissed at him under her breath. "Or the m-word is coming back out and I don't care who hears it."

Marly had never been to a dance before and she only had one dress that was at all appropriate: a yellow cotton sundress with tucks down the front. It was missing a couple of buttons and her mother made her fish around in the button dish for replacements. She stood in her robe waiting while Mom took *forever* to sew them on. Sylvie lent her a poufy net petticoat to go underneath her sundress, but only after Aunt Betty intervened. The bouffed-out skirt looked more grown-up, but not by much, and Marly only had her patent Mary Janes to wear. Talk about little kid shoes. She looked like she was going to church.

Mom let her borrow a pair of white gloves with little floral eyelets all over the backs, and she tied a yellow ribbon in Marly's loose hair.

"Lovely," Mom said absently. But Marly knew she looked her fourteen years and no more.

Sylvie and Priscilla, on the other hand, looked like full-grown women. Cilla's blue tulle made her bust look bigger than it really was, and Sylvie was pert as heck in her pink chiffon with the big buckle at the waist. Marly's brothers were in their sport coats, their hair Brylcreemed and their shoes shined to a high gloss (courtesy of Mom). They had a flask hidden and kept passing it back and forth when Mom wasn't looking. On the way out to the car, Marly picked some seaside daisies and tucked them into the ribbon in her hair.

Although she wasn't exactly sure what a dance should be like, she thought they were meant to be fun. And this one wasn't. A dance floor had been cleared in the middle of the same dining room where they'd had luncheon earlier but there weren't any decorations or anything. A band played watered-down standards, while old people shuffled around, stepping on each other's toes. There were sandwiches and a little tray of cream cakes but otherwise it was slim pickings. Marly's brothers disappeared into the billiards room, which was no girls allowed, and Mom and Aunt Betty joined Mrs. de Marche and a bunch of squares sitting in the far corner.

Sylvie had a string of partners all night and no inclination for a pity dance with Marly, while Priscilla hogged Freddie. Which left Marly where she always was—nowhere. She bet if her dad had been here, *he* would have asked her to dance. But he was never here. Dad did nothing but work.

Marly tried to catch Freddie's eye, but he was busy staring down at Priscilla like a goof. She sighed and ate a bunch of sandwiches, roamed the foyer, did laps of the patio, and grew more and more restless and despondent. Being fourteen-but-not-yet-fifteen was a total drag.

About the time the band launched into "Que Será, Será," Marly gave up. She headed outside and parked herself on the lawn under a maple tree, waiting out the rest of the night. She wished she'd brought her book. *Forever Amber* was a hell of a lot more interesting than this. Amber was in debtor's prison and had just taken a highwayman as a lover. Marly sighed and leaned back on her hands, gazing out at the dark bay.

She hadn't gotten a sail *or* a dance today. It was so unfair.

"Hey, pixie stick, everyone's worried about you."

Marly looked up to see Freddie de Marche crossing the lawns in his lazy, loping way.

"Liar," she sniped. "I bet nobody even noticed I was gone."

"Well, no, maybe not," he confessed, "but they will notice. Eventually. Maybe when it's time to leave."

"Not always," Marly grumbled.

The thing about not being wanted was you started to feel like you deserved it. Like maybe you *were* annoying, or drownable, or just plain forgettable.

"Are you skipping out on your first dance, kid? After all the fuss to get here." Freddie was wearing a preppy houndstooth sport coat. He looked pretty flash, all dressed up.

"Skipping out on my first and my last," Marly said definitively. "It's snoresville in there."

He gave her a knowing look. "It won't be snoresville when you're older," he promised, "and there's some boy you want to dance with. Closest thing to heaven, remember?"

Marly pulled a face.

"C'mon, half-pint, I owe you a dance."

"Forget about it." Marly sighed. "I don't need your pity."

"It's not pity," Freddie scoffed. "It's paying off my blackmailer, remember?"

"Well, consider her paid." Marly kicked her heels into the lawn. "I don't want any stupid dance anyway."

Freddie looked up at the sky. "Ah, you're killing me here. Where's your sass gone?"

Marly shrugged. "I don't want to go back in there."

"So we'll dance here."

"There's no music."

"Sure there is." He cupped a hand to his ear. "If you listen hard, you can hear that god-awful 'How Much Is That Doggie in the Window?' song playing."

Marly snorted.

"Do you know how to dance, or do you want to stand on my feet, and I'll shuffle you around like a little kid?"

"Get lost."

He grinned and tugged her to her feet. "Wait for it, in a minute they'll play something else. You don't want to waste your dance on Patti Page."

"She's so wet. I don't get why people like her."

"Tell me about it. My mom thinks it's cute. She turns it up every time it comes on the radio." He pulled her arms into position.

"Ugh, mine too."

"This is better," Freddie said as another sickly old ballad started up.

"Is it?" Marly wrinkled her nose.

He laughed. "You don't like romance, do you, kid?" To annoy her, he started singing along. "*Somewhere there's music, how faint the tune . . .*"

"Do girls actually fall for that?" Marly scoffed.

"They fall for *me,* kid." He dipped her without warning and she squealed.

"Why are you hanging out here with me?" Marly asked as he righted her again. "When you could be in there dancing with Cilla?"

"I'm being blackmailed, remember?" He caught her skepticism and shrugged. "Maybe because I also think it's snoresville in there."

"You said it wouldn't be snoresville if there was someone you wanted to dance with. Don't you want to dance with Cilla?"

"I did dance with her. A heap of times."

"Too many times?" Marly hazarded.

"Enough with the twenty questions, half-pint. Just enjoy the dance."

"You've got a high opinion of your dancing."

"Yeah, I do," Freddie said, giving her a spin.

He *was* a good dancer. It was different from the lessons at school with the boys, who held hands like they were being forced to hold slimy dead fish. Freddie de Marche, meanwhile, was a grown man and he didn't act like touching a girl would give him cooties. He spun her about on the lawn like dancing was a fun thing to do.

The band broke into a cover of "My Funny Valentine" and Freddie twirled her again, like he was Fred Astaire and she was Ginger Rogers.

"Now *this* is a good song," Freddie declared.

"If you say so." Marly was a bit giddy from all the spinning.

"I do say so." And he started singing again, his voice going all whispery. "*Sweet comic valentine, you make me smile . . .*"

"You're such a turkey." Marly laughed. He was no Mario Lanza or Frank Sinatra—he missed as many notes as he hit.

He dipped her again, this time slow and lazy, like he was in an old movie.

Marly had never gotten the appeal of those old films her mother loved. Not until this moment. But as the moonlight splashed through the maples and the faint strains of the band drifted over the blue lawns, Marly thought of all those silvery films and all those shimmery couples, looking like they'd been coated in moonlight. And when Freddie de Marche dipped her, she got the queerest feeling, like she was filling up with shimmery moonlight too. It was a tingly magical feeling, a midnight feeling.

Maybe she'd give dances another shot. Maybe this feeling was worth wearing too much tulle and painful shoes for. . . .

Somehow, as the song unfurled through the fragrant June evening and she stared up at Freddie de Marche, the shivery moonlight feeling became something more. It was like standing too close to the fire after coming in from the cold, when your body couldn't quite decide if it was frosty or toasty. Parts of her were blazing, parts shivering. Freddie was oblivious, twirling her as if she were a little kid. He gave her a playful bow when the song ended and actually chucked her under the chin like she was five years old.

But she wasn't five years old. And Marly was head over heels in a confusing, tumbled-up feeling that was going to ruin her life for many years to come.

TWELVE

"It's like the whole town just went to sleep," Flo marveled. She was sitting on the narrow little sill on one of the dormer windows in my room, staring at the street, which had emptied out for the summer. All the vacation houses were shuttered for the end of the season; the bright beach towels were gone from the fences, there were no children shrieking, and no baseball commentary or pop music drifting through the still air. The picnic tables at the lobster shack were empty, even though it was the middle of the day, and there was only a single lonely yacht slicing across the water.

"I guess it kind of did go to sleep," I said absently as I opened a box of books. I'd found a little teak bookshelf in the stack of furniture out under the tent and moved it up to my room. I wouldn't feel at home till I had my books around me. "It's hibernating until next summer."

"The campground was nearly empty when we left too." Flo sighed. "Are we going to be the only people here for the rest of the year? Won't that be weird?"

We'd waved the Overbecks off that morning, watching as the

rental truck turned the corner of Tinker Street and disappeared down Beach Road, heading home to Pittsburgh. I missed them already. This all seemed powerfully real now that Flo and I were alone in the house. And apart from Elton next door and Jake down on the corner, we did seem to be the only people left on our street.

Flo sighed again, the sound heavier. "I hope I like my new school."

She was sliding into the doldrums, I could feel it. I'd taken her into Rockport earlier to buy school supplies, spoiling her with money I didn't really have, letting her choose an expensive tin of colored pencils and a new backpack. I had a tight ball of anxiety in my chest, remembering all the new schools I'd attended as a kid, all the first days and being introduced to walls of judgmental faces, knowing I wasn't like the other kids, knowing they'd find me weird, knowing I'd be sitting alone at lunch.

"I feel you," I said fervently. "I hope I like my new job." Which also started on Monday.

Flo lapsed into silence, staring moodily out the window as I unpacked my books.

"Do you think Jake could get the old radio cabinet thing working?" she asked abruptly. "Can I go visit his puppy and ask him if he'll come fix it? I found all these old records in the room with the clothes, and I want to play them."

"Don't bother him now, babe, it's the lunch rush."

She snorted. "There isn't anyone there."

"Well, then definitely don't bother him. I don't want you alone with strange men."

"Mooooom," she said in drawn-out frustration. "It's *Jake.*"

"I said no." I looked up and saw her restless irritation. "If you need something to do, go unpack the rest of your things."

"I'm sick of unpacking."

"Then go outside and pick me some lilacs." It would be nice to have lilacs in my bedroom the first night I slept here.

She pulled a face.

"Read a book?"

"I'll be reading books all year in school. I don't want to waste the last two days of summer vacation *reading*." She cocked her head. "Why don't *we* go have a couple of lobster rolls and give Jake something to do. Then I can pet his puppy, because you'll be there."

"I need to keep unpacking, Flo-bug."

"But we've never even had a lobster roll! Don't you think that's sad, given we live in Maine?"

"Flo, I seriously need our stuff unpacked before I start work on Monday."

She gave me a look I rarely saw. A kind of wobble-lipped look, like she might cry. My heart sank. I hated it when she cried.

"What if I help you unpack the rest of this stuff, really quick, and *then* we go?" she said, blinking away her upset, still trying to find a way to get what she wanted.

The tightness in my chest constricted even further. She'd been such a good sport about this move, and all she wanted was to walk to the corner, pet a dog, and eat lunch with me.

"You're going to hate lobster rolls," I warned her, as I capitulated.

"I bet I won't hate lobster rolls as much as I hate Moxie," she said as she collapsed beside me and grabbed a handful of books out of the box. "You'd hate Moxie too if you tried it." She began stacking my books on the shelves, pushing the hardbacks into one row and the paperbacks into another. "Those records I found are probably worth a fortune," she chattered at me. "We could sell them online, you know. Dad says vintage vinyl fetches a lot of money."

I made a noise to let her know I was listening and opened another box.

"I'll take photos of them all, if you want, and work out if they're in mint condition. Dad says you get more money for mint condition." She paused as she pulled an envelope out of a book. "Hey. You've got a letter here you haven't opened. It must have got packed away by mistake." She handed it to me, then resumed her chatter about how to sell vintage vinyl.

My heart gave a lurch as I stared down at the letter. It was the one that had arrived on the day I'd first started scrolling treasure houses. The one Suni had handed me as we ate pizza and discussed which state we should live in. *Hazelton FCI* was stamped across the envelope.

Tina.

I folded it and tucked it into my pocket. I glanced at Flo, but she was more interested in hurrying through the boxes so she could get to the puppy than in my letter. Thank goodness, because she still didn't know about Tina and I wasn't ready to tell her yet. I didn't know if I'd ever be ready.

"Flo, I'm just going to, uh, grab a glass of water from the kitchen," I lied, slipping out of the room. "You're doing a great job."

Opening Tina's letters was like sticking your hand in a box without knowing what was in there. I felt guilty and vaguely nauseous as I headed downstairs and out to the back porch. We'd pulled the decaying screens out and cleared everything except the swing and the heavy old wireless radio. The old records Flo was obsessed with sat in careful stacks. Shakily, I tore open the envelope, so full of nervous energy that I paced as I skimmed her words, barely taking anything in. My stomach was in a knot, my heart racing, my hands sweating. My whole body was preparing for bad news.

Tina had loopy, girlish handwriting—her *G*s were big curls and her *O*s looked like bubbles about to pop. But there was no bad news. Her letter was chatty, full of gossip about her friends at Hazelton. Over the years, she had made a lot of friends in prison. And she'd once scored a lot of dope and pills from those friends. I'd stupidly thought being locked up would help her, that she'd get clean, but the federal prison was even worse than the state prison. The one and only time I'd gone to visit her, she'd been high on some kind of tranquilizer, barely even cognizant of my presence.

But she certainly hadn't been tranquilized when she'd written this letter. It was speedy and manic, leaping from topic to topic like a cartoon frog leaping onto lily pads. She told me how her roommate had found out her husband was cheating on her, and how he'd still had the nerve to turn up for his conjugal visit, and that Skye and Julia (whoever they were) were hooking up. Tina herself had a bit of a thing going on with one of the guards. "We got talking about *Real Housewives,* of all things!" she wrote, her loops getting even loopier. "Isn't that crazy?" The letter went on like that. Only at the end of the final page did she stop talking about herself long enough to be curious about me.

"Tate, that's the guard I'm friendly with, asked me if you went to college and I said yeah, she's clever, my girl. Not like her mother, haha! But when he asked me if you graduated, I couldn't remember. You did, right, Angel? And was it economics or accounting or something like that? I know I should know, but you know me, I'm a ditz."

I folded the letter sharply and put it back in its envelope. It hadn't been economics *or* accounting. It had been statistics, at Carnegie Mellon, where I met Tim. And where I got knocked up. So no, I hadn't graduated. Instead, I'd raised a kid and worked in a medical center.

But Tina knew none of that. Tina didn't know much about me at all, because I didn't tell her anything. She didn't even know where I lived—she was still addressing letters to Suni and Wayne's house, as she'd done for years.

Even though it was my choice not to tell her about my life and it wasn't a choice I regretted, it still hurt that she didn't know me. It was a razor-sharp old hurt, deep to the bone.

"Flo!" I strode to the hall and called up the stairs. "Flo! Forget the books, let's go for lobster rolls." All of a sudden unpacking seemed much less important than taking my kid to lunch on her last weekend of summer vacation.

Debussy was down at the Oxeye Hardware Store (and Lobster Shack). That giant orange fluffball seemed to own the whole town. Doris left a bowl of kibble out for him in the general store, and he often loitered at Jake's so he could be there to gobble up scraps. Today, since there wasn't a crowd of summer folk dropping food for him, Debussy was sprawled on one of the picnic tables, sunning himself. He acted oblivious to Hazel the puppy's intent stare. She was tied up to the post again, staring at Debussy with laser focus. There was now a big comfortable dog bed on the porch next to her, and a bowl of water.

There was no sign of Jake, so Flo rang the brass bell that hung beside the service window.

"Hey, neighbor," Flo called, when Jake finally appeared. "Hey, neighbor" was what everyone in Oxeye said when they popped in to our house.

"Hey." He was wearing a baseball shirt and jeans today. But his feet were still bare, and his hair was still tousled.

"We've come for lunch," Flo told him.

He looked surprised.

"It's going to be our first night sleeping in our house," Flo explained, "and it's the last weekend before school, so we're having lunch to celebrate. Or calm our fears. We're eating our feelings, basically." She considered the empty chalkboard. "What happened to your menu?"

"Season's over, kid. We're only open on the weekends now."

"It *is* the weekend," I reminded him.

"Yeah," he said. "But there isn't anyone here."

"*We're* here," Flo told him firmly.

He sighed. "Fine. But I don't have the *full* menu available. I only have lobster rolls and coleslaw."

"Isn't that what you always have?"

He gave her a sour look. "No. In peak season I also serve fries and onion rings. And hot dogs for kids who don't like lobster."

"You don't have hot dogs today?" I said nervously, knowing Flo was going to hate her lobster roll.

He took one look at my expression and sighed again. "I guess I could break out a hot dog or two if I had to."

"If you don't have any customers, you should join us for lunch," Flo suggested.

"Flo, if I never eat a lobster roll again, it will be too soon."

"You have to eat something, don't you?"

"I had a big breakfast, I'll be fine."

"Your loss. We'll have two lobster rolls with coleslaw and a couple of cans of lemonade," she said.

"Make that water," I corrected. "And perhaps throw in a backup hot dog. . . ."

While Jake fetched our lunch and Flo played with Hazel, I took a seat at the prime picnic table overlooking the bay. The day was still, and the sound of gulls carried across the cliffs. Tina's letter was burning a hole in my pocket. Since Flo was distracted, I eased it out of its envelope again. As I reread it, I noticed new details. *Gemma from my meetings has met a guy online. . . .* I'd skimmed over it before, but this time I noticed the word *meetings.*

Meetings? As in Narcotics Anonymous meetings?

But wouldn't she have told me if she was going to meetings again?

"Here you go." Jake broke me out of my thoughts, sliding a tray with a bunch of red baskets onto the table.

"You made fries and onion rings," I blurted, surprised. I hid the letter under the table.

He looked uncomfortable. "Don't get weird about it. I just felt like fries," he said as he sat down opposite me. His knees brushed mine under the table. I glanced up, wondering if he'd felt the zap of electricity like I had.

His gaze met mine. His blue-green eyes turned hazy, and my stomach rolled a lazy somersault. He *had* felt it.

"It's a feast!" Flo declared, joining us, breaking the tension.

"Hold on, kid. You need to go wash your hands if you've been petting the dog and cat." He pointed at the store. "There's soap and a towel in the kitchen. Go wash up but don't touch the fryer—that hot oil is dangerous." Jake passed me a bottle of water and put a can of Moxie in front of Flo's spot.

"She wanted—"

"I know," he cut me off. "Hush and don't spoil the joke." His double dimples dented, showing his amusement. Hazel barked. Jake sighed and went to untie her and bring her over to the picnic table. Then he muttered under his breath about his sister being slow to pick up the damn dog.

"How come you don't want to keep her?" I asked. "She seems like a nice dog. And she likes you." That was an understatement—she was giving him the most adoring look.

He grunted. "I'm not ready."

"Oh." I hazarded a guess. "Those pictures inside, of the golden retriever. That was your last dog?"

He hid behind his plastic sunglasses—black and orange ones today, with the price sticker actually on the lens. "Ben. He died in March. He was old." Jake seemed relieved when Flo came skipping back.

"I love onion rings," she chattered, reaching for a handful. Then she spotted the orange can. "Hey!" She picked it up and shook it at Jake. "I *hate* Moxie."

"Not anymore you don't," he said, eating a fry. "You're a Mainer now. You'll love it."

"Mom's a *Mainah* too," Flo said, copying his accent. "She can drink it." She parked the shook-up can in front of me.

"No, she's not. She's still from away. But you—you're a kid, so you get to be a Mainer. Adults have to live here for a few decades before we decide they're no longer from away."

Flo shook her head at him.

Jake gently removed the Moxie can from in front of me. We

both knew it would explode the moment someone cracked it open after the shaking Flo had given it.

In my entire life, I'd never eaten lobster before. I figured it would taste like crab sticks, and it kind of did, but it was a million times better. Jake's place looked rough and ready, but his food was excellent. The bread from Doris's was toasted crisp on the outside but was fluffy and soft on the inside; the mayonnaise and scallions were the perfect contrast to the lobster itself, which was fresh and delicious and not fishy at all.

"That's gross," Flo decided, sliding her lobster roll my way and reaching for the hot dog and more onion rings.

"Lucky your mom likes it," Jake said, sounding pleased. His double dimple had reappeared.

"Do you open for weekends all year?" I asked, eyeing the second roll and wondering if I could fit it in.

Jake laughed. "God no. You should see this place in the winter. It's like an ice planet. Blows a gale, gets buried in snow, and everything that's not buried is frozen solid. I close up the lobster shack just after Halloween. Until then, we get tourists staying in the campground on weekends, popping out to see the fall color and enjoy some last seaside air before winter. But after October, there's no one. Even most of the locals head off on vacation. Last year Alan and Roger went to Greece for a bit, and Elton went to stay with his kids in Massachusetts."

"Are we going to be the only people here?" I asked, chagrined, not liking the thought. I imagined Oxeye empty except for us. It would be like living in a ghost town.

"No. Josie at the library stays. She prefers to take vacation in July. Colleen at the café usually sticks around, and so does old Tom at the gas station. And I'll be here. Mostly. I might go to my sister's place for Christmas, though."

I heard Hazel whine and glimpsed Jake's hand slipping under the table to toss her a fry. He caught me looking and scowled.

"Found anything interesting in the old house?" he asked, pushing the puppy away as she tried to lick his hand.

"It's all interesting," I admitted, "there's just so much of it. Flo keeps finding all these cats."

His eyebrows shot up and he glanced at Debussy, who jumped down from the neighboring picnic table.

"Porcelain cats, crystal cats, wooden cats." Flo had lined them all up on the little desk in her room.

"I have a cat count," Flo said through a mouthful of hot dog. "Twenty-seven cats so far."

Jake seemed relieved that we were only talking about figurines, which made me nervous. Was there another Debussy around?

"I found records too." Flo proceeded to tell him about them in detail. "There's a heap by this guy called Eddie Fisher."

"You know he was Princess Leia's dad," Jake told her. He reached down and took hold of Hazel's collar as Debussy stalked closer, drawn by the smell of lobster.

"No, he wasn't. Darth Vader was Princess Leia's dad."

"I mean the actress. Eddie Fisher was Carrie Fisher's dad. She played Princess Leia."

"How do you know that?" Flo seemed impressed.

"I don't know." He shrugged. "I'm fond of useless facts, I guess."

"Well, there's a heap of Eddie Fisher records, and a heap of Elvis records."

"They might be worth something."

"I *know*." She gave him a look and then explained the whole concept of mint condition to him and how she needed to find out if the Elvis records were *mint* before listing them to sell online.

Jake listened patiently. "Well, you know what might be easier than selling them online? There's a store on Main Street in Camden that specializes in vinyl, CDs, and cassettes."

"What's a cassette?"

Jake explained it to her.

"Oh, cool. Maybe I'll find some of them in the house too."

"I wouldn't be surprised." He glanced at me. "If you're interested, I can introduce you to Sammy, who runs the store. She's always on the lookout for new stock."

"That would be great," I admitted. I'd been feeling a low-level dread at the thought of supervising Flo selling things online.

"But we can't sell any of it yet, not until I've checked it out," Flo said hastily. "And we need you to fix the wireless radio to do that, Jake."

"You don't have another record player you can use?"

"Nope," said Flo.

Jake sighed. "Listen, Flo, those things are impossible to fix—the electrics are too old. Even if it was fixable, it would be way out of my league. But I think there might be a portable record player in the front room. I remember seeing it."

"There is?" Flo lit up. "I didn't see one."

"It looks like a little suitcase with a handle. But it will need fixing too. I know for sure you'll need a new needle."

"Can you come do that?"

"When?"

"Today," Flo said, as though it had been patently obvious. "After you close the store. Mom can feed you dinner."

I gave her a sour look. I had so much to do before Monday. I didn't need to be feeding our local hardware proprietor.

"You don't have to do that," Jake said hurriedly.

"Yes, we do," Flo assured him. "It's the least we can do."

"Is it?" That came out before I could think.

Jake seemed to be repressing a smile, judging by the way his mouth hooked up in the corner. "Well, I'll have to go buy a needle for you. So that's probably worth dinner. What's for eating?" he asked Flo, throwing me a playful glance.

"Macaroni and cheese," Flo told him.

"Since when?" I said sharply.

"She makes great macaroni and cheese. She never buys the packet stuff; she makes it from scratch. Which is sometimes a shame, because I like the packet stuff. Homemade is never as orange, have you noticed that?" Flo finished the last bite of her hot dog.

"Thanks for volunteering me to cook," I scolded her as we walked home.

"I picked the macaroni and cheese because it's your best," Flo told me kindly. "You don't want to scare him off."

"I don't want to . . . what?"

"Well, he's the only guy in town who isn't old or gay." She gave me a knowing look. "And you like his muscles *and* his lobster rolls."

"Florence! I'm not looking for a man."

"How often do you meet a man who can also fix your front door? You don't want to look a horse gift in the mouth."

"Gift horse," I corrected. "And where on earth do you get these ideas?" I muttered as I followed her up our front steps.

"Suni and Alison."

I groaned. I'd have to remind them again to stop gossiping in front of Flo.

"I'm going to start sorting those records," she said, heading happily for the back porch.

Still, at least she wasn't anxious about school on Monday anymore.

While we'd made the kitchen livable over the last week, we hadn't completely cleared it out—most of the drawers were still jammed with stuff. I needed a cheese grater to make dinner, but the drawers seemed to hold everything under the sun except a grater. If I didn't find it soon, I'd have to hunt through my own stuff, which would be a pain, as I had no idea which box mine was in.

I swore under my breath, wishing Flo hadn't asked Jake Abernathy to dinner.

I could hear Jake and Flo out on the porch, messing around with the record player he'd dug out from the parlor. It was a 1950s thing in an aged, yellowing case, with built-in speakers.

"You knew the lady that lived here, didn't you?" I heard Flo saying as I hunted. Her voice carried through the open kitchen door. "The lady that lived here before us, I mean."

"I did," he said shortly.

I wondered if he knew where she kept her cheese grater. I'd found rubber bands, paper clips, a host of salt and pepper shakers, bundles of pens and pencils, and another cat. This cat was a pepper shaker, a smooth little porcelain tabby with three holes in the top of its head to shake the pepper out of. I put it aside for Flo to add to her collection.

"How did she live here with all this stuff everywhere?" Flo asked.

"With difficulty," Jake grunted.

"She was a hoarder, right? I read about hoarders on Wikipedia. And there's a whole TV show about hoarders. I watched some clips on YouTube. It's sad. Was the lady who lived here sad?" Flo asked.

I eavesdropped, curious about Marly, the lady responsible for all this mess. I finally found the cheese grater in an old bread box. As well as an ancient calculator that was out of battery. Nothing surprised me in this house anymore.

"No one's sad *all* the time." Jake sounded philosophical. I peered out to the porch and saw he was bent over the vintage record player. "She just had trouble letting things go."

"How come?"

"Well, I don't know. Maybe all these things reminded her of times when she was happy. Or maybe they just made her feel safe. Or—" He made another grunting noise as he fiddled with something. "Maybe she just liked *stuff*, you know?"

"I *don't* know," Flo said firmly. "I've never had room for stuff before. I've never even had my own room." And, to my horror, I heard her start to describe our life in a way that made it seem sad and small.

"All three of you always slept in the same room?" Jake asked, sounding surprised.

"All two of us."

"No, I mean, when your dad was there."

"My dad wasn't there. He's in Seattle now, but before that he lived in Shadyside in an apartment with four other guys. They were nice enough, but they sure drank a lot of beer."

I winced.

"Mom wouldn't let me stay there overnight, which Dad said was understandable and I shouldn't be mad at her for. But I did get mad at her. They had so many gaming platforms and they had all the good cereals."

"What are the good cereals?"

"You know, the kind moms hate. Lucky Charms, Cap'n Crunch, Apple Jacks, Cocoa Puffs, Honey Smacks, those ones."

"That's sugar, not breakfast."

"That's why they're *good*."

"They'll make your teeth fall out." I heard him rummage around in his toolbox. "You're better off eating eggs."

"Mom makes me Quaker Oats a lot. They're only good with honey, though."

I listened to Flo complain about my food choices as I chopped broccoli for the macaroni and cheese. She hated when I put broccoli in it, but after hearing her complain about my oats to Jake, I was putting in extra.

I remembered all those school breakfast programs I'd crept into as a kid. Plastic trays with cartons of milk, chewy bagels. The best days were when there was a little plastic cup half full of cut-up strawberries. I remembered the shivery, exposed feeling of arriving at the school on no sleep, sitting hunched over my plastic tray, wishing I was at home with my mom but glad to fill my empty belly. After school I had watched reruns of *Bewitched* and *Happy Days*, shows where kids sat down at tables while their mom poured them orange juice and handed them plates of scrambled eggs and crispy bacon at breakfast time. My mom didn't do that. If she was home and we had any juice, she'd drink it straight out of the carton, standing at the open refrigerator in her T-shirt and underwear.

I *did* make Quaker Oats a lot for Flo, mostly in the winter on those dark sleety mornings when it was hard to leave bed. I made them the old-fashioned way, in a saucepan, and they were creamy and hot when I poured them into her bowl. The sight of her spooning them up made me so happy I had to turn away so she didn't see me tearing up. She didn't know how much those oats said.

"I like oats," Jake admitted, making me feel like he could read my mind.

"It's grandma food."

"Yeah, so? I like my grandma."

"I don't really know my grandma—she's in Cincinnati but I've never been there. I met her once when I was three, when she came to visit my dad, but I don't really remember it." As far as Flo knew, she only had one grandma. "Mom says I'll get to see her at Dad's wedding this November."

I checked the instructions as I struggled to get my countertop oven preheating. I glanced at the big black range and tried to imagine cooking the mac and cheese in it. You could lose a whole roast turkey in that monster.

Once the macaroni and cheese was in, I dipped out to the porch with the bug spray.

"Looks like it's the moment of truth. Which record do you want to try?" Jake asked as I sprayed Flo liberally. He was on his knees in front of the vintage player, so they were about the same height.

"This one," she said, picking the first one off the closest pile.

"*Dean Martin Sings*?" He turned it over in his hands and slid the record out of its sleeve. "You a Dean Martin fan?"

"I doubt it," she said, completely oblivious to me. "But I won't know till I try, right?"

I watched Jake gently lower the record onto the ancient turntable. His baseball T-shirt stretched tight over his shoulders and back and I felt a not-unpleasant swirl in my belly. Flo wriggled forward until she was bending over his shoulder.

"Don't scratch it," Flo warned. "You'll damage the value."

"And the music," he said dryly.

The needle dropped and there was a familiar scritch-scratching sound I remembered from when Tim and I lived together.

Brassy music sounded faintly from the small holes in the case.

Flo twiddled a black knob and the trumpets soared, a little fuzzy-sounding.

"High five, kid, we did it."

As Flo energetically slapped Jake's hand, I felt an odd weakening. It was a wave of feeling that was unfamiliar to me, an eddy of something sad and sweet and bright and sharply pleasant. Oh God, was I about to *cry*?

"I might just pick some flowers for the table," I said, turning away. What was *wrong* with me?

I grabbed a pair of garden shears and a basket from the laundry, where Wayne had left a neat little collection of tools for me, and headed out into the garden. Dean Martin's whiskey-warm and lazy voice was crooning, "*Who's your little who-zis?*" as I passed the big white wedding tent full of culch on my way to the garden. I could hear Flo laughing at the silly lyrics of the song as I picked the late roses, which were fat and old-fashioned and highly perfumed. I sheared off wands of lilacs too. Around the outbuildings were thick beds of hydrangeas, all in pastel shades of pink and green and palest purple, and I snipped with abandon. There were thickets of small daisies everywhere, and taller wildflowers whose names I didn't know. I cut armfuls of everything, not knowing what was weed and what was wildflower, and not caring. It was all beautiful. And cutting flowers stopped my tears.

"Is there still a garden left?" Flo asked, her eyes widening when I came in with my overflowing basket.

"I doubt she even made a dent in it," Jake said. His marble-glass blue-green eyes were amused. He was sitting cross-legged on the floor, the denim of his jeans outlining his strong thighs.

"Look, Mom, we have Beatles albums! Jake says they'll be worth a lot!" She held up *Rubber Soul.*

"I said they *might* be worth *something*."

"Can I get you something to drink now that your work is done?" I asked Jake, as Flo took the needle off Dean Martin and swapped him out for the Beatles. She was treating the records like they were made of glass, which made me smile.

"Sure." He uncoiled from the floor. I was painfully aware of his closeness. That smell of wood shavings and sea salt curled around me.

"Um . . ." I tried to pull my thoughts together. They were scudding about like clouds in a strong wind. "Beer? Or iced tea?"

"Whatever you're having is fine."

Right. Okay. "Beer," I blurted. In the fridge I had a variety of boutique Maine beers Wayne had bought to try. He'd left them for me. "To ease the pain," he'd joked, giving me a squeeze as he'd said goodbye.

As "Drive My Car" exploded tinnily from Flo's record player, Jake followed me into the kitchen. He leaned against the doorframe, hands in pockets, watching me as I dropped the flowers on the table and rummaged through the fridge.

The evening was bluing and the kitchen felt unsettlingly intimate.

"Ah, do you mind turning on the overhead lights?" I said, wanting to dispel the intimacy as fast as I could. "What kind of beer do you like?"

Jake flicked the switch and the bare bulbs blazed to life. "Whatever you're having is fine."

"I have pale ale from two different places in Portland, IPA from Bangor, lager from Augusta, or stout from Bar Harbor?"

"Pale ale." He sounded amused. "Doing a tour of the state in there, are you?" he asked as I handed him the aggressively fluorescent can.

"Something like that." I took a pale ale too and went to find us glasses. Suni had organized the cupboards, but the glassware was a carnival of jelly jars, wineglasses, tumblers, champagne flutes, and highballs. Some were crystal, some dime store finds. I grabbed a couple of oversized wineglasses and handed him one.

"Not using the range to cook?" he asked as he cracked his can and poured its contents into the glass.

"To be honest, I'm afraid of it," I confessed.

"I'm calling this one mint!" Flo shouted over the music.

"Good stuff," Jake called back, without looking away from me. "The woman who bought *this* house is afraid of a little old range?"

"Yes," I said fervently. "It's terrifying. I mean, where do you even start?"

"I'd recommend time travel." This time the double dimples led to an actual smile. "Will you keep it, do you think?"

"It doesn't really seem right to get rid of it," I admitted. "It feels like part of the house. It would be like knocking down a wall."

"Well, people do that too."

I shook my head. "It feels wrong to remodel an old house that much." I thought of the houses I'd seen renovated in reels online. "Have you ever watched TikToks of treasure houses?" I asked him, as I opened a cupboard door to reveal wall-to-wall vases. Marly must have liked cut flowers a *lot*.

"Have I ever watched what of *what*?" Jake took a seat at the scrubbed wood kitchen table as I filled a couple of vases with water.

"Treasure houses." I explained the reels, telling him specifically about HandyMom24 and her farmhouse in Washington. The red door and the paddling pool and the Christmas lights, a life built on a foundation of culch. "I like the ones where people bring the house back to life, not the ones where they remake them into something entirely unrecognizable. For some reason, it makes me sad to see an old house gutted."

Jake nodded. "Because they lose their identity."

I blinked. That was exactly it. "Yes. Somehow it erases everything it's ever been, all the good as well as the bad. Like wiping someone's memory."

He gave me an odd look. Then he nodded. "The family wanted to sell to someone who'd love the place for what it was," he said gruffly. "I guess they knew what they were doing when they let you take it."

I blinked, surprised by the emotion in his voice.

He glanced at the range. "Best keep the range then, if you want to keep the character of the house."

"Yeah . . ." I said slowly, following his gaze. He was right, it was part of the house. Losing it would diminish the charm of the kitchen. Even if I didn't ever cook on it, I could put some of the pretty teapots on display and a potted plant or two. And then the house would stay whole, and I would still think of Marilla and Green Gables every time I walked into the room.

Jake ran his fingertips over the flowers on the table. "You know what these are?" he said, taking a white petal gently between his fingers.

Startled, I turned back to the table. "Daisies?"

"*Oxeye* daisies. The town's named after them." He gently tugged one from the tangle of the basket and twirled it between his fingers. "They grow all down the coast." He pointed at the wall. "You ever notice the wallpaper in here?"

Daisies. I had never looked closely at the white floral print, but now it seemed obvious.

The Beatles died abruptly. Then Elvis came on singing "Blue Suede Shoes."

"Do you know what the purple flowers are, the ones that look like starbursts?" I asked curiously as I bunched the lilacs into a fluted porcelain vase to take upstairs to my room. The rest of the riot of late-summer flowers went into a glass vase for the kitchen table.

"Wild bergamot," he said, taking a long draft of beer. "And the tiny pink ones are swamp milkweed, the fluffy white wands are sweet pepperbush, and the large flat-faced pinky-purple flowers are raspberry. You should find fruit out there soon."

"Are you an amateur botanist?" I asked, impressed.

"Just a happy gardener." He slouched back in his chair. "I'm more familiar with vegetables, though."

I remembered the vegetable beds in the yard behind his store. Not for the first time, I wondered why he was here in Oxeye. "Was your hardware store a family business?" I asked, unable to hide my burning curiosity.

"Nope." He didn't elaborate.

"Did you always want to run a hardware store?" I smiled. "And lobster shack."

"Nope."

I took the hint. Elvis gave way to Doris Day.

"Flo, you'll have to listen to more than one song to work out if the record is in mint condition," I called to her.

"No, I won't! Jake showed me how to examine them for scratches. I'm just playing these because I want to know what they sound like." The first verse of "Tea for Two" chirped at full volume from the porch.

"She's got a lot of energy for a kid who doesn't eat sugary cereal," Jake said.

I laughed.

"Her dad's getting married, huh?"

I darted a glance at him, but his expression was deliberately bland. "Yes," I said simply. I felt nothing about Tim getting married.

Okay, that was a lie. I felt a wild stinging sense of rejection that Tim was getting married, and not to me—even though I didn't want him anymore. Tim and I were woefully incompatible. I have unrelenting abandonment issues, and he abandons people.

He'd left me with a baby and moved into student housing with a bunch of other thoughtless, selfish man-babies, playing beer pong and sleeping in and gaming and fucking around, while I was changing diapers and reading to her and not sleeping and worrying about bills.

Jake took a hint and fell silent.

I felt self-conscious as I set the table, aware that he was watching me. I met his eye and my stomach did a slow-rolling tumble. He didn't look away. His greenish gaze was clouded and intense.

Doris Day ended abruptly, and the evening hush was thick and luscious in that bare-bulbed kitchen. I could hear the low hum of the little oven, the chatter of birds nesting for the evening, and the distant roar of the ocean against the cliffs. The heavy perfume of flowers mixed with Jake's salty-woody scent and made me feel light-headed.

The moment drew out, and out, and out.

"Hey, Mom? Jake? Who's Chet Baker?"

The spell broke and I backed away from the table, flushing. Oh God, had I been staring at him?

Had he been staring at *me*?

"MOM!"

"I don't know," I called back.

"JAKE?"

"I don't know either, kid. Just play him and see." Jake seemed unsettled too.

Chet Baker, it turned out, played the sexiest music in the world. A languid trumpet sighed a long, sensual note. Jake shifted in his chair. That music, combined with Jake Abernathy watching me, made serving macaroni and cheese a dizzying exercise.

"Is Chet the singer or the trumpet player?" Flo asked, confused, appearing in the doorway with the liner notes.

Whoever was singing had a soft, fretful voice. *Don't change a hair for me . . .*

"Oh, he's both," she said, reading on.

Not if you care for me . . .

"He's good-looking too." Flo held out the album cover so we could see the dark-haired man in the white T-shirt. He had a James Dean/Marlon Brando vibe. "Or he was. He's probably dead now, isn't he, if he lived in the black-and-white times?"

"The black-and-white times?" Jake asked.

"When I was a kid, I used to think the past was black and white like the old movies," Flo told him, dropping her album cover on the sideboard and joining Jake at the table.

"When you *were* a kid?" He scratched his nose.

"Oh, Mom, you put broccoli in it? You want the guy to like you, don't you?"

"Flo!" I blushed. Oh my God, she had no shame.

"I'll still like her," Jake drawled, the longing trumpet in the background making his words sound loaded.

"Way to ruin macaroni and cheese," Flo grumbled at me.

"Go wash your hands and stop complaining, or you can cook next time."

"I will," she grumbled, "and my macaroni will be properly orange. Come on, Jake, you have to wash your hands too." She shooed him off his chair.

Jake brushed past me on the way to the sink and I felt a shock bolt through me. He felt it too. I could tell by the way he tensed up.

I was so busy pretending not to be unsettled by Jake's presence that I wasn't paying attention to Flo, who went hunting through the sideboard for a hand towel. At least I wasn't paying attention until Flo screamed.

"What is it? Is it a snake?" I'd been having nightmares about snakes slithering in through the open porch.

Jake was already there before I reached her. I heard him swear.

"Is it a snake? A spider? A rat?"

"Chill, Mom!" Flo was crouched over the open cupboard in the sideboard, Jake peering over her shoulder. "Don't scare them!"

"You're the one who screamed! And scare what exactly? Please don't let it be a nest of mice."

"It's *kittens*!" Flo beamed at me.

"No." I closed my eyes. Not in my sideboard. Not in my kitchen.

"And a mama cat too! Aw."

"Ah hell, I thought I'd got her out," Jake grumbled.

"What? You knew?" I was appalled.

"I knew she was pregnant. I just didn't think she was back in the house."

"I'm going to call her Mac," Flo declared. "And all these little ones are Cheese."

"You can't call them Mac and Cheese," Jake scolded her.

"No, you can't," I agreed. "Because we're not keeping them!"

"And because you can't give pets silly names," Jake said firmly. "It's not respectful. You don't see people named after food."

"They're not pets, Jake," I protested. "They're strays."

"My best friend in Pittsburgh is Candy Swivert," Flo offered smugly. "She's named after food. And your dog is Hazel—what about hazelnuts?"

"She's not called Hazel*nut*. And she's not my dog."

"Well, these are my cats and I'm calling them Mac and Cheese. The fat kitten there can be Mozzarella, that one can be Cheddar, that skinny one String Cheese. . . ."

"They're *not* your cats," I told her firmly, "and you're not naming them, because you're not keeping them."

But neither Flo nor Jake was listening to me.

"What if I name her Marly after the woman who lived here?" Flo asked Jake.

"Absolutely not."

"Mac it is then." Flo cooed at the kittens. "And this one's going to be called *Velveeta*."

THIRTEEN

September blew in fresh as new linen. The days were brassy and bright, with golden light and gusty breezes, the leaves turning scarlet and amber in the woods. Whales came to the bay: humpbacks and minkes and, once on a buttery mellow Sunday afternoon, an enormous North Atlantic right whale and her calf. The sight of her cresting the water, her tail arching through the air, was something I didn't think I'd ever forget. Flo had found an old telescope in our piles of junk and liked to stand at my bedroom windows with it trained on the water for a glimpse of a fin or tail.

Flo had found the transition to sixth grade in her new school harder than either of us would have liked. It gave me flashbacks to my own childhood and rooms full of unfriendly faces.

"They all have friends already," she complained her first week.

"They can't add one more?"

She didn't even deign to respond to that. She just stomped upstairs to her room and her cats. The only thing that pulled her out of her mood that whole weekend was the Sunday lobster bake on the beach. The Oxeye residents were celebrating the end of summer and reclaiming their little beach at the foot of the cliffs from the tourists.

"We do it every year," Josie confided as Flo and I followed her down the winding path to the sand. "Isn't it lovely to finally have the beach to ourselves?" Oxeye daisies bobbed in the gusty breezes, and the scudding clouds caused the sunlight to fall in dramatic shafts on the restless ocean. Josie was carrying a heavy basket stuffed with corn and potatoes. Flo and I had been assigned the ingredients to make s'mores and Flo was swinging the shopping bag energetically as she scurried down to the beach, where Jake and Tom from the gas station were tending to a smoking pit in the sand. I knew the first thing Flo would do when she got down there was pepper them with questions.

"You could cook a whole horse in there!" she exclaimed as she regarded the hole in the sand. "How big is this lobster we're baking?" She didn't wait for me to respond, skipping off ahead to ask Jake, who would definitely have the answer.

I felt weirdly shy as I approached the knot of locals on the sand, even though they'd been in and out of my house regularly since we moved in. Doris and Gary from the general store (and bakery) were setting up camp chairs upwind from the fire. Doris was in a lime-green windbreaker, her orange hair a blaze of color as she bustled about. Her short, garrulous husband Gary was wearing a threadbare fisherman's beanie and a coat that was tight on his barrel-shaped frame.

"You'll need to dress warm," he'd told me cheerily when Flo and I had swung by the store for graham crackers and marshmallows. "It's the wind that chills you. Doesn't matter how sunny it looks, those bay winds can turn you blue. Even in September."

Gary beamed at me now, as he saw we'd taken his advice. Flo's scarf was flying behind her as she approached the cooking pit, and I had my windbreaker zipped up to my chin.

"You weren't wrong about the bay winds," I told Gary ruefully, trying not to stare at Jake as he greeted Flo. Jake's smile was broad and white and wreathed in dimples. It was the happiest I'd ever seen him.

"Colleen's coffee will warm you up," Gary told me with a wink. "It's got a fair shot of whiskey in it."

As promised, Colleen provided me with a steaming tin mug of whiskey-laced coffee. Colleen ran the café on Beach Road; she had silver-streaked dark hair, cinnamon-brown eyes, and an impressive amount of jewelry on her small frame. She wore large pressed-tin earrings and layers of necklaces made of sea glass. She always seemed pleased to see us when we popped by her café. Roger kissed me hello and instructed me to sit down and start shucking the corn with Josie and Elton. They clearly had a well-oiled routine for the lobster bake. Jake and Tom set a giant steel tub on the hot rocks in the pit and filled it shallowly with seawater, and as it was set to boil, we shucked corn and peeled potatoes and chatted over the boozy coffee. Flo was sent off to gather up seaweed, which was apparently going to be used to cover the food as it baked.

"How long has this been a tradition?" I asked as I tossed another ear of cleanly husked corn into the waiting basket. I kept one eye on Flo as she carried an armful of drying seaweed to the pit.

"Oh, a long time. Back to the days when this was a resort town," Doris told me, shuffling her chair closer. "As soon as the summer folk went home, Saint-Cyr used to throw a lobster bake for the staff. A farewell for the season and thanks for all the work. And since most of Oxeye existed to serve the resort, the townsfolk used to get invited too."

"They were a grand affair," Gary told me. "Not like this modest little cookout. There would have been people everywhere." His hand glided in front of him, as though he were conjuring an image of the past. "Picnic blankets and games and kids playing. A whole row of cookout pits and an ice cream cart. There's a framed photo of one of the historic Saint-Cyr lobster bakes in the library—Josie can show you next time you're in."

Josie nodded agreeably. "It's from the late fifties, I think."

"Saint-Cyr used to be where the campground is?" I asked, remembering the signs we'd seen when we stayed there. My gaze drifted to the wooded spit at the far end of the beach.

"It was demolished in the seventies." Elton sighed. He too was staring at the campground.

Doris nodded. "Crying shame too. It was a landmark in these parts."

"My folks worked there," Tom told me as he came to collect a basket of shucked corn to toss into the steel tub. "My pa was a waiter. He had a fancy suit with shiny buttons. He would have waited on Jake's folks when they came up from Boston. Yours too, Elton."

"Waited on *me,* you mean. I stayed there when I came courting Sylvie." Elton sounded wistful.

My ears pricked up. "And Jake's folks stayed there?" I was dying to learn more about Jake. He was closemouthed about himself.

Tom grew cagey at my questioning. "Everyone's folks stayed there. There wasn't nowhere else to stay." He turned his attention back to the cooking. "And then when it closed during the recession, in the seventies, there wasn't anywhere to stay at all. At least not until the county opened up the campground."

"Was that when Jake's people bought a house in town?" I asked Elton. "After the hotel closed? Did Marly buy my house then? Jake's aunt . . . ?" I fished, guessing at their relationship. I was desperate to learn more about Marly as well as Jake. The glimpses of her we'd found in the house were tantalizing. A book with her name scrawled inside the cover, the old magazines, the button dish. All the cats. Why *had* she collected so many porcelain cats? And how was she related to Jake?

But at my mention of Marly and my house, I sensed the mood shift.

"Ah, I think we're ready to put the vegetables in." Doris got up and ended the conversation.

Josie caught my confusion. "No one likes to upset Jake," she told me quietly as she gathered up the bucket of potato peelings and corn silk. "He'd rather we just move on and forget the past when it comes to the house."

My gaze flew to Jake, as he helped Flo with a long tangle of seaweed. For someone who wanted to move on and forget the past he sure spent a lot of time in my house, giving advice about how it should be restored to its former glory. His cable-knit fisherman's sweater pulled tight over his broad shoulders as he moved. He was more at ease than usual, laughing as he and Flo piled a veritable mountain of seaweed on top of the giant makeshift cookpot. He showed her how to tuck the seaweed down so it formed a lid.

I had enough baggage of my own to understand there were reasons why people might not be forthcoming about their lives. For some reason, Jake didn't want to talk about Marly, or about his relationship to my house. I could respect that. I didn't want to talk about my past either. I wondered if we'd get to a point where either of us would be comfortable opening up. . . . As if reading my mind, he glanced up. His gaze held mine, his eyes serious, then appraising.

"Mom, when you're done having your stare-off with Jake, can you pass me the hand sanitizer? I stink of seaweed." Flo waved her noisome hands in front of my face.

I blushed as red as the coals in the firepit. I noticed Doris and Gary exchanging amused looks and I swore Alan and Roger were smirking. I was so embarrassed I could barely look at Jake again.

It turned out the lobster bake was an all-day affair. Doris and Roger regaled us with stories about how hard the coming winter would be as we ate our way through not only lobster but also char-grilled steak, buttered corn, steaming potatoes, and then blueberry cheesecake and s'mores. By the time I licked the last of the marshmallow-smeared chocolate from my fingers, I was as relaxed and happy as I'd been in years. Tom lent Flo his binoculars and she whiled away the late afternoon searching the horizon for whales, then we wandered the length of the curved beach, gathering driftwood and chips of green and amber sea glass.

By the time the evening star was glittering in the east, Flo was languid and yawning. “I like it here.” She sighed as we traipsed back up the trail to the top of the cliff. “I’m glad we found this treasure house, even if it does come with a school full of buttheads.”

“Flo!”

“What? I can’t say ‘buttheads’ now?” But she was still grinning, and she looped her arm through mine as we headed home.

FOURTEEN

"It's like there's some kind of secret language I don't know," Flo grumped in her second week at her new school. "There's this one girl, Lainey Mullins, and she whispers every time I walk past."

"Maybe she's saying nice things about you?"

"Mom, you can't even say that with a straight face."

"Maybe sign up for extracurricular activities?" I suggested. "You might meet people that way?"

"I registered for cross-country," she told me a few days later, drumming her fingers on the car door as I drove us home.

"Great idea."

"Okay," she declared the following week, as she climbed into the car, muddy from running through fields. "No luck at cross-country. Do you think I should join the dance squad, try out for field hockey, join debate club, or audition for the school play? Where would I be most likely to find my people?" She held up a hand. "And don't say do all of them, because there's only so many hours in a day, and this school treats homework like it's a way of life. I need *some* time off."

I stole a glance at her. She looked like a mountaineer about to scale Everest, she was so grimly determined. "Ah . . . I'm not sure. Which would you prefer?"

"I think the problem with field hockey is that you spend so much time running and whacking the ball that you don't get to talk to people, and dance squad has a stupid amount of sequins. So maybe debate club or the play?"

"What play are they doing?" I asked. Flo had never once shown any interest in drama, and I was dubious it would keep her occupied for long.

"*Annie.* It's about some orphan kid." She exuded irritation. "Look at what I've come to! It's *hard* to make friends in Maine."

Not for the first time, I was flooded with admiration for my kid. My reaction to new schools and unfriendly kids had been the exact opposite of Flo's. I'd tried to make myself invisible, retreating to the corners of the library to read alone, leaving the school campus as soon as I could at the end of each day. Flo had none of those instincts. She treated finding friends like a hill to be climbed, rather than a personal failing.

"I got a part in the play," Flo told me in the final week of September, as she threw her backpack in the backseat of the car.

"That's fantastic," I said, hoping it was. I'd been nervous about her auditioning for a musical, since she'd never had a singing lesson in her life.

"Don't get excited, it's not a speaking part."

"It's not? Who are you playing?"

"You mean *what* am I playing," she said, sighing.

"Oh . . . ?"

"I'm Sandy," she said in a long-suffering tone. "The *dog*."

I tried not to laugh. "Oh. Well, at least you don't need to memorize lines."

"And Lainey Mullins got the part of Annie," Florence groaned, closing her eyes and thudding the back of her head against the headrest. "So every time I'm onstage, I'm onstage with *her.*"

I cleared my throat. "Well, maybe you two can make friends during rehearsals."

"She called me Fido, Mom. 'Congratulations, Fido,' she said, in front of *everyone.* I swear to God, if I didn't like the school lunches here so much, I'd give up. Do you know what we had today? *Calzones.* I gave Chef Tonya a high five and told her she deserved a raise. She said she'd settle for no more budget cuts."

"Well, that's something."

"You know, the only thing that makes me feel better about being Lainey Mullins's dog is the fact that she has to wear this red curly wig that makes her look like Ronald McDonald. At least I'll be in a dog suit, so no one will recognize me."

"That is also something."

Despite her slow start making friends, Flo seemed her usual garrulous and spirited self. "What about you?" she demanded. "How's your friend situation? Have you made any at work?"

"Not a friend exactly, but a few friendly acquaintances."

"I believe in you. You can take them from friendly to friends."

"Thanks, Flo."

"Cupcakes might help."

"I'm not baking cupcakes."

"You're no fun."

Everyone I worked with was nice enough and I didn't think I'd need cupcakes to make friends. I just needed time. I'd always been slow to get to know a person and that was just the way it was.

It turned out that Dr. Parker Nock and Dr. Maud Gerrish were married, and they had very different ideas on how the practice should be run. Maud felt doctors should be like trusted family members, comforting and supportive; Parker felt they should be experts who should be listened to. Maud wanted the waiting room to look homely and be filled with toys and fish tanks and posters of cats hanging from branches; Parker thought waiting rooms should be bare and quiet, with no *nonsense.*

"We find it hard to keep an office manager," Shirleen, one of the medical assistants, sighed during my first week. "I've been here for five years, and they've been through three in that time. Not everyone can cope with umpiring their matches, if you know what I mean."

Dr. Gerrish would order donuts for the break room and Dr. Nock would tell me donuts were the cause of many early deaths and to get a fruit basket instead. Dr. Nock would put the call waiting music onto smooth jazz and Dr. Gerrish would change it to easy listening pop. Dr. Gerrish would let the Girl Scouts sell cookies by the front door and Dr. Nock would then declare that the Junior Anglers should be able to sell raffle tickets too.

"Zoe, what the hell is that stoned-looking teddy bear out in the waiting room?" Dr. Nock complained in my second week. "Don't you think it's insensitive to the opioid addicts to have a stoned stuffy sitting out there?"

"Um, do you mean the Care Bear?" I hazarded. "That's Sweet Serenity Bear, Dr. Nock."

"This is a serious place, Zoe. People come here with actual problems. Do you think they want a stoned Care Bear goggling at them?"

"Um, no. I'll move it out of the waiting room, Dr. Nock."

"Don't just move it. Get rid of it!"

When Dr. Gerrish found out that Sweet Serenity Bear was gone, she was anything but serene. "That bear keeps the little ones calm when they come for their shots!" she snapped.

"Yes, of course, Dr. Gerrish," I said.

"You get online right now and order me a full set of plush Care Bears, thank you, Zoe. I want all the happy-looking ones. No Grumpy, you hear me, Zoe?"

"Yes, Dr. Gerrish."

"Get Funshine and Love-a-Lot and Hopeful Heart. And I want another Sweet Serenity!"

"Oh, I didn't throw her out, Dr. Gerrish." I pulled the Care Bear from my desk drawer and held her up.

"Well, thank goodness for small miracles," she exclaimed, snatching Sweet Serenity out of my hands. "I'm putting this right in front of that old grump's door." She paused, a gleam coming into her eye. "Actually, Zoe, go on and order a Grumpy Bear after all. I think I'll put it on his desk."

The first couple of weeks working there were stressful. I felt like I was being tossed back and forth like a hot potato. But after that, I relaxed into it and just let them bicker (flirt?) with each other. It seemed to be one of their love languages.

The work itself was more interesting than the glorified call center back in Pittsburgh. I ran the accounts but also managed the practice, everything from staffing rosters to ordering supplies. It was busy but smooth, with patterns to the week that soon felt oddly comforting. Aside from Shirleen, there were a couple of nurses, and a few other medical assistants who handed out lollipops and stickers to children and adults alike. During my lunch breaks, I read *House Beautiful* and *Home Living* (which were bountiful in the waiting room thanks to Dr. Nock, who didn't believe in gossip magazines) and I scrolled reels about renovations for ideas for the house.

"What do you think of this?" I asked Shirleen, holding up a magazine spread, which showed a screened porch painted a moody shade of dark blue-green.

"Oh nice. You wouldn't think a dark color like that would work, would you?" She shook her head, her bleached hair swinging stiffly. "Interior decorators are genius, aren't they?"

"I got it into my head to paint my bedroom deep burgundy after reading one of those things," admitted Carrie, another of the medical assistants. She was reading one of the gossip magazines

Dr. Gerrish had brought in, which we all hid from Dr. Nock. "But my room doesn't look anything like the pictures in the magazine. I feel like I'm sleeping inside a womb."

"Oh, Zoe, are you renovating?" Erica was currently knitting a winter coat for her daughter's dog and peering over Carrie's shoulder at the pictures of celebrities on the red carpet.

Shirleen laughed. "If you can call what Zoe's doing *renovating*." She gave me a look. "Go on, tell her," she prodded.

I told her, preparing for the usual politely masked horror. But Erica surprised me.

"Oh my God, I love treasure houses!" Erica dropped her knitting needles in excitement. "I've never met someone who bought one in real life! Got photos?" she demanded.

"You know about treasure houses?" I sat up straighter.

"Do I! I'm obsessed. *Obsessed.* Are you making reels? What's your Instagram?"

"Oh no, no Instagram." I shut that down fast. I wasn't posting anything where Tina might one day find it. I didn't need her seeing photos of my house and my life and my *kid.* My life was strictly private. "I'll show you photos on my phone, though."

Erica made excited noises as I showed her images of our junk-filled rooms.

"And this is the porch you want to paint green?" she asked, as she zoomed in on the details of our currently screenless and stripped-bare porch. "And what's that?"

She was looking at the other end of the porch.

"The, uh, laundry." I had to laugh at the look on her face. "It's in original condition," I joked. "With vintage features."

"Oh, dear God. Rip that off, honey. You could make one big, long, lovely porch. It wouldn't take much to take down that corrugated iron and put up frames for screens instead. Wouldn't it be a big space then? Forget that dark green, though, stained timber would be nicer."

"I like this white porch here," Carrie said, pointing at another page in the magazine. "It's got Kennedy compound written all over it."

"I don't think I'm the Kennedy compound type," I said dubiously, staring down at the nautical white indoor/outdoor room.

"Well, what type are you?"

I thought about it. "I don't know."

"Whatever you do, keep it simple." I jumped a mile as I realized Dr. Nock was standing behind me, staring down at the photo on my phone.

"The focus is supposed to be on the view, not the room," he said. "Looks like a nice big garden." He took an apple from the fruit basket on the table and wandered off again.

He was right, I realized, as I went back to the magazine. The reason I was drawn to the page with the blue-green room wasn't the color of the paint, it was the way the woods glowed beyond the frames of the screens.

"What kind of flooring have you got?" Erica asked, finishing off the dog coat.

"Floorboards on the porch side, brick on the laundry side."

"Do you want to keep it like that or change both to brick or both to boards?"

"I don't know." I sighed explosively. "There are too many decisions to make. And I don't know what kind of person I am," I said plaintively. How could I be over thirty and not know what kind of person I was, whether or not I was a Kennedy compound type, or even if I preferred bricks to boards?

"Do as little as possible," Dr. Nock advised as he returned to fill his coffee mug. "Old houses are not to be messed with. Buff them up and smooth off the edges and then leave them be."

I'd said something similar to Jake, I remembered, about letting houses be what they were. "But don't you think it'll look odd if half the floor is brick and half is board?"

"Do *you*?" His gray eyes were clear and uncompromising.

"No," I blurted.

"Well, there you go." And off he went again.

"Girls?" Tam, the last of the receptionists, who was managing the desk while we lunched, stuck her head into our little kitchen/common room. "I've got an emergency!"

The mood shifted, everyone alert.

"Oh, not *that* kind of emergency. It's just about this evening's NA meeting. My mother's had a bit of an episode in the home, but I'm supposed to be here to help Dr. Nock tonight. Can someone sit in for me? It's just doing the coffee and snacks and tidying up after."

"Ah, honey, I can't. I'm babysitting tonight." Erica was regretful.

"I've got friends coming over to rewatch the Anthony season of *Bridgerton*," Carrie said, not sounding regretful in the slightest.

"Sorry, Tam, it's Zumba night." Shirleen did a shimmy.

Tam looked increasingly tense.

"I might be able to do it," I said tentatively, even though the mention of Narcotics Anonymous made my stomach clench. "I just need to check my planner to see what time I have to get Flo. I haven't got our schedule memorized yet." Tam followed me to my desk, all but wringing her hands. "What time is the meeting?" I asked as I skimmed the week.

"Six till seven-thirty."

Flo had her first rehearsal for the play from five to eight. She hadn't been thrilled to hear she'd be at school that late and had suggested we get burgers for dinner on the way home. I suggested she get excited about the leftovers in the fridge.

"I can do it," I told Tam, who sagged with relief. I tried to ignore the sweaty feeling I had at the thought of the meeting itself.

"Oh, thank you so much." She started packing up. "I could have left Dr. Nock to do it by himself, but he never locks up properly. . . ."

"All I have to do is coffee?"

"And put out snacks. He has a bag of apples over there—but I usually put out the rest of the donuts too. Oh, and tissues. You'll need tissues out. And then tidy and lock up after. Thank you, you're a godsend."

"I hope your mom is okay."

She teared up. "Thanks, Zoe."

FIFTEEN

I hadn't realized the meeting was a Nar-Anon Family Group. I'd thought it was a regular NA meeting, but it turned out those were on Mondays. This one was for partners and families of addicts.

People like me.

"I trust you know that everything that happens here is completely anonymous and private and you're not to repeat any of it to anyone," Dr. Nock told me firmly before he opened the doors. "And for God's sake, get rid of those Care Bears."

I stayed discreetly out of the waiting room during the meeting, surrounded by Dr. Gerrish's Care Bears, but I could hear the whole meeting through the open door.

"Last week I went to a movie with this boy in my class," a teenage boy said softly. "He's really wholesome. His mom and dad are dentists. He paid for my popcorn, and he was really sweet and held my hand, and then he walked me to my car and kissed me goodnight. And then I got home and found *he'd* turned up again. And there they both were, sprawled in the living room, and there was vomit—and she was barely breathing and . . . I can't forgive myself for this . . . I kind of hoped she'd stop . . . I wanted . . . I just wanted it over. Even if it meant she . . ."

Memory can be a freight train. And there you are on the tracks with your back to it when it hits. You don't even see it coming.

Or sometimes you see it, but you can't move fast enough.

And sometimes you see it and you don't even try and move. You just let it hit.

I was taken to foster care three times because Tina overdosed, but there were other overdoses, ones that only she and I knew about. Sometimes she overdosed and I didn't call for help, because I didn't want to be taken away. Like the time she shot up with the lady next door, without knowing what was in her spoonful, and she slumped through our front door, passing out cold. I was seven. She stayed out cold for most of the day and I thought she'd stopped breathing. I held my hand under her nose and felt nothing. I went and got a mirror and tried to catch condensation from her breath. Nothing. I pressed my ear to her chest to see if I could hear a heartbeat and held my hand on her skin to see if she was cold.

And I remember feeling a muddy electric buzzing inside me, like a live wire fallen into a puddle, sizzling. I felt it in my guts, a crawling, loose, prickly feeling like I might lose control of my bowels. I feel it now, as though I'm back there. I feel it in my veins, like someone dumped poison into me. At the time it was an animal feeling, and my instinct was to get low, to crawl under something, to hide like a defenseless creature. But I couldn't leave Tina. I sat there with my hand on her, thinking she was dead.

I only knew she wasn't dead when she wet herself. The smell was ammoniac, astringent. As soon as the hot stream hit my leg, I made a keening sound. I didn't have any control over it, the noise coming out of me. It scared me. But I kept making it.

After hours of being maybe-dead, Tina had stirred, making thick senseless murmuring sounds. Then she dragged herself to bed, still soaked in her own urine, leaving me there in the puddle. As she started snoring, I shook violently, juddering till my teeth chattered.

We never spoke of it. I don't even know if she knew she'd almost died—she probably didn't. But I knew. And the smell of ammonia still gives me that loose, hot feeling in my stomach and I still feel the press of the floorboards into my knees and the heat of her urine on my leg. I smell certain cleaning products and I'm seven years old again and sure my mother is dead.

I knew what the teenage boy in the Nar-Anon group meant when he said he hoped his mom would *stop*. I knew the endless tension of waiting for someone's chest to rise again. Of just wanting it to end, one way or another.

Even though I needed her, sometimes I needed her to *stop* even more.

"Are you okay?" Dr. Nock asked when the meeting was over and he caught sight of me cleaning the coffee machine. "You're very pale."

"Tired, I guess," I said, feeling exposed.

He eyed me. "These meetings can be tough to listen to."

My hands shook on the glass pot. "Addiction seems like a terrible thing," I said, trying to sound like a passive bystander and not like someone who'd just been flattened by the memory train. "Have you been running these long?"

"A few years. Opioids have been bad around here. Fentanyl especially. And now we have ketamine too." He sighed.

Ketamine. I remembered my mom when I'd visited her in prison. She'd practically been drooling, completely unaware her mouth was even open.

"It's a horse tranquilizer, you know," Dr. Nock said in his laconic way. "Originally. Now there's good research on its possibilities for treating depression in humans—there's a nasal spray that's very promising. But that's not what these folks are taking. They're dosing with enough to anesthetize a horse." He sighed again, staring at the empty circle of chairs. Then he seemed to shake himself. "Now, where are those stupid bears? I'm going to put them in my wife's wastepaper basket." He disappeared into the back room to gather up the Care Bears.

Dr. Nock was the old-fashioned sort and walked me to my car as we left for the night. "Get yourself some food, Zoe. You're looking sickly." He gently slapped the car on the side as I drove off. As soon as I was out of the parking lot, I felt the shaking start. My teeth chattered.

My mom hadn't died, I reassured myself. Not that time, or any of the times. She was still breathing. And if she *had* ever stopped breathing, it wouldn't have been my fault. Not that time, and not even the last time, when I wanted with every fiber of my being to put her out of her misery.

I was thirteen that time and she'd been in her meth era. She'd been gone for a few days and clearly hadn't been sleeping or eating. I didn't ask her where she'd been or what she'd been doing. Meth made her compulsive—she was likely to have spent eight hours peeling off her nail polish or talking to a cashier at a gas station. Once she'd been picked up in a dime store for counting all the red things in the store, including every red jelly bean she could see through the clear plastic of the packaging.

That day she came home after all those days away, when I didn't know if she was alive or dead. Tina was tweaking by the time she returned, irritable and mean as a toddler due for a nap. She had sores around her mouth because she kept chewing on her lips and she was paranoid and unable to sleep, even though she was clearly desperate for rest.

Tina paced the apartment as I tried to do my homework, muttering under her breath. I kept my gaze fixed on the tip of my pen as I pressed it too hard into my notebook.

Mom, don't. The thought was so bright it seemed as though it must be written in the air in neon.

The feeling of waiting for a person to explode is a caged feeling, like you're holding all the stress of it inside your rib cage and it's moving, writhing, slithering, coiling up to strike, and your ribs are bars too fragile to hold it in. I'd take surreptitious looks to check where Tina was as she crisscrossed the floor.

There was a violence to her pacing and muttering.

What would I do if she came at me? I played the scenarios out in my head.

Tina never actually *had* come at me. Most of my life she'd gravitated toward drugs that didn't turn her into an angry zombie: molly, which made her cloyingly affectionate, or oxy, which made her drowsy. Now and then she got her hands on coke or bennies. But this, the meth, was the worst—at least for me. When I was twelve and thirteen, she started alternating between ice and oxy, swinging between being a wretched, scratching, wakeful creature and a slumped-over shell of a person. Meanwhile, I struggled to sleep, always listening for Tina coming home, and I found myself struggling to breathe at sudden moments, like someone had dropped me into the ocean and expected me to breathe seawater.

The day I almost killed her, I felt like my lungs were filled with fluid. There was no room for air. She paced, scratching, muttering and whispering and making vicious hissing noises, shuffling wall to wall, shushing and fretting and chewing at the air. I couldn't breathe no matter how much I told myself the room was full of air, not water.

Mom, I couldn't say. *Mom, stop it. Please stop it.*

She didn't stop it. And then she started to cry, desperate tired crying, like she couldn't bear herself, like she wanted to stop pacing but couldn't, wanted to stop muttering but couldn't, wanted to rest but couldn't.

Then she had her phone out and I knew what she was doing.

I hated it when dealers came to the apartment. I hated it when *anyone* came to the apartment. I went and hid in the bathroom until she'd scored, every nerve of my body listening for voices and waiting for the front door to close.

"Baby?" Tina's voice was jittery, stuttering over the syllables. "Angel?"

She was talking to me. She was alone and holding a little twist of cling wrap, inside of which was an oily brown square of ice. Her hands were shaking and she couldn't get the cling wrap off it.

"Angel, help Mommy."

And that's when I almost did it. I almost shoved that whole brown chunk in her mouth. She was too agitated to find a needle or a pipe, so I knew she was going to eat it. Partly because she was grinding her teeth in anticipation. And for one very possible moment, as my unsteady fingers peeled back the cling wrap, I was on the edge of killing her by feeding her the entire cube. I just wanted it to stop. The thought was so intrusive that my hand actually moved toward her mouth.

"No, baby. Baby, no. Mommy needs some for later." She was so deep in the agony of withdrawal that she balked at the thought of ever feeling that way again. She carved off half to rewrap and handed it to me because she was shuddering by that point, her fingers spasming. As the ice disappeared into her sunken mouth, I had a vision of ramming the half I was holding in after it. Of holding her jaws shut and waiting for the full overdose to hit her system. All I could think, as that vision made my hand twitch, was that it would be *over.* No more waiting. No more listening. No more no more no more.

I was early to pick Flo up, which wasn't a good thing when I was in this juddery, shivery state. My thoughts were flying and I had that live-wire feeling flicking about inside me. Agitated, I got out of the car, feeling the urge to pace, the way Tina had paced the apartment, *crisscross, crisscross.* The comparison made my skin crawl.

I headed for the swings and sat down.

It was full dark and the golden orange streetlights around the parking lot were like fat fireflies. I could smell the ever-present ocean and hear the soft sigh and kiss of the water in Camden's safe harbor. I closed my eyes and tried to concentrate on being here on the swing, in this moment.

"Hey."

"Oh my God!" I flew off the swing like someone had yanked me on a string. My heart was in my mouth.

Jake. It was just Jake.

He was open-mouthed and wide-eyed, holding both hands up, palms out, as though I were holding him at gunpoint.

"Oh *God,*" I exclaimed, pressing my own hands to my galloping heart. "You scared the hell out of me."

"Sorry." His hands were still in the air. "I, uh, just saw you here and thought I'd say hi."

"What the hell are you doing in a school playground in the middle of the night?"

"It's seven forty-five."

"You know what I mean. It's *dark.*"

"Yeah, well, that happens at night." He slowly lowered his hands. "I'm just here to pick up my niece. She's in rehearsals for a school play."

"Oh." My heart was still racing. In fact, it now felt like it was racing *and* stumbling. Partly from memories of Tina, partly from having the pants scared off me, and partly because . . . well, Jake. The man was stupidly good-looking. The streetlights cast sharp shadows on his face and accentuated the hollows of his cheekbones, the dip where his dimples hid.

"I, ah, didn't realize you had a niece," I said lamely.

"I have three of them."

I sank back down onto the swing, trying to calm my galloping heart.

"Is Flo in the play too?" He joined me on the swing set. He was wearing a light sweater that hugged his chest.

I nodded. "She's playing the dog." I let out a slow breath. At least Jake had pulled me back from the past. I could feel my feet on the ground and the sharpness of the fall air.

There was a beat of silence. "And is she . . . happy . . . about that? Being the dog?"

"What do you think?"

"Well, I know Lainey would hate it."

I jerked on the swing. "Your niece is Lainey Mullins?" Oh, Flo was going to *hate* this.

"You know her?"

"No. It's just that Flo's mentioned her. She got the lead in the play, right?"

"Always," Jake said dryly. "Lainey was born to take center stage." He laughed. "If she'd got the part of the dog, she would have made placards and marched on the principal's office. She probably would have made me glue glitter all over those placards too."

"Flo seemed happy to avoid having to sing," I admitted. "She's only really doing the play to make some friends."

"Is it working?"

"I'll let you know. This is only the first rehearsal." We lapsed into an almost comfortable silence.

"Oh," said Jake, turning his swing toward me. "I meant to say, I'm putting in an order for firewood this week. You want me to order you a delivery at the same time? October's just about on us and it's going to get cold."

For a guy who had resting grumpy face, he sure was solicitous.

"Wayne said I should probably get the chimneys checked before I light any fires," I said regretfully. I'd been looking forward to a winter fire crackling in the parlor. Once I cleared out the parlor and could get to the fireplace, anyway. My house was just an endless list of things to do. But at the same time, the thought that it was *my house* filled me with a cozy warm feeling.

"I can look at your chimneys," Jake volunteered.

I shook my head. He'd done so much for us already. "It's fine, you don't have to—"

"All good. I'm checking Elton's too."

"Okay. Thanks."

He had a very reassuring presence. He was like the solid mass of the cliffs at the edge of Beach Road, immovable and calm. There was a permanence to him. Like he knew what he was and felt no need to be anything else.

"How come you live in Oxeye?" I asked abruptly. We'd never finished that line of questioning on the night we found Mac and the Cheeses, and I was still burning with curiosity about him. While I couldn't imagine Jake anywhere but Oxeye, he was an anomaly in a place made up primarily of vacationers and retirees. He was just about the only full-time resident. And me and Flo, of course. "I mean . . . how did you come to run the hardware store and everything? Are you from here?"

He gave me a sideways look that seemed a little wary and a little shy. "Not exactly," he said slowly. "I mean, my family summered on the coast every year when I was growing up, but we came from Boston, mostly. But the coast has a pull on you, you know? Or on my family, anyway. This place gets in your blood. No one is watching the clock in the summer, no one is in a rush to be somewhere else. And you spend the rest of your life wishing you could get back to the timeless summer at the seaside."

I was speechless. Usually, Jake was a man of few, mostly grunted, words, and yet here he was speaking like a poet. And he *kept* talking.

"When I was a kid, we spent nine months of the year in Boston." His accent became a more refined New England drawl as he went on, "And three months in Oxeye. I liked the Oxeye months better."

"And the hardware store? How did that happen?" I wrapped my arms around the chains of the swing and lifted my feet from the ground.

"I used to work at the lobster shack down in Rockport for cash during summer, back when Graham Gillis ran the hardware store.

He used to daydream about attaching a lobster shack to the place—giving Rockport a run for their money. And, I don't know . . ." Jake leaned back to look at the sky, which was a loose sprinkling of stars. "All through college, I just kept thinking about it. About the rhythm of the days, about the ocean out the window, about living a simpler life. I look at my brother-in-law, billing in two-minute increments and always glued to his emails, and I can't imagine doing that. This, though . . . It just felt . . . right."

There was so much more I wanted to ask him. Did he have any regrets about it? How old had he been when he bought the hardware store? Did he get lonely in a town full of older people? Did he date . . . ?

But we were interrupted by the gymnasium doors slamming open and a stream of kids flooding out, their voices bright in the cool, clear air.

"Lainey!" Jake called across the grass, lifting a hand so he was visible.

"Oh. My. God. She sent you *again*?" A tall girl with an even taller attitude streaked across the lawn in our direction. "Probably forgot she even has a kid."

"If she'd forgotten she had a kid, I wouldn't be here, would I," Jake observed, his voice mild.

"Where's Hazel?" The girl skidded to a stop in front of us. She looked a lot like her uncle—the same wild sun-streaked hair and double dimples. She gave me a cursory look, then directed her full attention at Jake. "You can't leave Hazel all alone, Uncle Jake, it's *mean.*"

"I didn't leave her alone." He bristled. "She's in the back of the truck." He jerked his thumb at the parking lot. "I've only left her there a minute."

I saw Flo approaching, eyeing Lainey. She was dragging her backpack over the lawn, something I was always scolding her not to do.

"Stop it, you monster. You'll ruin it," I chided her, scooping it off the ground. It was so heavy I groaned. "What have you got in here, rocks?"

"Yeah." She rolled her eyes. "I packed a bunch of rocks to bring to school."

"Hey, Flo." Jake didn't exactly smile, but the lines beside his eyes crinkled.

"You know Flo?" Lainey looked back and forth between them, her long hair swinging.

"Sure I do. She lives on my street."

Lainey's eyes widened. "Wait. Flo lives in the *junk house*?"

"Don't call it the junk house," Jake snapped. "It's just a house."

"A house *full of junk*. Mom says—"

"Lainey," Jake said in warning. "Don't be rude. You're talking about their house now."

It was Lainey's turn to roll her eyes, the gesture reminding me so powerfully of Flo that it made me wonder if they taught it in school.

"It's cool you're both in the school play," Jake said, changing the topic. He shot me a pleading look, as though begging me to rescue him from the conversation.

"Did you know Flo's my bitch?" Lainey asked Jake, her face all innocence.

I couldn't hide my shock. I reached for Flo, but she stepped back.

"Lainey!" Jake was appalled.

"What? She is, she's playing my dog."

Flo seemed unfazed by Lainey's rudeness. I guess she was used to it.

"Get in the car," Jake growled. "Now."

Lainey groaned. "Are you going to tell Mom I used the b-word?"

He gave her a stony look and pointed at the car.

"Seriously? You're such a snitch, Uncle Jake."

"Jesus, Flo, I'm so sorry," Jake apologized, once Lainey had dragged herself off to his truck, complaining the whole way. He was all kinds of embarrassed, and pretty mad.

"It's okay, Jake, I'm not actually her bitch," Flo said. She seemed vaguely amused.

"Well, sorry a thousand times over and . . . just more sorry. I'll definitely be telling her mom. And Liv's a hard-ass, so Lainey will know about it."

"You seem to be taking that little witch in stride," I said suspiciously as we walked to the car. Across the parking lot I could see Jake telling his niece off.

"I'm playing the long game." Flo opened the car door. "Burgers?"

"Leftovers."

"Even after someone called me a b-word?"

"Even then."

"And Jake thinks *Lainey's* mom is a hard-ass."

"Language!"

She rolled her eyes again, turned on the sound system, and queued up Spotify.

SIXTEEN

Flo and I slogged through evenings and weekends of sorting through treasure and trash. We had a few fun moments going through bags of cheap plastic toys. There was one bag full of little colored balls with holes in one end and plastic protrusions at the other. We didn't know what they were at first and had to google them—original 1950s "pop beads." You could pop them together to make jewelry.

"It's pretty nasty jewelry," Flo said, after she'd made a dozen or so bracelets and covered her wrists in them. "Although on Etsy people are selling bracelets like this with vintage beads for five dollars, so they're not total garbage."

When we went into the café the next morning and Colleen saw them around Flo's wrists, she just about melted.

"Oh lord, I had those when I was little!" She bent over Flo's stack of plastic beads. "My sister and I used to sit for hours popping them together. I had a set that was supposed to look like 'genuine pearls,' and actually they kind of did. I wore that necklace on my first day of high school and didn't I look fine."

"You can have some if you want," Flo volunteered. "We have way more than we need." She unpopped her bracelets and offered them to Colleen. "That's okay, isn't it, Mom?"

"Of course." The glow on Colleen's face as she took the junky little plastic beads made me smile.

"Coffee is on the house today, then," Colleen said, and when she served us, those pop beads were snug on her wrists, blazingly bright against her skin.

It turned out there was a lot of valuable culch in our house—or *usable* culch as Flo would say. Some things were worth money and some things weren't, but even the stuff that didn't have cash value had other kinds of value. Roger had grown teary at the sight of a battered old cookie tin. It was bright chartreuse, with brown and orange mushrooms all over it. It was very dented, but the colors were probably as bright as they were on the day it was bought. Roger had barely been able to speak as he put his hands on it.

"Are you okay?" Flo had asked, alarmed.

Roger nodded, but when he met my gaze, he was in tears. He pressed his lips together and tried to find his voice. "My mother had this canister," he said, his voice stretched. "It used to sit on the top of the refrigerator, where we couldn't reach it. When we were allowed a treat, she'd pull it down and pop the lid." He was losing his battle with the tears. "Only the store-bought biscuits went in *this* tin." Roger's smile was wobbly. "For her, store-bought was the best."

We sent him home with the tin, and he cradled it the whole way down the street. The next time I was at his house, I saw it sitting with pride of place on top of the refrigerator.

Slowly, we were making headway. We sold most of the records to Sammy from Vintage Vinyl & More in Camden, and Alan was helping me list online the old furniture we didn't want to keep.

"You have some absolute gems here," Alan told me as we went through it all out on the lawn. Jake had rigged up a couple of floodlights in the tent so we could sort things after work, now that it was dark early.

I photographed the "pieces," as Alan called them, and he wrote up the descriptions and measurements. We had a deal that he could have first bid on anything he saw that he liked. Luckily for me, he liked a lot. He took an old church pew and a couple of bentwood rocking chairs, and a whole bunch of lamps. The mid-century furniture sold easily online, the older stuff less so. I got an eye-watering amount of money for an old fifties teak bed that was, as Flo would say, in mint condition. There was a kidney-shaped rosewood writing table that Alan had high hopes for. He turned down several generous offers, even though I almost died each time he did.

"This is antique English rosewood, Zoe," Alan told me, looking horrified at my instinct to accept the first offer. "Ounce for ounce, this wood is worth more than gold!"

"You should be an antique dealer," I told him when I had a wad of cash in my hand and the rosewood table was driving off in the back of a van.

"I used to be one," Alan said, looking a touch smug. "But I'm retired now."

"Running a bed-and-breakfast is retired?"

"Blame Roger for that one."

To thank him for all his help, I gifted Alan with an art deco wooden clock he'd been eyeing. He put it on their mantel in the B&B and sent me a photo of it immediately. *Divine,* he captioned it. *Not thanks enough,* I wrote back. I seriously didn't know how I could have done it without him. By late October, we'd cleared the biggest objects from the tent and the house.

As we worked, the sound of Jake's power tools was a steady purr and whir. He'd put his hand up to help me repair the porch, which I was paying him for. I wouldn't let him do it for free. He'd ripped down the corrugated iron walls of the laundry in a single day but had balked at pulling out the heavy concrete trough.

"That's staying," he told me, stepping back and wiping sweat from his forehead. He pushed his safety goggles up. "I mean, it could come out, but it's not an easy job."

I considered the old trough with its cast-iron water pump. "Does the pump still work?" I asked.

"Nope. It's too old. Hasn't been maintained."

I considered it. It wasn't without its charms. Much like the old range, it gave off *Anne of Green Gables* vibes.

"You could turn the trough into a water feature or something," Jake said. "Or fill it with dirt and make it a planter."

I nodded. "Sure. It can be like the range in the kitchen. A big, weird feature."

He grunted, apparently pleased.

Jake had an odd relationship with the house on Tinker Street. He was both attracted to it and repelled by it. At least that made more sense now that I knew the house had been in his family. People got sentimental about things. I imagined what it must be like to be attached to a place. The only place I'd ever been attached to was Suni and Wayne's. The driveway of lilacs, the perfect lawns, and the soothing eggshell blue of my room. I'd been staring at Elton's cheery lemon-drop-yellow front door lately and thinking that it would be nice to have a colored door too. Maybe I could paint mine eggshell blue to remind me of Suni and Wayne. . . . make them part of the house, the way I'd become a part of theirs.

I was missing them dreadfully. I'd always known they were important to me, but I hadn't realized how much they were in the fabric of my days until they weren't anymore.

Jake had designed screened frames for the porch, and while he was at it, I'd asked him to order vinyl panels to winterize it. "By the time I get this done, we'll be looking at snow weather, so you might as well do it all at once," he'd said approvingly.

He disappeared on weekends, as did Roger and Alan, because October was the month of what they called "leaf peepers"—tourists coming to admire the fall leaves. I didn't need to leave my own yard to go leaf peeping. Our garden and the woods were ablaze. Elton pointed out the tree species to me and Flo as he helped us harvest our crab apples and we helped him harvest his McIntoshes. Hardly any of our crab apples had survived the birds, but Elton's trees were covered in nets, and he had a bumper crop.

"The oranges and yellows are maples," he said, pointing to the bright pops of color in the woods that lapped at our backyards. Flo was up a tree, snapping off apples at pace, but I was paying close attention. I wanted to know the names of everything.

"Most of those there are sugar maples," Elton told me, his finger outlining them. "The mountain maples go red as red can be, and the white ash turns purple."

In our yard, the white oak was turning a rich dark burgundy, the moosewood was festive yellow, and the hornbeam was sunset shades of gold and pink and scarlet, each leaf seeming to glow from within. The bushes that had scratched at us the day we arrived were mountain holly, otherwise known as catberry (which seemed apt, given all the cats we kept finding, both porcelain and real). Hud had excised them from the path beside the house, and from the yard in front of the porch, but those that remained had turned a burnished orange-red, the red berries still hanging thickly in their boughs.

"Elton, I think we should turn some of these apples into apple pie," Flo announced from up high.

"Do you now?"

"I do."

"Do you have a recipe?"

"No, but the internet does."

"Do you know what's better than the internet? Gary Laughton's secret recipe. Back when the bakery still made pastries and the like, the leaf peepers came from all over to buy Gary's apple pies."

"Can we do it in our kitchen, so I can keep an eye on the kittens? They get upset when I'm gone too long on weekends."

"I'm sure they do, and I'm sure we can."

Flo and Elton cajoled Gary to take an afternoon off from the store, which Doris only allowed because Flo asked the Laughtons to dinner after the pie baking.

"You can *eat* the pie," she'd promised Doris.

Flo was big on asking people to dinner. On the Sunday of the pie baking, she also asked Elton, Jake, and Colleen.

"Colleen's going to show me how to properly whip cream," she told me. "By hand."

Flo had become a regular visitor around town. She ran errands to the store for me and went to the library to donate books from our house and stopped by the café and the hardware store just to say hi. I was sure she was scoring snacks everywhere she went.

"I could have shown you how to whip cream," Gary Laughton told Flo when he found out about Colleen and the cream. He sounded a little hurt. He was wearing an apron Flo had dug out for him. It was a 1960s floral affair in lurid colors. It weirdly suited him. Gary was balding and rosy, with big eyebrows that made me think of bunting.

"Yeah, well, the cream is just an excuse, Gary," Flo whispered, her voice carrying across the kitchen to where I was sorting a drawer. "Colleen gets lonely."

Gary's bunting eyebrows shot up. "She does? Colleen doesn't strike me as the lonely type."

"Lonely types never do," Flo said sagely. "Like Mom here. She seems perfectly normal, don't you think? But she's not. She's actually a very lonely person."

"Flo!" I felt myself turning bright red.

"What! You are." Flo leaned into Gary. "She *is*," she whispered, in the same carrying voice.

I stood there in shock. She thought I was lonely?

"Well, now, I think everyone has their lonely times," Elton said quietly, pausing from peeling his apples. He gave me a kind look and I blushed even harder. Great. Now everyone thought I was weird and lonely.

"After Sylvie left me, I thought I'd just about die of loneliness." Elton sighed.

"Your wife *left* you?" Flo turned away from her lesson on how to make pastry and gave Elton her full attention.

He smiled at her. "Not in the way you're thinking. She got early-onset dementia. It started with a little memory loss, but she was in her forties, so she thought it was just the Change."

"The Change?" Flo perked up and I knew she'd be thinking of werewolves or shape-shifters.

"Perimenopause," I told her.

"What's that?"

"A conversation for a whole other day." We both turned back to Elton.

"First my Sylvie forgot how to tell time. And she was different, angrier. By the time she was fifty, she wasn't herself anymore. She withdrew, couldn't sleep, couldn't quite recognize people. Even me."

"Wow, that sucks," Flo said, sitting down next to him.

"Yes, it really does."

"What was she like before she lost it?"

"Flo!" I really needed to teach her some manners, I thought, my ears burning. "*Before she got sick,*" I corrected.

"No, it's okay," Elton said, and he was smothering a smile. "It's an apt description."

No, it's not, I mouthed at Flo. She rolled her eyes.

He resumed his peeling. "And to answer your question, Sylvie was pure sunshine, Flo."

"Yes, she was," Gary Laughton agreed heartily. "Now, Flo, watch this part. Most people use a food processor for this, but an old-fashioned pie needs to be made the old-fashioned way."

Reluctantly, Flo left Elton's side and went to watch Gary rub butter and flour together through his fingers.

"I remember the summer Sylvie brought you to Oxeye, Elton," Gary said with a puttering little laugh. "You were so smitten, she could have told you to jump off the cliffs and you would have."

"I sure would have. And I would have died a happy man doing it."

I listened to the two of them reminisce as they taught Florence how to bake a pie. They painted a picture of a cheerful, optimistic girl who liked pink roses and going to the movies, Elvis Presley and summers by the sea.

"She was happy with a simple life, was Sylvie," Elton said, his voice warm. "And it was so heartbreaking that it happened to her after she'd watched it take her Aunt Lori." He shook his head. "They were so close. They understood each other. In a family of big personalities, they were the quiet ones. It was hard on Sylvie, watching Lorraine suffer, and it must have crossed her mind that she had the same thing. I hate the thought of it. Her knowing—" His voice cracked, and he stopped talking.

"What a life she had, though, eh?" Gary said gently. "Summers here her whole life long, even till the end, with all her favorite people around her. She wasn't one for apple pie, though, was she? Lemon chiffon, from memory."

"No, that was Marly," Elton corrected softly. "Sylvie loved apple pie—she always made me cover the trees so the birds wouldn't eat the apples, and we came back during leaf peeping season to harvest them every year."

"And now here we are, still harvesting them," Flo marveled, her eyes glued to Gary, who was dripping vinegary water into the bowl of floury butter. "And still making apple pie."

"Here we are," Elton agreed. "That's the way this life works. There are always apples to harvest."

"Except on our trees," Flo told him. "The birds ate almost all of our crap apples."

"Next year I'll loan you a net."

Next year. Elton's words cast a spell, and suddenly I could see us through a dozen flickering falls, harvesting apples and making pies, falling into a homely, enduring pattern, just like Elton and his wife. It made me feel warmed through.

While the pie crust fired in the oven, Flo went to check on her kittens. They had a bed now and a litter tray, and a bunch of toys Flo had found around the house—balls and bits of yarn.

"You've got a cat count?" Gary said as he noticed the chalkboard Flo had propped up on the counter.

"Both real and porcelain now," I said with a sigh. We were at thirty-nine cat figurines and seven and a half actual cats. The half was Debussy, who didn't technically live with us but was around enough to count for something.

Today he came in through the back door with Doris and Jake, who were carrying pumpkins and a couple of bottles of wine. Debussy went straight to the rag rug in front of the cold range and set himself to bathing.

"I thought Flo might like to make jack-o'-lanterns," Doris huffed, dropping her pumpkin on the table.

"Smells good in here," Jake said, as he put his pumpkin down too.

"Apple pie is a home smell," Gary told me with a wink, as he gave Doris a wet kiss.

"What was that for?" she asked suspiciously.

"We were talking about Sylvie," Elton explained. "It's made him appreciate you more."

"Ah, Sylvie." Doris made a sad face. "I miss her. Who else would talk celebrity gossip with me? This one here"—she patted Gary's round belly—"doesn't even know what a Kardashian is."

"I know what a Kardashian is," Gary scoffed. "One of them broke the internet with her butt. You'd have to be dead to have missed that."

"Gary! There's a child present," Doris scolded him.

"Sorry, Flo."

"That's okay, I wasn't listening. I was trying to teach Cheeseball how to stand up on his hind legs. Velveeta can do it, so I told him he can do it too."

Jake let out a long-suffering sigh at the kittens' ignominious names.

"I hope no one minds a pizza delivery for dinner," I apologized to them all. I only had the counter oven, and it was full of pie.

"No one ever minds pizza," Flo exclaimed.

"And at least you have the honor of eating pizza in our dining room," I told them all as I pulled down wineglasses.

They made *ooh*ing and *ahh*ing noises as I took them through to the front rooms, which I appreciated. Now that Alan and I had sold the excess furniture, I'd been able to haul a lot of the junk out to the tent. The dining room had been emptied out except for the furniture I was keeping and the stacks of paintings, which I'd left against the wall behind the door.

I'd kept the dining table, which Alan had told me was solid oak in the French farmhouse style. Not in mint condition, but that was fine with me, as I'd be too scared to use it if it were. The chairs were also oak, according to Alan, ladder-backed with battered seafoam-blue upholstery seats.

"Oh, pet, look at the job you've done!" Doris was beaming at me. "It looks amazing."

"It looks empty, that's all," Flo told her. "It's pretty plain. I think we should paint the room a bright color. Like pink."

"We're not painting it pink."

"Do you think we need a fire yet?" Flo asked hopefully. "It's cold, don't you think? Doris? Gary? Don't you think it's cold?"

Jake had checked the chimneys and stored a load of wood for us in the wood hutch near the outbuildings, but we hadn't had a fire yet. Mostly because the parlor was still too cluttered, and I'd only just cleared out the dining room. I turned to check with Jake and found him hanging back on the threshold of the dining room, looking pale and haunted.

"You okay?" I asked him.

"Yeah." He seemed to gather himself. "Yeah, sorry. It's just . . . nice. Seeing the room like this. The table . . ." He shrugged. "It's nice."

"I'd forgotten what it looked like," Elton joked. He sat himself down at the table. "This was where I sat when I first met Sylvie's folks."

It took a minute for that to sink in. "Wait. *This* was Sylvie's family place?" I remembered the first day I'd met Elton, when he'd said this house held some of his happiest memories. I glanced at Jake. "Does that mean you and Elton are related too?"

Jake shrugged. "I told you, everyone's related to everyone around here."

"Are *you* related to him?" I asked Doris.

"Lord, no. My people are from Augusta."

"I don't know exactly what our relation is," Elton admitted to Jake. "Second cousins by marriage?"

Jake shrugged.

I frowned. "So, Marly was who in all this? Sylvie's sister?"

"Marly was Sylvie's cousin," Elton corrected me.

I would have liked to learn more, but Colleen arrived then, bringing a container of cookies and another bottle of wine. She'd dressed for dinner in a flowing knit top that came down to her knees, and she'd turned her pop beads into a long loopy necklace. She had a pair of jingly sea-glass earrings in.

"Oh, my goodness, look at this!" she exclaimed, as she came into the dining room. "You've been so *busy*."

"We have," I agreed, pleased by her enthusiasm.

"Mom! Pizza's here!" Flo came barreling out of the kitchen, holding up my phone. "Jake, can you come help me carry it?"

"Nope," Jake said, "I'm building the fire."

"Fine," she huffed. "Mom?"

"I'll come with you, Flo," Doris told her. "Let your poor mother sit down for a moment." Doris pushed me down into a chair. "Gary, you can pour the wine."

Outside the October night was chilly, but in our dining room, with the leaping fire, everything was cozy.

"Flo is right," Doris said as she handed out plates and paper napkins. "The place needs some color. You should definitely paint it."

"Put some of those paintings up too," Gary suggested, waving his wineglass in the direction of the stack behind the door.

The wine and warmth relaxed me. I felt myself melting back into my chair. Even with the walls bare, without a rug on the floor or any ornaments, I liked this room. I liked those fogged-up porthole windows, and the way the oak furniture anchored the room. And I loved the little hatch to the kitchen, which was currently open so we could talk to Flo and Colleen as they whipped the cream for the dessert.

"It's nice to hear laughter in here again." Elton sighed.

"It is," Jake agreed, swirling the wine in his glass, eyes downcast.

I would have given anything to know their thoughts. Jake's particularly. Again, as though reading my mind, he looked up and met my gaze. I felt the shock of it through to my toes and fingertips.

"Ta-da!" Flo exclaimed, as she brought in the apple pie. "Elton's apples; Gary's crust; my filling," she said with pride. Gary had directed her, but she'd done every step of the filling herself. "And Colleen's whipped cream. It's a team effort!"

"Don't forget the butter and flour and cream were from my store," Doris chipped in.

"And what about me?" Jake complained. "Don't I get to be part of the team?"

"You get to be the best part of the team," Flo scolded him. "The part that *eats* the pie."

He didn't argue with that. In fact, he was trying not to smile.

SEVENTEEN

Boston, Massachusetts, and Oxeye, Maine, 1956

When the invitation came for Sylvie's wedding, Marly was livid. "What is *this*?" she demanded, thrusting the card in front of her mother. It was a dreary March Monday in Marly's junior year; she had only collected the mail because she liked to get the paper to check the society pages. Sometimes Freddie de Marche was in there, grinning at the camera in that overconfident way of his. That way that made Marly shiver all the way to her toes.

Mom was sitting at the kitchen table in her dressing gown, staring out the window at the melting sludge of snow, lost in thought. She frowned at the invitation Marly was holding in front of her nose.

"She's getting married at the summer place on Tinker Street!" Marly raged. "Did you know about this?" she accused. "Getting married at Tinker Street was *my* wedding idea!" Marly dropped the invitation on the table and slammed around the kitchen getting breakfast.

"You're not getting married," Mom said, sounding irritated. She was irritable a lot these days. It made Marly feel like screaming. She couldn't say *anything* to her mom anymore without Mom being difficult.

"Oh, isn't that lovely." Mom's irritation evaporated as she examined Sylvie's wedding invitation, her expression turning dreamy. "I do love a wedding."

Marly scowled. Her mom loved *Sylvie.* She didn't even care that Sylvie had stolen Marly's wedding idea.

"I called dibs on the Tinker Street garden for weddings." Marly had been dreaming of her wedding. To Freddie de Marche. Which would happen under the tree where they'd first met.

"You can't call dibs on a garden."

"Yes, you can. I said I wanted to get married in the garden and I wanted to carry daisies and *look.*" Marly pointed an angry finger at the daisy on the invitation.

"Marly, try and be happy for your cousin."

"I *am* happy for her. I'm just not happy she stole my wedding idea." Marly slapped the newspaper down on the table and flipped straight to the back. She scanned the page as she crammed her burned toast in her mouth.

"She didn't *steal* your wedding idea. She just wants to get married at the coast. You're not the only one attached to the house on Tinker Street, you know. Or to daisies." Mom gave a heavy sigh. "It will be nice to go back to the beach. It's been a long time between summers."

Marly felt like throwing the paper across the room. It was bad enough it was Monday and she had a history quiz, but now Sylvie had stolen her wedding idea, Mom was being annoying, *and* there was no Freddie in the society pages.

"I'm going to call Bet about Priscilla's wedding," Mom said, heading for the hall.

"Sylvie's wedding," Marly corrected.

"What?"

"Sylvie. It's Sylvie getting married."

But Mom wasn't listening. She was already out in the hall and Marly could hear the whir of the phone as she dialed.

"Have you noticed Mom's been weird?" Bobby said, as he came into the room on a wave of drugstore aftershave. He'd been home from college for the weekend and seemed in no hurry to get back, even though Marly knew he had Monday classes.

"Mom's always weird," Marly told him shortly.

"No, I mean, extra weird. Did you notice that last night she couldn't turn the television on?"

"You mean she was lazy and asked you to do it."

"Marilyn, stop being a pain in the ass for five minutes. I'm serious."

He never called her Marilyn, so she listened.

"I watched her. She genuinely couldn't figure out how to turn it on. And she had a face like . . . I don't know . . . a confused little kid or something."

Marly frowned. "Maybe she had a headache?" But now that Bobby mentioned it, Mom *had* been a bit weird. She'd forgotten to pick up Dad's dry cleaning a few times, which Marly had suspected she'd done on purpose to annoy him, because Mom was tetchy with him a lot lately. But *that* was weird too. Because she wasn't a generally tetchy person. Marly's parents usually rolled along side by side peaceably. Neither of them liked conflict.

Since all the boys had gone off to college it was usually just Marly and her folks at home. But Marly had been busy at school. She wrote for the school paper and was on the student council. But even as busy as she was, she couldn't help but notice that she and Mom hadn't been getting along. She'd overheard Aunty Betty telling Mom that it was "just teenage girls" and "it would pass." Marly had been annoyed, because she thought it was a Mom thing, more than a Marly thing.

"You really haven't noticed anything?" Bobby said, exasperated, sitting opposite her and leaning forward. "Because I'll tell you, not having seen her for several weeks, she's *different.*"

"Maybe she's a bit distracted? She has been losing her keys a lot," Marly admitted. "She had to get new ones cut the last time." Which wasn't like Mom. Mom had a little glass dish in the kitchen where she always put her keys.

"She called me Virgil this morning," Bobby told Marly, frowning. "And when I told her I wasn't Virgil, she seemed really confused."

Marly frowned, her gaze drifting to the wedding invitation on the fridge. Mom had called it Priscilla's wedding. Not Sylvie's. Even though she'd only just read the invitation. Okay, so maybe she had seen Mom confused a few times. Maybe Mom had even mentioned being confused, last time Aunt Betty and Sylvie were over. But Aunt Bet had just said it was a "time-of-life thing," whatever that meant.

"Maybe it's a time-of-life thing?" Marly repeated to Bobby now, with a shrug.

Bobby, being Bobby, didn't drop it, though. He scowled at Marly and then went off to find Dad.

And then Dad got Mom to go to the doctor.

"It's just time of life," Mom and Dad reassured Bobby and Marly when they got back. Mom seemed terribly embarrassed about it.

"It's lady business," Dad said, seeming even more embarrassed.

But why would lady business make you forget how to turn on the television?

Mom's lady trouble only seemed to get worse over the following months, as Mom forgot more than just names. She started forgetting how to get places and often had to stop at a pay phone and call

Marly for directions. When she couldn't get Marly, she called Dad in a panic. By the time June rolled around, both Marly and her father were plenty worried. Mom took Marly to Oxeye early for the wedding, so they could help Aunt Bet make wedding favors and decorations, and to keep Sylvie happy and calm. Dad and the boys planned to join them later, for the actual wedding weekend. But when Marly slid into the front seat of the station wagon to leave Boston for the coast, she found Mom staring at the dashboard, confused.

"Mom?" Something was wrong. There was a frightened look on her mother's face.

Mom held the key in her hand. She was frowning and a little bit teary.

"Mom? Are you okay?"

"I don't know where this goes," her mom said in a small voice. She held up the key.

"What do you mean?" Marly felt a shiver of fear.

"This." She shook the key. "I know it turns the car on. But *how*?" She sounded terrified.

"Here." Marly leaned over and pointed at the ignition.

But her mom had started to cry.

"Hey." Marly had only ever seen Mom cry at movies and funerals and didn't know what to do.

"Don't tell your father," Mom begged. "He's worried enough as it is."

Marly had a cold quivery feeling in her stomach. *Dad* was worried? Dad, who barely ever showed an emotion?

Mom handed Marly the key. "Can you drive?"

Marly had finished driver's ed, but it was a long way to Oxeye from Boston. She kept darting glances at Mom, who wept for the first half an hour and then snappishly told her to keep her eyes on the road. When they got to Tinker Street, Mom acted like everything was perfectly normal and didn't mention it again.

Mom had sailed into the house, carrying her lace veil, which

Sylvie was going to borrow, and calling out "We're here!" just like she always did.

"You were right," Marly told Bobby when he arrived with Dad and Paul and Virge. With Sylvie's bridal shower set to take place at Tinker Street, Dad had splurged for Marly and the boys to stay with him at Saint-Cyr. This should have made Marly gleeful. But Mom's weirdness had ruined it.

Marly was sitting in the middle of Bobby's neatly made hotel bed as he unpacked his suit and hung it up. Paul was in the shower, singing "Heartbreak Hotel" at the top of his voice, and Virgil was still downstairs flirting with the girl at the front desk. Marly took advantage of getting her brother alone to tell Bobby about the car incident.

Bobby looked troubled.

"Lady business doesn't make you forget how to put a key in an ignition," Marly told him vehemently. "Aunt Betty's older than Mom. Surely if it was a time-of-life thing, she'd be having it too?"

"Okay, well, I guess we just keep an eye on her and talk to Dad again." He checked his watch. "We've got the bachelor party soon. I'll talk to him when we get back."

Marly flopped back onto the bed, feeling all messed up. The door to the balcony was open and the woodsy seaside air floated over her.

"Isn't there a girls' thing this afternoon?" Bobby asked. "Don't you have to get ready?"

"No." Marly pulled a face at the ceiling. "I wasn't invited. They said I was too young."

Bobby guffawed. "Too young for what? Getting giggly on one drink and playing parlor games and all that garbage?"

Marly nodded. "I even made the stupid deviled eggs and chicken salad, and now I'm not allowed to go eat any of it." She propped herself up on her elbows.

"Still, you'd probably rather be here anyway. You can laze about by the water."

True. Marly considered her nails, trying to seem casual. "Is Freddie going along on this bachelor thing?" She hadn't seen him yet, but she knew he'd been invited to the wedding as Priscilla's date, and she assumed he'd be staying at Saint-Cyr, as he always did.

"I assume so. Elton said it was a big party. And Fred might be his brother-in-law soon, if Cilla has anything to do with it, so he's bound to be there."

Marly scowled.

"Hey, can you chase up Virgil for me? Uncle Don told us not to be late."

Marly took the hint. She headed downstairs to rustle up Virge, wondering if she might bump into Freddie de Marche. She was wearing her new pencil skirt and her most fitted blouse, just in case.

Virgil was still at the desk, leaning on his elbow, smooth-talking the girl behind it. There was a tall vase of white lilies bursting over their heads, filling the foyer with perfume. Virge had a buzz cut and looked like a typical football-playing meathead. Which he was.

"Hey, Virge, you'll miss your bachelor party," Marly called as she crossed the black and white tiles.

Virge winced. "It's not *my* bachelor party," he assured the pretty girl. "It's for my cousin's fiancé."

"They say they're going fishing, but I don't believe them," Marly told the girl cheerfully, also leaning against the counter. Virge glared at her, and she gave him an innocent look.

"You little squirt!" Virge griped when the girl had excused herself to serve another customer.

"You'll be late for your boat," Marly told him, sticking her tongue out and backing out of his reach.

She loitered around the foyer, waiting for her first sight of Freddie de Marche for the summer. The last time she'd seen him had been at the engagement party at Aunt Betty and Uncle Don's place. Priscilla had been in a sour mood, probably because, as the eldest, she'd always assumed she'd get engaged first. Cilla had been sour with Freddie too, because it was his fault she had to stand there, faking a smile, as her peppy little sister received all the congratulations.

"I don't see how getting married is an *achievement*," Marly had said to Freddie, as they watched the families posing for photographs. "When I grow up, I might not even tell anyone when I get married."

"I could almost believe it," Freddie had said with a grin, "except you've got such a big mouth."

He'd been wearing a blue plaid sport coat that made his eyes look a darker blue. They were still clear as water, though, with a sparkle. That sparkle did distracting things to Marly's pulse. Freddie had hung back with her most of the evening, avoiding Cilla's bad mood and the endless ribbing from her family about popping the question. Thinking of the sparkle in his eye that night had sustained Marly these past months, but now she was hungry for more.

"Well, hey, short stuff."

Marly's heart leapt to her throat as she turned to find Freddie jogging down the *Gone with the Wind* stairs of Saint-Cyr's foyer. He was in navy shorts, with a sweater tied around his shoulders and a pair of sunglasses tucked into the neck of his shirt. His dark hair was longer than she'd seen it before, at least on top, and it bounced as he jogged.

Freddie whistled as he took her in. "Look at you. Bet you're breaking the boys' hearts at school."

Marly hated that she blushed. She wanted to seem cool and poised and, well, grown-up, and here she was turning red as a strawberry.

"And look at you," she responded, "all dressed up just to hook some fish. What are you planning to do, wink at them and hope they'll jump in the boat?"

He laughed. "My plan is to drink beer and watch other people hook the fish. How about you? Ready to shower the bride?"

Marly didn't tell him she wasn't invited—it would only remind him that she was too young. For parties, and for him. "What time does your boat come back?" she asked.

"I assume before dark—then there's a fish fry." He turned at the sound of hooting and grinned. "Here comes the lamb to the slaughter."

Elton was being playfully heckled as he came down the stairs with his phalanx of friends. He was a gentle guy, with floppy blond hair and big brown eyes. He took the teasing in stride.

"Have fun at your shower," Freddie told Marly, and then he was off, slipping into the tide of men, all headed down to the shore.

Marly's dad broke away from the tide and came over to kiss her on the forehead. "Marly, you can charge your meals to the room. Don't stay out after dark, you hear? You go straight back to your room."

"Sure. Have fun," she said lamely as she watched them go.

When she was fourteen, she would have been in seventh heaven to be let loose at Saint-Cyr, but it really wasn't much fun when you were seventeen-almost-eighteen and all alone. She drifted out to the patio and watched the bachelor party pour down to the pier and out onto a waiting vessel. She leaned against the railing and wondered what kinds of things were happening up at the house on Tinker Street. Were they really sitting around eating deviled eggs and playing silly parlor games? Or were there more adult things that Marly couldn't know about yet? She thought there must be, or she would have been invited.

She passed a lazy day at Saint-Cyr by herself, eating an early dinner alone, the highlight of which was the dessert cart. She had lemon chiffon pie. But it wasn't satisfying.

The thing was, Marly realized as she looked around the dining room at the other diners, life was no fun alone. She thought of

Sylvie and Elton with their arms around each other at the engagement party, both shining with happiness and giving each other secret looks. And she thought of Freddie de Marche and his fake laziness, which hid a repressed and restless energy. If Freddie had been here eating dessert with her, the night would be entirely different. The dining room might have some charm. When he was here, Saint-Cyr's old-fashioned fustiness became timeless charm, the little covered candles on the table seemed magical, the square music romantic. Freddie de Marche had that power. He made everything seem *alive.*

On the wedding day, Marly took as much care with her appearance as the bride did. Thank goodness she'd talked her mom into letting her wear the same dress as the other bridesmaids, even though she was only seventeen. As she turned in the mirror, admiring the way the ice-blue silk taffeta tea dress clung to her, she imagined Freddie's face when he saw her. No one would dare call her a kid when she was wearing this. The dress had a high neck and no sleeves and was inspired by something Sylvie had seen Grace Kelly wear in a movie. Sylvie's own dress was designed almost exactly after Debbie Reynolds's dress from when she'd married Eddie Fisher the year before. She and Mom had decided Sylvie was far more the Debbie Reynolds type, and the lacy organza with its sweetheart neckline and cap sleeves suited her sweetness and pep perfectly. Marly, meanwhile, didn't feel at all sweet in her dress, thank goodness.

Her hair was pinned up, just like the other bridesmaids', with a spray of daisies just behind her left ear. The only difference between her and the others was that they wore heels, while Mom had made Marly wear flats, and they had pearl chokers, while Marly only had a pearl bracelet.

"It doesn't matter if you look different," Cilla had said, cutting off her protest as they got ready together in the main bedroom. "You're the *junior* bridesmaid, you don't have to look the same."

Cilla was depressingly lovely in her tea dress. Her hair was cut in the Italian style and it framed her face beautifully. The color of the dress made her blue eyes shine.

But Freddie didn't love her, Marly reassured herself. She knew he didn't, because he didn't behave the way people did in books and movies when they were in love. His gaze didn't follow her, he didn't share secret smiles with her, he didn't give her a look like he wanted to devour her whole.

He didn't look at Marly that way either. But that was only because he thought she was just a kid. *That* was a perception she could change.

"Oh, I'm so nervous, I could *die*," Sylvie gasped, pressing her hands to her midriff.

"That's as it should be." Aunt Betty chuckled. She was decked out in a deep cerulean silk suit, with a little hat with a net. "You're lucky you're not sick from the nerves like I was. Remember that, Lorraine?"

Marly was the only one who noticed that her mother didn't respond. That she didn't even seem to recognize her own name. She was standing at the edge of the room, holding the lace veil with a faint frown on her face.

"Mom?" Marly went to her, concerned.

"Oh, honey, don't you look lovely." Mom's big hazel eyes, so like Marly's own, were soft with appreciation. "You got so beautiful."

Marly was shocked to find tears pricking. "Thanks, Mom."

"And this will finish it perfectly." Mom lifted the veil to Marly's hair.

"Oh no. No, Mom, that's not for me. That's for Sylvie." Marly caught her mother's hands. She hoped no one had noticed. "It's Sylvie's wedding, Mom, remember?" She searched her mom's eyes. They were confused. "Here, Mom, let me." Heart pounding and hands sweating, Marly took the veil to Aunt Bet, who pinned it in Sylvie's honeyed hair as the girls chattered. But in the corner, Mom still looked anxious and confused.

Marly slipped downstairs and found her father. "Daddy? Can you come?"

Marly's father was a self-contained man. He'd been away at the war for the first few years of her life and had always been reserved and a bit awkward with her. He knew how to act with boys; with Marly he wasn't so sure. But she felt comforted by his stolidness on Sylvie's wedding day.

"Just bring her out onto the landing, honey," Dad said calmly. "And I'll escort her down for the ceremony."

She could tell he was worried, but he gave her a nod, like he'd take it from here.

Marly brought her mother out.

"Well, what is this?" Daddy said, taking Mom's hands and kissing her forehead softly. "Did an angel fall to earth?"

Mom sagged against him. "Walt . . ." she said in a small, uncertain voice.

"I know, honey. It's okay." He kissed her again. "I'm here. Now let's just go down to the garden and take a seat, okay?"

Marly watched her father lead her mom downstairs and found she was trembling like a leaf. Her father looked up as they reached the hall and caught her eye. He gave her the faintest of smiles and then passed out of sight. Marly had never loved him more than she loved him in that moment. And she'd never been so afraid.

"Marly!" Priscilla's head popped out of the big front bedroom. "There you are! Don't go disappearing. It's time!"

Numbly, Marly took the small bunch of carnations and daisies and took her place in the procession. Uncle Don had joined them and was already weepy as he regarded Sylvie in all her lacy glory.

"Aunt Bet?" Paul had arrived to escort their Aunt Betty down the aisle to her seat.

The wedding itself went by in a blur. The makeshift altar had been set up near the rose garden, which was in vigorous full bloom, and the powdery sweet scent of roses mingled with the sea air. Uncle Don cried through the whole wedding, and so did Mom, but Marly didn't think they were crying for the same reason. Marly's heart was hurting in her chest. As she walked down the aisle, she saw her father holding her mother's hands and she almost cried herself.

What was wrong with Mom?

She was so caught up in her thoughts, she didn't even look for Freddie de Marche in the crowd, even though she'd spent all morning fussing over her appearance for him. It wasn't until the ceremony was in full swing that she remembered and darted a glance at the crowd. He was up the back on the aisle, so she must have walked straight past him.

He was in a suit, with a bow tie, and his hair was slicked back neatly. He had a brooding expression, at least until he caught her staring at him. Then he winked.

Marly blushed and jerked her attention back to the bride and groom.

Elton Coutts was beaming ear to ear, his blond hair in a side part, and his brown eyes shining. He looked like a man who'd just found the pot of gold at the end of the rainbow. And Sylvie was giggling and blushing and acting the schoolgirl. They were so cute it was sickening. Marly's attention wandered again, this time back to her parents. Her mother was leaning into her father, and he was still holding her hands, his thumb stroking hers.

And to her horror, Marly found herself crying, in front of all those people.

EIGHTEEN

It was Halloween and Flo was at the school dance. I'd finished up at the NA family meeting—something I'd been helping out with more regularly—and was in the car waiting for her. I'd brought a box to sort through while I waited. I was glad of the distraction because the meetings always threw me. Today I'd listened to a woman describe going no-contact with her son and I'd felt a sharp sting of recognition. I didn't want to think about all Tina's unanswered letters and the fact I hadn't visited her in years. It was a relief to distract myself with boxes of culch.

I never knew what I'd find in the boxes. I'd found one full of old tin toys, which had turned out to be quite in demand on eBay. And another one of vintage Christmas ornaments, which were an unexpected joy. They were a mix of glass in various abstract shapes and bright colors, shiny and tactile, and there was a kitschy little angel tree topper holding a candle. I'd kept that box aside, to revisit in December.

As I pulled on my thick down jacket, beanie, and gloves and opened up the back of my hatchback, I wondered what I'd find. I climbed in and sat down with my legs crossed, leaving the hatch up. It was only forty degrees out, but there was a beautiful sea fog rolling through Camden and I wanted to enjoy it as it crept across the parking lot in thickening veils, muting the streetlights and the sound of music thudding from the gymnasium. I'd brought a thermos of hot tea to keep me warm.

This box had been up in the "costume room" as Flo called it. We'd found a little clutch of boxes when she'd hunted through the racks of clothes for something to wear for Halloween. In the end Flo had chosen an old black suit and painted her face white, with black shadows under her eyes and cheekbones.

"I'm from the black-and-white times," she told me, posing.

If it didn't win the prize for best costume, it might at least win for most interesting. It was certainly weird.

This box was labeled *MARLY'S*. The handwriting was firm and decisive. Dying of curiosity, I'd packed it into the car, so I'd have something to do while I waited for Flo.

Inside there were a few old diaries—the kind you use to keep track of your appointments, not the personal kind. The oldest one was from 1957. It was well thumbed and full of notes. It was when I saw the words "Homecoming Dance" on a Saturday night that I realized the diary belonged to a teenager. Teenage Marly, to be precise. The first page listed her contact details, giving the name Marly Orcutt, an address in Boston, and a phone number that didn't seem to have enough numbers. I turned the pages. There were dates for her SATs, which seemed to correspond with a week when there were a lot of appointments: "Mom: Dr. Wesley"; "Mom: blood tests"; and "Mom to hospital." There was no record of her mother ever coming out of the hospital, but lots of visiting hours were listed.

There was a single wrist-length white glove in the box. It had little flowers in open lace on the back. And there was a heavy hardback book without a cover. I hefted it out and looked at the spine. *Forever Amber*. I'd never heard of it. I flipped the pages and found a series of old postcards and letters tucked between them. The first was a screamingly bright graphic postcard that said "Greetings from New Jersey." Inside the letters were beachy pictures of cartoon people having fun in the sun. I flipped it over.

Hey, pixie stick. Did you get the cat I sent you? It's to start your collection. x F

It was postmarked from Fort Dix, New Jersey, and dated November 1956.

There were postcards from West Germany, Korea, Hawaii, Japan, and then Washington, DC. More than one asked if the recipient (Marly, I assumed) had received her latest cat, and I began to get an idea of why there were so many figurines of cats in our house.

There was a postcard from late 1957, the writing all tiny and cramped so it would fit on the card:

> *Kid, you kill me. Nothing from you for all those months, and then you write me the* War and Peace *of letters. I must have sent you a postcard a month and NOW you write, right when I'm leaving. I'll send you a letter when I get where I'm going. Hopefully they'll bounce on your other letters—assuming there are other letters. If there aren't, write some, will you? I'm sorry to hear about your mom. I can't imagine what it must be like. Hang in there. Promise I'll write. x F*

And write he did, whoever he was. There were dozens of postcards, from all over the world, and letters written on thin onionskin airmail paper. The dates ranged from 1956 to 1962.

> *I can't tell you much about my day-to-day, short stuff, or the censors will black out so much of the letter there won't be any letter left. Instead, why don't I tell you something about a guy I met last week. He's a very mannered sort,*

soft-spoken, with a sideways smile. Very southern and prone to deferring to others. Which might not be what you'd expect from a man who makes girls scream just by walking into a room. He doesn't live in barracks but rents a private house. Maybe so he's got somewhere to store his blue suede shoes and his hound dog.

Oh my God, he was talking about *Elvis,* I realized, checking the envelope and date. West Germany, 1958. I felt a thrill run through me.

There was a postcard from Paris in 1962: *I was supposed to be here with a girl I know, but she stood me up. x F*

And one from Palermo: *I'm getting fat on leave in Italy. Thinking I could live here when I'm discharged. x F*

There was another brief airmail letter, written in a more unsteady hand: *I heard you got engaged, pixie stick. E wrote and told me. I keep thinking about that time I saw you in Maine, when I came back from leave. I'm an idiot, I guess. Anyway, I wish you nothing but the best with the guy who was smart enough not to be an idiot.*

Then there was a postcard from Maine later that year: *I'll wait.*

That was the last one.

I blinked, coming back to myself and the trunk of my car. I felt like I'd been transported back in time. Who was he, this *F*? And what had happened between him and Marly? She'd kept his letters and postcards, so he clearly meant something to her.

I unpacked the rest of the box but didn't find out anything more about *F*. I'd have to ask Jake what he knew. And if he didn't know anything, or wouldn't answer, I'd ask Elton.

I was in the middle of cramming everything back in the box when I saw Flo and the other kids coming out of the gym. "What happened to you?" I gasped, when I saw the red smeared all over her face. But it wasn't blood—it looked like some kind of paint or marker.

"Lainey Mullins happened to me," Flo said flatly. "It's lipstick. She said it would turn me Technicolor."

Now *I* was tempted to use the b-word. "I'm talking to your teachers. Where are they?"

"No, Mom." Flo grabbed me by the arm to stop me from charging toward the gym. "Don't. I'm all good."

"You're all good? You're getting bullied by that horrible kid."

Flo patted my arm. "Don't crash out. I told you I'm playing the long game."

"What does that mean?"

"You'll find out. Eventually." She got in the car. "Come on, it's cold."

"But—"

"No," she said, cutting me off. "Trust me. I know what I'm doing."

I paused. She wasn't crying or upset, she wasn't raging. She was telling me she was handling it. I tried to listen, but it was hard when I wanted to wring Lainey Mullins's neck.

The week after Halloween, Tim came to collect Flo for his wedding. Her teachers had given her work to do while she was away, and she was thrilled to get out of school for a week. He came in on an early-morning flight on Saturday and Flo and I picked him up from Augusta airport, which was a tiny regional airstrip surrounded by sodden parkland. Augusta itself was the capital of Maine and a pretty little place on the banks of the Kennebec River, about an hour west from Oxeye. It was a cool misty morning as we drove through, the fall leaves bright in the watery morning light.

Flo was bouncing with excitement at seeing her father. I was nervous. I hadn't seen Tim in person for months and was anxious that he'd say something negative about the house, and the fact that I'd moved our kid to rural Maine. Not that he could talk. He'd moved across the country and left her behind.

"There he is!" Flo went flying when she saw him emerge from the little red-roofed building. She threw open the car door and ran as fast as her legs would carry her, flinging herself at him. My heart pinched to see how much she loved him.

He looked good, I thought reluctantly. Tim was tall and lanky, in an olive-green duffel coat with an oat-colored sweater and dark jeans. He had a good haircut for a change, his brown hair styled with product. Wedding hair, I thought a bit meanly, assuming Alyssa was responsible for the makeover. He was still smiling as he climbed in the backseat of the car, his round glasses fogging up almost immediately. He laughed and took them off.

"I'm sitting in the back too," Flo announced, sliding in after him.

She'd left the front door open, so I leaned over and grabbed for it, feeling graceless. "Hey, Tim," I said. "Welcome to Maine."

"Hi." He dropped his arm around Flo and squeezed her. "Thanks for picking me up."

"Dad, we packed my bag in the trunk because we didn't know what you'd want to do. Do you want to drive around looking at things and have lunch, or come see our house?"

I waited for his answer, hoping he'd pick the first option. We'd made a lot of headway, but the house was still a mess.

"What kind of question is that?" Tim said. "Of course I want to see your house! I want to see your bedroom and where you eat breakfast and brush your teeth. And can we drive by your school? Is there anywhere else I should see? I want to know everything about your life."

I bristled, feeling surveilled. But Flo was glowing with pride and happiness.

"You should see our whole town," Flo insisted. "It's not very big, so it won't take long."

"And do you like living there?"

I drummed my fingers against the wheel as I listened to him

question her, feeling tense. Luckily, she was a fountain of enthusiasm.

"Mom, we should start the tour with my school in Camden and drive home that way," Flo instructed from the backseat. "Dad, you should see these towns, they're so pretty." She then told him all about her cats, in detail.

"And how many do you have?" Tim sounded a little concerned.

"Forty-nine and a half."

I saw his double take in the rearview mirror. "Only seven and a half are real," I said hastily.

"You have seven and a *half* cats?"

Flo explained, love for those kittens radiating from her. It almost made the vet bills worth it.

It rained on and off as we drove through the patchwork of autumnal countryside. But by the time we reached Camden, the clouds had eased and sea smoke was rising from the harbor as we took Tim on a tour of the town. It curled around the anchored yachts and billowed at the shore.

"Wow," Tim said, impressed by the beauty. Flo beamed.

I chauffeured and Flo chattered, showing off her school and listing the types of whales and seals in the bay. The sun came out as we drove down the coast, turning the rusty cliffs amber and striking spangles off the ocean through the smoke.

I saw Oxeye through fresh eyes as we drove into our town. Compared to Camden and Rockport, it was down at heel.

Flo played tour guide, pointing out the café and the summer houses, explaining how the hardware store sold *lobsta rowls* in tourist season.

"Wow, look at those woods," Tim said as we turned the corner.

I'd gotten used to the thick balsam woods on our street but saw it anew now, a mass of untamed forest. Low mist was gathered in dips and pockets close to the ground among the fallen needles.

Our house looked better than it had back in July, but it was still a witchy-looking place. The front yard was cut back hard and it wasn't pretty. The lilacs had been pruned and were naked stalks jutting up from their thick old bases, and most of the out-of-control cottage garden had died back to a mulchy brown mess. Now the jungle was gone, you could see the broken porch palings and the cracked windows. I'd booked a glazier to come later in the month, and Jake had volunteered to fix the palings, but there was just so much to do. Seeing the place through Tim's eyes, I noticed the missing shingles, the flaked paint.

But Tim was far more impressed than I thought he'd be. "Wow, it's *big*," he said. He got out of the car and looked down the short cul-de-sac to the cliffs. "And you have a prime ocean view!"

The cold November air was heavy with wet pine and the scent of the sea.

He looked at Elton's place next door. "That gives you a good idea of what it could be," he said admiringly.

"Wait till you see inside," Flo told Tim, grabbing his hand. She went to pull him around back, the country way.

"Hold it," I called. "Let him come in the front."

The porch out back was still a work in progress, while the front hall was completely clear. It made a much better first impression.

"Zoe, this place is something," Tim said, his nose pink from the cold, after Flo had given him the tour. Our house got *cold*.

"If we're staying here for the day, I'll light the fire," I said apologetically.

"Let's stay," Flo told him. "Then we can play with the kittens. They're going to miss me so much this week."

Tim seemed happy enough with that. I lit the fire in the kitchen grate, glad Jake had made sure every single fireplace was usable, because our furnace was garbage.

"How are you going to get through the winter?" Tim asked ruefully as he warmed his hands by the fire. "This place is archaic."

Flo had scampered off looking for her cats in the labyrinth of the house, leaving us alone.

"I have a guy coming to put in a heat pump this week," I told him. "It's costing an arm and a leg but there's a rebate, and Jake—uh, my friend—says it will save me hundreds each year on my bill." I leaned closer to the fire, cold to the bone. "All I care is that it works." I shivered. The nights had got so cold. Flo and I had piled on the quilts and slept in our beanies, with ski socks on and hot wheat bags held to our chests. "And we thought Pittsburgh was cold!"

"Seattle's pretty cold too," he told me, "but probably not as cold as Pittsburgh. It rains more than it snows." We kept the conversation to the weather, both avoiding each other's eye. It was weird, having him in our house. He didn't belong.

As he and Flo played with kittens by the fire and I served sandwiches and hot chocolate, I marveled at the fact that I'd ever loved him. He seemed like a stranger.

In the afternoon, Jake came by to resume work on the back porch. He was bundled up for the cold, a scarf looped around his neck and a beanie on. He came into the kitchen gingerly, eyeing Tim. They shook hands like a couple of kids sizing each other up on the playground.

"Jake's our neighbor," Flo told her dad. "He runs the hardware store and makes the *lobsta rowls.*" Flo tugged on Jake's arm. "My dad's a tech bro," she told him.

"Flo," Tim protested, "don't say it that way. I work for a technology company that investigates energy alternatives."

Jake nodded. "Cool." He glanced at me. He had his surly face on again. "I'd best get to work. There's some weather coming in and it would be good to have your screens up." He disappeared out to the porch.

"Friendly guy," Tim observed, amused.

"He is," Flo assured him. "He's just a slightly grumpy friendly guy."

Leaving the two of them in the kitchen, I followed Jake out to the porch. "Jake?"

He grunted, already bent over his toolbox.

"I was wondering if I could leave the fire lit in the kitchen when I take them to the airport—is that okay? Will you be here for a couple of hours? If not, it's fine, I'll put it out." Although I dreaded coming home to a frigid house.

"I'll be here," he said, glancing up. His blue-green eyes were kind.

"Thank you." My relief was palpable. Not just because the house wouldn't be as cold when I got home, but because someone would be here. I wouldn't come home to an empty house.

"You okay?" he asked with studied casualness, his voice gentle.

I half laughed, half groaned. "Yes. No? I don't know." I braced myself to go back into the kitchen. "It's hard to send her off, you know?"

He nodded. "I'll keep that fire lit, I promise." He gave me a sympathetic smile. "It's always better to come home to a fire burning than an empty grate."

"Thank you," I said again, my throat tight. "For everything." I gestured at his toolbox and the porch.

"My pleasure." Something in the rough warmth of his voice made my breath catch. "How long is Flo gone for?" he asked.

"The week." I flushed.

"You'll be lonely," he said softly.

For some reason, I broke out in goosebumps. "I have a lot to do," I said, backing away. "I'll try and get through the junk in the parlor. It will be a good opportunity. . . ."

"Yeah, well," he said as he rose to his feet. "If you get lonely, you know where to find me."

Was it me or was there a load of meaning in that sentence? My flush became an outright blush. His light blue-green gaze was steady, clear. There was definitely no mistaking what he meant.

"You'd best get to the airport."

Yes. The airport.

My heart was thudding as I went back inside and rounded Flo up.

Had that been an invitation, I wondered? My mind whirred as I drove Flo and Tim inland, back to Augusta. I'd caught Jake's steady blue-green stare on me a few times this past week and it made my blood run fast.

Jake was possibly the sexiest man I'd seen in real life. From his tumbled, sun-streaked hair to his wildly expressive eyebrows, to that double dimple and those lips . . .

Not to mention his big muscular hands, and his shoulders, and his abs and his *all of him.* I mean, I'd have to be *dead* not to have thought about it.

But he was my *neighbor.* It would get super awkward if it didn't work out, wouldn't it?

I shook my head to clear it. There was no way I could hook up with my neighbor. Especially when he was doing renovations for me. I'd end up an awkward mess every time I ran into him in town. Not to mention my house might not get renovated.

By the time we got to the airport, I'd managed to banish thoughts of Jake and was falling into a blue hole thinking about saying goodbye to Flo for a week. On one hand, it would be nice to have some alone time and not have to do the school runs. On the other, no Flo.

She'd never gone to stay with Tim like this before. This would be the longest we'd ever been apart. I felt like I was pulling my own heart out of my chest and putting it on a plane to send it across the country.

I spent most of our goodbye trying not to cry like a baby.

"I wrote out instructions for the cats and left them on the kitchen table," Flo said, pressing a hot kiss on my cheek as she bent between the car seats to say goodbye. "Send me photos so I know they're alive."

"Won't you want to know if *I'm* alive?"

"I'll know because you're sending me pics of the cats," she said with an eye roll. "I love you, Mom."

"I love you too." I peppered her with kisses. "Have fun." I glanced at Tim. "And good luck," I said, forcing a smile. "I hope you have a beautiful wedding day."

"Thanks, Zoe. I'll send you pictures," he said, patting my shoulder, "so you know *she's* alive. I know how you worry."

He made it sound like I was neurotic. "Thanks," I said dryly. "Fly safe. Let me know when you arrive!"

I watched them walk together into the airport, him tall and lanky, her small and energetic. I sat there in the car and waited for their plane to take off, feeling a tightness in my chest. And then their small commuter plane taxied down the runway and they were off, soaring into the iron-gray skies. It was only four o'clock, but it was growing dark, the streetlights flaring in the misty air. As I drove home, the rain kicked in, and the sound of it against the windshield made me feel lonely. I turned up the music to keep the feeling at bay.

Flo had called me lonely. It had stung because she was right. I *was* lonely—and always had been. And I wasn't sure I knew how to be any other way.

The weather swept in as I curled down the coast, and the woods were churning in the winds as I turned onto Tinker Street. The front light was on at my house when I pulled into the driveway, and I could see smoke being tossed into the night as it emerged from the chimney at the back of the house. Jake.

When I dashed around back, trying to get in before I was saturated, I found the porch empty but the lights on. Jake had hung all the clear PVC sheeting, which snapped a little on its anchors in the wind, but it did an astonishingly good job of protecting the porch from the weather.

"Wet out, is it?" Jake drawled as he emerged from the kitchen. He had his hands in the pockets of his work jeans and was trying to keep a straight face, but I could tell he was pleased by his work, and even more pleased by my reaction to it. His double dimple was a deep dent.

"This looks *incredible.*" I turned on the spot, taking it in. I could barely tell it was raining outside.

The porch was almost done. Jake had finished all the timber screens and oiled them up, and the space had an open, airy feel. A lick of paint on the back wall and in that little bathroom and the porch would be ready for decorating. I felt a sizzle of excitement at the thought.

"I'll bring a belt sander tomorrow and get to work on those old floorboards," Jake said, leaning against the doorframe. "They'll take no time to refinish, and then I'll clean and seal the bricks and you'll be able to move some furniture back in."

I heard a bark.

"I hope you don't mind," he said, glancing over his shoulder. "I brought Hazel up. She gets separation anxiety if I'm gone too long."

"The cats—" I started, alarmed.

"They're fine. They're in the hall. I've tied Hazel up by the table."

True to his promise, Jake had kept my fire alive in the kitchen. The room wasn't exactly warm, but it wasn't cold. Hazel looked up when we came in, her tail thumping.

"You need to hang your storm windows," Jake told me mildly. "You're lucky we haven't had any real bad weather yet. It can really blow here on the coast." He reached down to pull on Hazel's ears. "Want me to do that tomorrow?"

"Oh, no, you're doing too much for me already."

He gave me an amused look. "You know how to hang them yourself?"

I bit my lip. The answer was clearly no.

"Why don't we split the difference, and I'll show you how to hang them?"

"All right."

We stared at each other. The silence extended between us, the only sounds the fire crackling and Hazel's snuffling.

"And then maybe you might want to have dinner with me tomorrow?" Jake said slowly, without dropping his gaze.

"Dinner?" I winced as my voice cracked.

His double dimple dented.

"Um, sure," I stumbled. "You mean out, or . . . ?"

"I mean at my place," he said, his voice still slow and careful, like he was worried about spooking me.

"At *your place*?" I sounded like a parrot.

"Yeah. I don't like to leave Hazel alone. She tends to chew on everything in reach and then she keeps me up all night checking I'm still there."

I couldn't break away from his gaze. It was hypnotic. My fingers and toes were tingling.

"I'll cook," he said, gathering Hazel's leash. "Okay if I leave the tools here till tomorrow? Oh, and I secured the tent. Should be okay through the storm."

"Ah, thanks." I followed him out to the porch.

"Was that a yes to dinner at my place?" he asked nonchalantly as he prepared to duck out into the cold, rainy night.

"Ah . . ." I shouldn't. It would complicate things. But then I thought of Flo next to Tim on that plane; Tim getting married; me eating alone in my kitchen tomorrow; Flo calling me lonely . . . "Yes," I blurted impulsively.

His blue-green eyes twinkled. "Good."

Hazel barked in agreement.

"What can I bring?" I rubbed my hands on my jeans nervously.

"Your appetite." There was that twinkle again.

Oh God. What was I *doing*?

NINETEEN

On Sunday morning I slept in, stretching luxuriously in bed. Flo had messaged late that she'd gotten to Cincinnati okay, and then I'd finally been able to sleep. It was unsettling being without her but, oh, I'd forgotten how nice it was to sleep in. I'd only woken up because my phone vibrated with Flo demanding a proof-of-life photo of her cats.

The sweet little things were gamboling around the stairs, their mother watching over them from the landing. Mac was a fluffy tabby with intelligent yellow eyes. She meowed good morning as I shuffled out to take the photograph. I sent the photo off to Flo, then fed the tumbling little fluff balls, made coffee, and went back to bed with my book. From my pillowy bed I could see the rain lashing the windows and the ocean roiling in the bay. It was a perfect day to do nothing at all.

My phone vibrated again, and my heart kicked up a notch when I saw it was Jake. But his message was a prosaic one. *See the weather report? Best get those windows up sooner, rather than later.*

It was no wonder I'd thought he was an old fisherman when I'd only had his messages to go on. He texted like an old man, with punctuation and everything, and of course on the day of our date, his message was about the *weather.*

I frowned at my phone screen. Then I punched open my weather app and winced. Gale-force winds and heavy rain were predicted by evening. Possible thunderstorms. My phone buzzed for a third time.

I'll be up at your place in an hour. I'll bring my ladder.

I groaned. But I didn't say no, because my stupid pulse was racing at the thought of seeing him again. Instead of luxuriating in bed with a book on my Flo-less Sunday, I raced to the bathroom and quickly showered so I could shave my legs and make sure I was, uh, prepared, in case anything happened. There was no harm in an abundance of caution.

"Do you have a rain slicker?" Jake asked, when he turned up at my door. He was dressed like a fisherman for real now, in a bright yellow rain jacket and fishing pants, with a beanie on under the hood. It should have looked ridiculous, but actually it looked stupidly hot. He was the kind of guy I could imagine at the wheel of a trawler in high seas. My gaze flicked to his big, strong hands.

"Zoe? You'll need a rain slicker."

I flushed and tried to focus on the task at hand. I did indeed have a rain slicker. It was, however, bright cerulean blue with white polka dots, and not terribly functional. I dug it out while he waited on the porch. It barely covered my butt, I thought ruefully, as I buttoned it up to the chin. He gave me a dubious look when I emerged, which I completely understood. I did not belong on a fishing trawler in any way, shape, or form.

I was drenched in two minutes flat.

"The storm windows are out in here," Jake told me, leading me through the sodden garden to the stone outbuilding. He wrenched open the splintered old door to reveal stacks of storm windows under sheets. "Sorry, I should have reminded you to do this before now," he said, as we carried the heavy things out.

"It's not really your job," I pointed out.

It took us about half an hour per window, a bit longer with the complicated ones like the portholes and the dormers, so most of my Flo-less Sunday was spent out in the weather. Not that I did more than help carry windows and hold the ladder. There was absolutely no way I would ever be able to do it myself. Jake's offer to "show" me so I could do it in the future had surely been facetious.

When we finished the final window, we collapsed on the front porch swing, both wet and tired.

The rain was sheeting down again, pouring in waterfalls from my broken gutters. Jake followed my gaze up to the roof.

"Want me to fix those gutters next week?" he asked.

"I really should just employ you on a retainer." I wondered how much it would cost.

"Maybe I'm just finding reasons to see you," he said lightly.

I felt his words thrum through me. "We live on the same street. You hardly need a reason." I felt absurdly shy.

There was a buffeting gust from the northeast, and it howled in the eaves above us. Out over the ocean, thunder rumbled from the dark clouds stacking up on the horizon.

"Got those windows up just in time," he teased.

"Looks like it."

"Is there anything you don't eat?" he asked, abruptly changing the subject. He turned to look at me, his face only inches from mine on the two-seater swing.

I shook my head. I couldn't think of anything. But to be fair, I could barely think of my own name when he was looking at me.

"Is six-thirty too early for dinner?"

I laughed. "I have a kid, remember? I'm used to early dinner and early bed." I blushed, not registering what I'd said until I'd said it.

"I'll keep that in mind."

Oh, that twinkle. He had the most incredible eyes. They were like summer shoals in a tropical ocean.

"Make it six then," he said, as he rose from the swing. "I'm not going to complain if I have more time with you. You can keep me company while I cook."

Now, that sounded appetizing. I watched him flip up his rain hood as he stepped off the porch. The squall was blowing in from the ocean, sending flurries of rain whipping across the cliffs.

I'd forgotten to ask him about Marly's postcards and the mysterious *F*, I realized as I watched him disappear into his hardware store.

I must have tried on ten different outfits and changed my underwear four times. In the end I settled on my new jeans and a soft, wine-colored sweater. It was only his house, not a fancy restaurant, and everything else felt too formal. I did wear lace underwear, though. Just in case.

I fed the cats and bedded them down in the hallway, grabbed an umbrella and a bottle of wine left over from the pizza night, and dashed through the rain before I could lose my nerve. The lights above the hardware store were blazing through the darkness, and I could hear the ocean making a terrific roar against the cliffs as I reached the porch. The door to the store was locked. I realized I didn't know how to get up to his private rooms.

"Hey."

I couldn't tell where his voice was coming from. The suck and sigh of the wind was too loud. I huddled, wincing as the rain lashed at me.

"Hey! Zoe!"

I looked up. Jake was on the balcony. He had to lean over to see me, and he took the wind full in the face.

"Come around back," he called down. "The side gate is open. You can come up the back stairs."

I found the gate—there was a MIND THE DOG sign—and let myself in, dashed across the muddy yard and up the back stairs to the balcony.

"Ah, you're drenched," he said, sounding concerned. "Let me get you a towel." He opened a French door into the apartment and a blast of warm air eddied out at me.

The legs of my jeans were sodden, and my boots were covered in muck from the yard. I slipped my shoes off and left them on the balcony.

"Maybe bring them in," Jake suggested, catching me at it. "They're liable to blow away if the wind picks up."

"Seriously?"

"Seriously." He fetched me a towel while I carefully put my muddy boots just inside the door. I took inventory of the room while he was gone. It was open-plan, a space that had clearly once been two rooms. The kitchen was to my left—simple, with pale wood cabinetry and a modest island. On the far-left wall was a brick fireplace with a roaring fire; Hazel was snoozing on a dog bed in front of it. French doors on both sides opened to the wraparound balcony. In summer he'd be able to throw the doors and all those sash windows open and let the sea air flow in. He'd also have views all the way down to the spit. Although, tonight, all I could see was darkness. The windows on the ocean side were slick with rain and the balcony looked drenched.

The room was painted a warm, creamy off-white, and the furniture was mismatched but cozy. There were bookshelves on every spare wall between the windows, I noted approvingly. The room smelled delicious too. Something good was cooking.

Jake reappeared through the door next to the fireplace, carrying a fluffy white towel. He tossed it to me. "Here you go."

I handed him the bottle of wine in exchange for the towel,

aware that my hair was a mess from the wind. So much for taking care with my appearance, I thought as I tried to dry myself off. I didn't have high hopes for drying the jeans. They were soaked through from the thigh down.

"It's going to be quite a night, by the looks of it," Jake said as the wind kicked at the windows.

"Hope you've got your storm windows up," I said dryly.

He grinned at me, the double dimple in full flight, and my heart tumbled over. "Why don't you dry off by the fire. Can I get you a glass of wine?"

I nodded, trying not to drip on his rug as I crept toward the fire. The warmth was divine.

"I've got white in the fridge if you prefer?" Jake offered.

"I'm easy," I said, then winced. God, everything was sounding suggestive tonight.

Jake was wearing a well-laundered flannel shirt in soft gray and sage green and jeans that clung lovingly to his long, hard legs. His shirt was open at the neck, revealing his collarbones and a triangle of burnished skin.

"I didn't do fancy for dinner," he warned me as he poured a couple of glasses of Chardonnay. "I just roasted a chicken."

"It smells amazing." I took the wine from him. He smelled amazing too—that woody, salty, warm Jake smell.

I had no idea what to say next. I'd forgotten how to date.

Jake was watching me, a small smile playing on his lips. He was amused by my nerves. Although, to be fair, he looked a little nervous too. And the place had clearly been cleaned to within an inch of its life. There was a candle burning on the coffee table too—an expensive scented one. I doubted it was usually there. Jake didn't strike me as a candle guy.

He lowered himself to his velvety overstuffed sofa and took a sip of wine.

Lightning spiked in the east, illuminating the black sheet of the ocean.

"Wow." To get away from my nerves, I moved to the window to watch the storm approach. The world outside was monochrome as the distant lightning flickered. Faint thunder grumbled.

"It's still a ways off," Jake said, not moving from the couch. He stretched an arm across the back of the couch and watched me.

A net of lightning split the sky, and I silently counted until the thunder rumbled.

"You were not at all what I was expecting when I heard someone was interested in the house," Jake said, and even though he spoke quietly I jumped.

"You made that clear when I met you."

He pulled a face at the memory. "Sorry. I can be an ass. It's too much time spent alone—I forget how to act with people." He rubbed his cheek. "But also, you are a *madwoman* for buying that place."

"No," I said, screwing up my courage to go and join him on the couch. "I am a *desperate* woman. Do you have any idea how expensive housing is?" I lowered myself to sit next to him.

He rested his chin on his palm. "Hi," he said.

"Hi." I took a shaky sip of wine. "I haven't done this in a while," I confessed.

"What? Talk?"

"Funny." I fiddled with the hem of my sweater. "You know what I mean."

"Well, you're doing fine so far." He lowered his voice to a conspiratorial whisper. "If it helps, I haven't done this in a while either."

I didn't believe him.

"It's a small pool around here," he said wryly. "And I'm related to most of them."

I suppressed a smile. "I guess that's true. But, I'm not sure if you're aware, there's a whole range of new technologies now that allow you to date *out* of your pool. Have you heard of Bumble or Hinge?"

"I'm an old-fashioned guy," he protested. "I like meeting a person in real life."

"I think I'm better *not* in real life," I admitted. "You can banter better when you have time to think about it."

"You are definitely better in real life," he said firmly. And then he inched closer, his woody scent wrapping around me. "Scripted banter is overrated." He met my gaze and my stomach dropped in slow motion.

"Aren't you worried," I breathed as he leaned toward me, "about what might happen if this goes wrong?"

"Don't you think about," he countered, sliding even closer, "what might happen if this goes *right*?"

"The thing is . . . I have a kid."

"Yeah, I know her."

"So I can't . . . just . . ."

"What? Enjoy yourself?"

I bit my lip. He hadn't even touched me and my skin was singing.

"Zoe," he said, and his low voice made me shiver. "I don't know what this is, or what it's going to be. I'm not making any promises."

I think my face fell because he smiled. And then he reached out a finger and traced the line of my jaw.

"*Except*," he murmured, "I promise to be nice, and I promise to be honest with you."

Every bit of me seemed to be focused on the patch of skin beneath his finger.

"I don't know what I want," I blurted.

"That's okay." He leaned closer. "What if I ask and you just tell me yes or no?"

His finger had migrated to my ear, tracing my lobe, which was stunningly sexy. Who knew.

"If I were to kiss you," he murmured, "would you want that?"

I thought about it. For about half a second. "Yes."

He took the wine from my hand and put it on the coffee table.

The lightning was flickering, casting bright sheets of light as he turned back to me. "I like that answer." He cupped my face with his hand and pulled me gently toward him.

When his lips touched mine, I just melted, like I had no bones.

Jake Abernathy tasted salty sweet. And God, he was a good kisser. He took it slow, his lips firm but teasing, gentle and slow. I pressed against him, and he wrapped his arms around me, pulling me close, the feeling of him holding me tight simultaneously comforting and so incredibly *hot*. My body felt like it was waking up from a long slumber, nerve endings I'd forgotten I even had zinging to life. I could feel his hard chest pressing into me, sending tingles through every inch of my skin. I deepened the kiss, wanting more. So much more. I had a fistful of his hair in my hand, as I wrapped myself around him. He moaned into my lips, turned on by my hunger. I wanted him more than I'd ever wanted anyone.

"I've wanted to do that since the day you walked into my store," Jake whispered when he finally broke the kiss.

I was breathless, my heart clamoring. "Funny, I don't remember getting that impression." I pressed closer. "I think I want you to kiss me again."

"You think or you do?"

"I do."

This time the kiss deepened much further, his hands sliding down my back as his tongue slipped along my lips. I opened for him and then things got even hotter. His tongue slid into me as his hands slipped under my sweater and onto my bare back. His palms were warm, sending sparks billowing in their wake as they ran over my skin. I tangled one hand in his hair and arched against him, wishing those big warm hands would keep moving. As though reading my mind, his hands traced the line of my spine, down to my ass. I moaned as he gave me a squeeze and hauled me across his lap. I could feel him hard against me and I gave his lower lip a teasing bite.

If the oven timer hadn't gone off, I'm not sure we would have stopped.

"Whoa," he said breathlessly, disentangling himself. "I meant to go slow."

"You sound like you knew what would happen tonight," I teased him shakily.

"I knew what I *hoped* would happen," he said as he got up to rescue the chicken.

I topped up the wine while he carved the chicken and set the table. The wind hissed down the chimney, sending the flames jumping, and the lightning marched toward us across the dark water. Then, as Jake set dinner on the table, a titanic *crack* sounded overhead, rattling the plates and the cutlery.

Hazel whined. She'd slept through the storm until now, but she was up like a shot, ears back and her tail between her legs.

"You're okay," Jake soothed her. But she came and cowered under his legs as we ate. The storm was building, throwing itself at the cliffs and the store. The thunder seemed to roll and crack from all directions as the rain whipped harder at the windows, pelting in sideways across the balcony. In the buttery glow of the streetlights, I could see the rain squall, caught and tossed by the winds.

Then came a deafening smack of thunder, and all the lights went out. The room shivered orange and gold with firelight.

"The power's out," Jake soothed a crying Hazel. "That's all, girl." He checked on me. "You okay?"

I nodded. "It's kind of romantic," I told him as I fetched the lone candle and moved it to the dining table.

"It would be if I didn't have a wuss of a dog." He laughed. Hazel seemed to be trying to climb him. He pulled her into his lap, and she burrowed her head under his armpit.

With Hazel taking center stage, we eased into a more relaxed mood, batting questions back and forth as we ate and the storm raged. Jake had Hazel on his lap, one arm securely around her as she whined and shivered.

"And you're sure you aren't keeping her?" I teased. Hazel looked up at him with pleading eyes, as though begging him to stop the storm. She licked at his neck and wriggled in his arms.

"I'm not ready," he said gruffly.

"You look like you are."

He pulled a face and changed the topic. "How did you get into the medical business?" he asked me.

I shrugged and also pulled a face. "I needed a job. I had Flo, and Tim wanted to go to grad school. He needed to keep his grades up, so I was the one who had to go work."

"Flo said her dad didn't live with you. . . ." Jake looked uncomfortable at his own curiosity. "Sorry," he mumbled. "I've just been wondering."

His discomfort was kind of adorable. "It's fine," I said, waving his apology away. "It's all water under the bridge now. We lived together for the first ten months after Flo was born. But it didn't work."

"*It* didn't work or *he* didn't work?" Jake sounded bristly on my behalf.

"A bit of both," I admitted. "But we were young, only twenty-one." I watched him comfort his puppy and felt a pang, remembering the long hard years when Flo was little. "He moved out and threw himself into campus life and I dropped out of my statistics and data science degree and worked in a medical call center, chasing people to pay their bills."

"You dropped out? That must have been hard."

I shrugged. "It was what it was. To be honest, continuing to try and study *and* work *and* look after a baby would have been harder. Impossible. And I don't regret it—I'd do anything for Flo."

"To a mother's love," Jake said, lifting his glass in a toast.

I swallowed, as thoughts of Tina swam to mind.

"She's a lucky kid," he added as we clinked glasses.

"She's a good kid."

"And now Mr. Campus Life is getting married," Jake prodded.

"And he lives in Seattle, which is what? Three thousand miles away?"

I nodded.

"Does it ever make you angry? That he got to finish his degree and have a whole life like he never even had a child?"

"Anger isn't useful." I shifted in my chair. Anger was never useful. "It's best to just move on."

"Seriously?" He fixed me with his disconcertingly straightforward stare. The candlelight cast shadows on his face and made his eyes shine. "But didn't you have dreams? You must still have dreams?"

"Not big ones," I admitted, feeling exposed. "All I've ever really wanted was a home. Predictability. A job, a place to live, food in the refrigerator, a library card. And I have all those things, Tim or no Tim."

He scratched his jaw. "Yeah, but he made all that a lot harder when he left you to deal with it. I think a little anger would be justified."

I pressed my lips together. Maybe it was the wine, or the intimacy of the firelight, or maybe it was just Jake, but I was honest. "Anger doesn't work," I said bluntly. "It's just a waste of energy. You're better off forgetting it and moving on. Anger doesn't keep you safe, it doesn't keep you fed, it doesn't keep your *kid* fed."

His eyebrows went up and I felt he was studying me closely.

I took a sip of wine, ignoring my pounding heart.

"But you still *feel* it?"

I shook my head. No. I refused to.

"I'll feel it for you," Jake volunteered, shaking his head. "I mean, what an asshole."

"He's not. He pays child support." Mostly. "And he calls her three times a week and sends her presents."

"That's a low bar," Jake rumbled, holding Hazel closer.

I fell silent. It was.

"Meanwhile you're competing for Mom of the Year," he told me.

I felt a lump in my throat, which was silly. Jake had only known us for a few months. But I didn't often get praised for my parenting, even though I felt like I was performing at an Olympic standard most of the time. It was *hard* being a mom, and there were no performance reviews.

"And that kid is turning out great," Jake added, giving me a half-smile. "I should know, too, because my niece is *not* turning out great. She watched *Mean Girls* and thought Regina George was inspirational."

I laughed. "You've seen *Mean Girls*?"

"Of course. I have a sister. And a bunch of nieces."

"Lainey is a bit . . ."

"Mean."

"I was going to say passive-aggressive."

Jake snorted. "There's no passive in it. I think it's because she's the youngest and her sisters do it to her. She's got a messed-up relationship with other girls."

"And what about you," I segued clumsily, full of my own questions I was dying to ask him. "How are your relationships with girls?"

"I like them," he said with a smile.

I rolled my eyes. "I noticed. I mean, what's your history?"

"We might need more wine for that one." He hefted Hazel under one arm and went to get the bottle I'd brought. "Fancy going back to the couch?"

I did. We left the dishes on the table and curled up on the sofa. Hazel hid between Jake and the cushions as the storm continued unabated.

"Now, where were we?" he asked, inching closer to me.

"You were telling me about your history with women," I prodded.

"I was hoping you might forget that."

"I didn't." I reached out to run my hand up his neck and into his hair. I felt him shiver.

"Well, it's a depressing patchwork," he admitted. "A lot of dating, a lot of heartbreak—"

"Yours or theirs?" I interrupted, enjoying the way he moved like a cat under my fingers as I ran them through his hair.

"Bit of both." He sighed. "It seems to bother people that I've got no ambition."

"You've got no ambition?" I was surprised. "But you run your own business."

"Yeah, but look at it. It's not like I run it for the money. It's a mom-and-pop business in a town with about thirty people." He shrugged. "The hardware store mostly makes its money servicing the farmers nearby and they can probably find better in Augusta. My main income is from the campground, which I manage but don't own."

"Who owns it?" I'd never even thought to ask before.

"The state does." Jake sighed. "They bought the land back in the seventies. There used to be a resort there, you know, the old-timey sort like from *Dirty Dancing*, where folks from away would come for the summer to play croquet and sail. It was out of fashion by the late sixties and burned down in the early seventies. Everyone around here thinks it was an insurance job. Anyway, the state bureau bought the land and reforested it and then set up a campground."

I tried to imagine a hotel standing where the campground was but couldn't. It looked like it had always been woodland.

"You feel like kissing again yet?"

I did, but I was also still curious. "How about a kiss, then a question?"

God, he was a good kisser. As soon as his lips met mine, I lost all sense of time. And sense in general. By the time we surfaced, I had my hand inside his shirt, tracing the warm velvety skin over those collarbones.

"Do you still remember your question?" he teased, leaning down to press a kiss to my neck, where my pulse was leaping.

"Yes," I said breathlessly. "I wanted to know why your lack of ambition was a problem."

His breath was hot on my neck as he sighed, making me shiver. "Oh, you know, people like a man with drive."

"You don't seem to lack drive," I said, aware of the double meaning as I rested my hand flat against his chest. I could feel his heart pounding.

"Now, that's where you're wrong." He leaned down and put his cheek on my shoulder. "One thing you need to know about me, Zoe, is I don't care a thing for money. Or for success. Or for any of the things real men are supposed to care about. I'm quite content wasting my life here in this dinky store, in this dinky town, living my quiet life, watching the seasons change, sailing and surfing and just generally letting the days go by." He rubbed his cheek against me. "Women generally find that disappointing. They might think they want a laid-back guy, but when they get one, they seem shocked I don't have a career plan or a desire to travel to Europe every year or whatever." He sat up again and passed me my wineglass. "I'm really happy being a loser."

"You're not a loser," I said vehemently, meaning it. "Oh my God, Jake, you have no idea. You should meet some of the men out there. You run a business—really two if you count the lobster shack—and manage another business, and you can fix *anything*. And I've only been here for a couple of months, but I can see why you don't want to leave. I never in a million years thought I'd be able to afford to live on the coast, and every morning I wake up and look out my window at that beautiful bay and I have to pinch myself. I go down the path through the woods, to the beach down from the spit, and I can't believe I get to stand there on that horseshoe of sand. It seems like anywhere else in the world it would be a private beach, with security guards to chase you off." I cleared my throat, aware I was giving a speech. "And, trust me, as someone who's had to grind in the city for many years, the thought of living a quiet life here sounds like heaven."

"Good thing you're living here, then, isn't it?" He seemed amused by my speech, but also kind of touched.

"I mean it, Jake," I said, remembering my childhood. "Your life is perfect."

Hazel let out a shuddery sigh in her sleep and I realized the storm had rolled away while we'd been talking.

"It's a little more perfect tonight," he said, sheepishly grinning at what a line it was.

I kissed him gently, the softness of his lips and his woody scent mingling with the smell of the fire and the perfume of the candle. "Your turn to ask me a question," I whispered.

"Are you going to sell the place once it's renovated and leave?"

I pulled back, surprised. "What?"

He shrugged. "I kind of thought you might. Flip it and move back to the city."

I was astonished. "No. This is our forever home." But I was also astonished at myself, because it hadn't even occurred to me, even though plenty of the treasure houses I watched on TikTok were flipped to sell. I frowned and pulled away from him. "Wait. Are you kissing me because you think it's safe because I'll *leave*?"

"No." Although he paused and then shrugged. "I don't know. I guess I was trying not to think about it at all and just stay in the moment. Because if I like you, and if you leave, that would suck."

"And if you didn't like me and I stayed, would *that* suck?"

"Oh whoa, no. That's not what I meant. And *you* might decide you don't like me. You might think I'm a bad kisser, or hate the stink of lobster after a while, or just get irritated by the way I breathe."

"You kiss great and breathe fine," I said shortly, still unsettled by the idea that he might only be interested in me because he saw me as temporary.

"And the lobster thing?"

"I'll let you know."

He laughed. "I think you're taking this harder than you need to."

"Probably." I slumped back against the couch. "I do that."

"Tell me about that?"

"No."

"Oh, you're upset." His blue-green eyes were kind.

"I have abandonment issues," I blurted. Then I cringed, not knowing why I'd said it. "And I'm making a mess of tonight. . . ."

"No, you're not. No more than I am." He took my hand and lifted it back to his chest. The flannel of his shirt was soft and his heart was still racing beneath it. "Let's just be messy." He rested his forehead against mine and stared into my eyes.

A frightening quivery feeling rose in my belly. This guy might be dangerous, I thought. I might actually like him. And then what would happen when things didn't work out?

"I want to take it slow," I told him.

"Okay." He smiled. "Does that mean no kissing?"

"No. I like the kissing."

I let myself surrender. It wasn't hard. His arms wrapped around me, and he slid back into the couch, pulling me with him. Hazel woofed and scrambled out from under him, padding sleepily to her dog bed.

Jake's hands slid down my back as he kissed me, his tongue lazily teasing. I felt his fingers brush the bare skin between my sweater and the waistband of my jeans, and then they were slipping under my sweater again.

"You're so warm," he whispered. "Are my hands cold?"

They weren't but they made me shiver anyway. I fumbled his shirt buttons open, wanting to get closer.

"I thought you wanted to take it slow," he mumbled against my lips.

"Not that kind of slow," I breathed, as I kept unbuttoning. "Emotionally, I meant."

"Oh." He groaned as my hand ran over his chest. "*Emotionally*."

I pulled his shirt open, revealing all that taut burnished skin.

"I've been wanting to do this since I first saw you," I admitted, running my hands down the ladder of his ribs and over the planes of his stomach. His muscles clenched under my touch.

His head fell back against the arm of the couch. "This isn't emotional?" he asked in a husky voice.

"Hush." I pressed my mouth to his. I didn't want to talk anymore.

I ran my hands over his exposed chest, enjoying the way he shivered at my touch. He smelled so good: pine and salt and that unique Jake scent that made me weak at the knees. I lowered my head to press a kiss to the column of his neck, where his heartbeat leapt beneath the skin. He melted into the couch, his eyes fluttering closed. Under my fingertips his nipples hardened. I circled them as I kissed his neck, letting my tongue flick over his galloping pulse. I wanted to kiss every inch of him, and I wanted to do it slowly, and thoroughly.

I felt Jake's hands under my sweater, and then I felt the sweater lifting. I helped him pull it over my head and I heard his indrawn breath as I sat, half astride him.

"You're so beautiful," he said thickly as he stared at me. Featherlight, his fingers ran up my spine and over my shoulders, tracing my collarbone before dropping down the curves of my breasts in their scallops of lace. I was so hot for him my nipples were pushing through the lace hungrily, my breasts swollen and aching.

"Touch me," I whispered. I took his hands in mine and pulled them to cover my breasts. I arched into his touch, which was hot and firm. He squeezed me and we both moaned.

"What do you want?" he asked as he ran his thumbs over my jutting nipples. I felt it like a shock.

"Everything," I admitted.

"Lucky for the both of us, that's all I think about when it comes to you." And he set out to prove it.

We woke up when the lights blazed on.

"Power's back," Jake said sleepily. He'd pulled the throw blanket over us. We were packed tightly together on the couch, my leg thrown over his.

"We really should have gone to bed. I have a king-size bed in there." He yawned.

"I like it here," I said, propping myself up on an elbow and watching him as he crossed the room to turn the light out. He was unselfconscious naked, but who wouldn't be with a body like that?

"I like that you like it here." He leaned over and kissed me. "I might just clean off the table before Hazel realizes she can reach the chicken."

"I can help."

"Nope." He pushed me back when I made to stand and tucked the blanket around me. "You want some coffee while I'm up?"

"It's the middle of the night," I protested.

"Nope. It's almost dawn." He reached for his phone and showed me the screen.

I yelped. It was six-thirty. "I have work!"

He laughed. "And you have plenty of time. No school run, remember?"

I sagged back against the couch. Oh. That took a good hour of craziness out of my morning.

"I'll make you breakfast, and you can watch the sunrise with me, then go home and get ready for work."

The sunrise was something to see from Jake's place. The storm had passed but the harbor was still windswept and tempestuous. We dressed and put our coats on and took our coffee out on the balcony in the frosty fresh morning.

I turned my face into the wind and enjoyed the briskness of it. Everything smelled like rain and pine. My skin tingled from the cold, and from Jake. He wrapped an arm around me from behind and held me tight against him as the eastern sky blushed pink around the edges of the gray banks of clouds. The first gulls took wing and I heard the long haunting cry of the loons.

"They'll be gone soon," Jake murmured, dropping a kiss on my head. "Once they've flown, we'll be in winter for real. It always makes me sad."

Coral and pink rays struck loose from the clouds, sending bars of light across the choppy harbor. I sighed and leaned back against Jake, thinking it was one of the prettiest things I'd ever seen.

"Do you often watch the sunrise, or are you a late sleeper?" I asked him.

"Ah, we're back to the questions. I usually watch the sunrise. My bed is there." He pointed at another set of French doors farther along the balcony. "So even if I sleep in, I can see it. Lately I've been getting up and taking the dog for a run. If you head down to the beach the morning after a storm, you'll find driftwood washed up. There's nothing a dog likes more than chasing thrown driftwood."

The mention of questions reminded me. "I did have something I wanted to ask you," I said, turning within the circle of his arm to look up at him. "I found some old postcards and letters in the house." I described them to him. "Do you know who *F* is?"

"Well, I'd have to look at them to be sure, but I'd guess the *F* stands for Freddie."

"Freddie?" I lit up. "Freddie who?"

"Freddie de Marche."

"De Marche? Like your cousin Perry next door to me?"

"Yeah," Jake said slowly. He was looking at me with an expression I couldn't read.

"He was writing to Marly, wasn't he?" My imagination had run wild since I'd read the letters. "Was it a tragic romance? I mean, she was the last person to live in the house, and I've yet to come across any happily-ever-after photo albums or his and hers monogrammed towels. There's really nothing in that house that seems to belong to him, except for the postcards. Did he break her heart?"

"Marly wasn't the last person to live in that house," Jake said, confused.

"She wasn't?" I asked, shocked. "But everyone calls it Marly's place." All the imaginings I had about my house wobbled like a tower of cards. I'd built a whole image in my head of Marly, the old lady of the culch.

"Well, it *was* Marly's place. She got the family shares in it and she used it for a summer place. But she never lived there."

"She didn't?" I couldn't hide my disappointment. "Then who did?"

Jake pulled away and a cloud fell over his face.

"Jake?"

He sighed. "Well, I guess I was going to tell you eventually. My mother did."

TWENTY

Oxeye, Maine, 1956

"I didn't take you for someone who weeps at weddings, pixie stick."

Marly jumped. She'd been hiding behind the outbuildings, trying to find some privacy to pull herself together. Dad had taken Mom inside somewhere; no one else seemed to realize that something was terribly wrong. The garden was full of chatter and music and the clinking of glasses. The June day was sparkling fresh and scented by roses. But Marly felt that nothing would ever be good again.

"It's awfully sappy of you," Freddie teased, but she could see he looked concerned.

Marly gave Freddie de Marche a sharp look, trying to hide her real feelings, which were hot and hurting. "All the best people cry at weddings."

He pulled his handkerchief from his pocket. "Here, I came prepared in case I got a case of the weeps too."

She took it from him and turned her back on him while she dabbed at her eyes.

"Those didn't look like tears of joy. Care to tell me what's wrong?" he asked gently.

"No."

"Fair enough." He leaned against the outbuilding at her side and looked up at the sky above. "Seems like everyone's getting married these days. You know my sister's getting hitched this summer too. My mom's already weeping."

"Are you going to ask Cilla to marry you?" Marly blurted. She hadn't meant to. It had just come out.

"God, no."

The vehemence in his voice made Marly's heart explode in her chest like someone had filled it with gunpowder. "Why not?"

"Because I don't want to marry Priscilla."

Marly turned back toward him, leaning her shoulder against the outbuilding and facing him front-on. "Well, why not?" She needed to know.

"I don't know."

"What do you mean, you don't know?" Marly was astonished. "You've been dating her for three years, even if you haven't pinned her."

"I haven't pinned anyone," Freddie said, sounding put out. "I never made any promises."

"Dating someone for three years is a kind of promise," she scolded.

"No, it's not. It's movies and walks and dinner. Not *marriage.*"

"Well, what's so wrong with marriage?" Marly thought of her father's tenderness with her mother.

"Nothing. But that doesn't mean I want to do it." He thudded the back of his head against the stonework of the wall. "I don't know. I guess I had an idea about the *right* girl. That there'd be something extra. Cilla's nice and all, and pretty and, uh, friendly, but . . ."

"But . . ." Marly repeated.

"Yeah. *But.*" Freddie shrugged. "It's just nice. And I don't want nice."

"What about me?" Marly said abruptly. She straightened up so he could see her properly in her fancy ice-blue bridesmaid's dress.

"What do you mean, what about you?" Freddie frowned.

"I'm not nice."

He was frowning even more now, those thick eyebrows drawing together. He honestly didn't understand her question.

She sighed, annoyed at having to spell it out. "Would you ever ask *me* to marry you?"

He laughed. "Sure, kid. In a decade or so."

Freddie wasn't taking her seriously. It annoyed her. No one ever took her seriously. She glared at him.

"You're joking, right?" He seemed to decide that she was and relaxed again. "Come on, let's go wish the happy couple good luck and get some food."

Marly felt like screaming but she didn't; she followed him back to the party, hoping no one would say anything about her crying like a baby through the ceremony.

Sylvie had drunk too much champagne and was loudly telling everyone she loved them as they gathered to wave her off. She'd changed into her going-away outfit, a pink suit and hat, and was still carrying her bouquet.

She hugged Marly's mother tightly and told her how much she loved her, but Marly could see that her mom looked stressed rather than touched.

"And you, Marly," Sylvie said, actually pinching Marly's cheek like she was a little kid. "You look so grown-up."

"So do you," Marly said dryly.

There were cheers as the happy couple reached Elton's car, which had been well and truly decorated with toilet paper and whipped cream. A placard hung from the rear: JUST MARRIED—HONK TO WISH US LUCK.

"Time to throw the bouquet," Cilla ordered, and then she got in position in the middle of the crowd.

Sylvie winked and threw the flowers straight to her sister.

Marly looked around to see if Freddie had seen it, but he was nowhere in sight.

"Pumpkin." Dad appeared, with his coat and her mother's handbag over his arm. "I'm going to take Mom back to the hotel room."

"Okay. I'll come."

"No, no." He forced a smile. "Stay. There's still cake out. The boys can walk you back later."

Marly watched as he led Mom to the station wagon, gently guiding her into the front seat. Marly's stomach was in knots, and she felt sad and small and faded. But that was nothing compared to how she felt when she stole around the oak tree side of the house, trying to avoid people, and almost ran into Freddie and Priscilla having a *scene.*

"What do you mean, you *enlisted*?" Priscilla whacked Freddie with the bouquet, which made a fleshy slapping sound against his chest.

Marly darted behind the catberry bushes, hoping they hadn't seen her.

"I mean exactly that. I enlisted. My buddy Cal just got drafted," Freddie said, "and I got to thinking about it. And I thought, why the hell not? I'm not enjoying law. In fact, I hate it. And if I enlist, I won't get drafted."

"If you enlist, you won't get *drafted*?" Cilla's voice was dripping with contempt. "What does it matter, either way you're in the army!" Marly had never heard her sound so angry before.

"Yeah. But I'll control how, where, and why. I can choose which branch of the service I go into."

Marly's head was spinning. Freddie de Marche was joining the *army*?

"And what does this mean for us?" Cilla asked tightly.

Freddie went very still and very silent.

"Do you expect me to be an army wife, hauled from pillar to post?"

He stayed silent.

"I see." Priscilla drew herself up to her full height and then slapped him roundly across the face.

Freddie took it. Then he placed his hand on his red cheek and softly said a single word. "Ouch."

"You don't get to say *ouch,*" Cilla told him fiercely. "You've toyed with me for years, and now that you've wasted my youth, you're running off to the *army*?"

"Wasted your youth?" Freddie got snappy himself at that. "Come on, Cilla, you're not even twenty-two yet."

Cilla made a sound like an angry cat. "Almost twenty-two and a bridesmaid at my own little sister's wedding." She threw the bouquet at him and then stalked off, her skirts swirling.

Freddie swore. Then he looked over at the catberry bush. "You can come out, half-pint. I saw you dive in there."

Chagrined, Marly inched out of the bush. "I didn't mean to eavesdrop," she said, although she kind of had.

"It's not really eavesdropping when one of the parties is shrieking." Freddie untied his bow tie. "I'm out of here, kid. You want me to walk you back to the hotel? You're looking pretty done with it all yourself."

Marly nodded. She had no interest in going back to the wedding party. "I'll just tell my brothers where I—"

"No need," Freddie said, wincing on her behalf. "They already headed off with Elton's brothers to some bar in Rockport."

Of course they had. Here she was alone, then. Again.

Except for Freddie. But even he was about to run off to the army and leave her.

"Come on, it's lovely weather for a walk." He offered her his arm and she took it. "Let's cut through the woods and then down to the beach."

As they crossed Tinker Street they could hear the sound of the wedding party winding down, glasses chiming as they were gathered up, voices grown soft and tired. The forest on the southern side was sleepy in the late afternoon, the dusty sunshine pouring through the firs. The needles crunched underfoot, and everything smelled like summer about to take full flight.

Marly felt the firmness of Freddie's arm under her fingers, and she fixed every detail of the moment in her mind, to relive later.

"So. You're joining the army," she said softly, as they meandered down through the woods to the road, taking a path that wasn't exactly a shortcut but was worth it for the beauty.

"I am." He pulled away from her, tugging his arm from her grasp. He took his jacket off and slung it over his shoulder.

"When?"

He looked up at the branches above them, the new budding pinecones just showing their little heads. "End of the summer."

"But . . . why?"

"Why not? I've got nothing else happening. Like I said to Cilla, the law isn't for me. I've finished a bachelor's degree, and I'm not interested in taking it further." He lapsed into silence as they reached the edge of the firs and crossed the road to the cliffs.

Marly frowned. "By why the *army*?" She followed him until the cliffs declined and the sandy path down to the little beach appeared. The seaside daisies were in full bloom along the path, nodding their heads in the breeze.

Freddie fished in his jacket pocket for his sunglasses and slid them on. Marly wished she'd brought hers. It was still bright out, the sun still a couple of hours away from setting.

"My old man was in the army, you know," he said.

The sandy path curved in switchbacks down to the beach. Marly stopped abruptly. "Keep your eyes on the beach," she told him firmly. "I want to take my stockings off and go barefoot."

"Sure, kid. Good idea." He didn't show the slightest inclination to steal a peek as she unhooked her stockings and rolled them down. He genuinely did think of her as a kid, Marly thought in disgust. Freddie took the time to take his shoes and socks off too.

She bundled the stockings up and crammed them in the toes of her shoes. "Okay. I'm done."

He didn't even look at her *then.* He just started off down the path again, his shoes swinging from one hand and his bare feet sliding through the golden sand.

"Your old man was in the army, you said," Marly prodded. She wasn't surprised to hear it. Mr. de Marche looked like he should be in a uniform.

"He stormed the beaches at Normandy." Freddie hopped off the path and onto the little horseshoe beach at the foot of the uneven cliffs. "He got a Silver Star. He was in the European theater for the rest of the war, including the Battle of the Bulge." Freddie stared out at sea. "He never talks about it."

Marly didn't know what to say, so she stayed quiet.

"I don't understand him at all, you know," Freddie said, turning back to look up at the cliffs. "But I keep thinking that at least he's *done* something. Served something bigger than himself." He bit his lip, making the silvery scar on his chin flash. "So, I don't know why the army, except that. And that the draft might get me anyway, so why not take control of it and do it in a way that suits me?"

He was going to join up and go away, like her father had gone away when she was a baby. Dad had also fought, but in the Pacific. He also had a Silver Star and never said a word about what he'd done to get it.

Freddie could be sent to Korea, where the war was over but the peacekeeping troops still sat. Or to West Germany, on the borders of the Iron Curtain. What if the Cold War turned hot? He might have to fight and maybe die.

"I love you," Marly blurted. She regretted it immediately. It had burst out of her because of the way he looked there, framed against the swelling waves, his hair blowing out of place, into his eyes. She told him, because if he left and she'd never told him, and then he died, she'd regret it forever. Looking at him there on the beach, pent up with three years of longing, knowing that if he could just *see* her then he'd see they were meant to be, she'd thrown caution to the wind.

But she knew immediately it had been a mistake.

Freddie had frozen. "What?"

Well, it was done now. And she wasn't about to pretend otherwise. "I love you," she said, this time more firmly.

He stayed frozen. The sea breezes gusted around them, kicking up glitters of sand.

"You can't go away . . . you can't go away to *the army* . . . without knowing that I love you. And that I'd marry you if you'd ask me."

Slowly, Freddie removed his sunglasses. He was squinting, but she could see that his gaze was full of pity. And that pity turned her stomach. "Ah, pixie stick," he said, sighing, "you don't love me."

"Don't *call* me that." Even though she loved it when he called her that. He never called anyone that except her. "And I do. I've loved you for *years.* I've loved you over every game of tennis and Monopoly, every time you took me out in a canoe, every time we walked on this beach."

"With *Cilla,*" he reminded her softly. "We did all that with Cilla."

"No. You might have. But I didn't. I did it with *you.*"

Freddie de Marche swore softly and looked heavenward to the June blue sky, as though seeking help from above. When he looked back at her, his pale eyes, the color of ocean shallows, were full of bittersweet sympathy. "Marly." He never used her name, and the sound of it on his lips made her shiver. "Marly, honey, you only *think* you love me."

She shook her head. No. This was love.

"One day you'll grow up and find a guy . . ."

"Stop treating me like a child," she said fiercely. "I'm seventeen."

". . . you'll find a guy," he said patiently, "and these feelings will pale in comparison."

"They won't," she spat. "They *won't.*"

He was looking at her so *kindly.* It made her want to kick and scream. This wasn't how she'd imagined this moment at all. In her daydreams, the scales fell from his eyes, and he *saw* her and knew he loved her.

"Listen, kid, you're a knockout," Freddie de Marche told her gently, "and trust me, you're going to knock some guy's socks right off."

"But not *your* socks," she said bitterly.

He looked down at his bare feet and tried for a joke. "What socks?"

It fell flat.

"Marly." He dropped his shoes and coat in the sand. "One day you'll thank me," he said, taking her hands. "For not being a molester after all." He shook his head. "You feel all grown up, Marly, but you're just a kid."

"So? So what if I'm a kid? I won't be a kid forever."

"But you are now." He sounded tired. "And I'm a lot of things, but someone who takes advantage of kids isn't one of them."

She tore her hands out of his. "I'll wait till you get back. Till you're out of the army. By then I'll be Priscilla's age. If she's old enough, then *I'll* be old enough."

Freddie laughed, but it wasn't mean. "Pixie stick, by then you'll have met a guy who'll turn you weak at the knees. A guy who knows a good thing when he sees it. You'll be getting married up there in that garden, with all your family around you, and I'll just be a distant memory—some guy who dated your cousin in those last golden years of your childhood."

"I'll never marry," Marly told him wildly. "I'll just have *cats.*"

"What are you talking about?" Even though he was exasperated and sad, he smiled.

"I'll be one of those cat ladies, who lives in a run-down old house with only cats for company. Like Miss Havisham in *Great Expectations,* but with *cats.*" Marly had the urge to kick sand in his face.

"Well, if that's the case, I bet you'll make the best cat lady the world has ever seen. And you'll leave a bunch of broken hearts in your wake."

"But not yours," Marly said, feeling bitter.

"Marly, you've got to understand. What kind of guy would I be, taking advantage of you when you're barely old enough to even know what love is?" He shook his head at her. "You don't want a guy like that. You want a guy who meets you when you're full grown and powerful."

"I *am* full grown and powerful," she raged. But they both knew it wasn't true.

The wind blew between them on the beach as the gulls banked overhead, their cries carrying over the cliffs.

"I'll write you," he said softly.

"Why? If you're just some guy who dated my cousin."

"Because the guy who dated your cousin likes you, kid. As a person. And he'd like to stay friends."

Marly felt bitterly humiliated. And shattered by the events of the day. Nobody wanted her. She *would* end up an old cat lady.

"Walk you home?" he asked gently.

"No. I'll get there myself." Marly lifted her chin.

"Okay." He put his hands in his pockets and gave her a sad look. "Take care of yourself." He caught himself about to call her "kid," she could tell. "Bye, Marly."

And then she stalked off down the beach, scrambling up the rocks to the trail that led into the woods, where Saint-Cyr lazed in its grounds.

Marly never forgot the vision of Freddie de Marche, standing there on the beach, a little speck of a person, staring out to sea.

And then he went off and enlisted, like an idiot, and she went on with her life, which felt smaller, scarier, and much less magical for the absence of him.

TWENTY-ONE

I could barely absorb the shock as I stood there on Jake's balcony in the frosty morning. Jake's *mother* was the last person to live in my house on Tinker Street? Not Marly? For some reason, I felt betrayed.

I felt even more betrayed when he told me she was still alive. The story I'd been telling myself about the woman who'd lived in my house came collapsing down around me. I'd painted a tragic picture of her, a romantic and solitary figure fading away in the clutter of her past.

"The agent said it was an estate sale," I said flatly.

"It kind of was. Just a power-of-attorney estate sale, rather than an after-death estate sale." Jake ran his hands through his hair.

"I don't understand," I said, shaking my head.

Jake shrugged, in that way he had that said nothing and everything. "Well. My mom has the family curse," he said. He seemed to slump, like he'd run out of energy.

"I don't understand." I was feeling like a parrot, my mind caught in a loop, unable to say anything else. It was *Marly's* place. Marly was the old woman in my imagination. Not Jake's *mother.*

"She has early-onset dementia. It's hereditary." He drained his coffee and opened the door, clearly done with watching the sunrise. "It's dotted through the family tree. Like some kind of fungus. My great-grandmother had it, Sylvie had it, my mother has it. There are a few more cousins and uncles and aunts in there too. It's a bitch of a thing."

I followed him inside, his words hitting my heart. "That's awful." I swallowed hard. "I'm sorry."

"It is what it is."

"And I'm living in *your mother's* house?"

"Yeah. I mean, it used to be our summer house, not our actual house, but after my parents' divorce, my mom moved there full time."

I stopped dead as it hit me it wasn't just his mother's house, it was *his* house. "Oh my God, no wonder you felt you could take the front door off. This explains how you knew where the storm windows were. And why you have opinions on everything to do with the house. It's *your* house."

He shook his head vigorously. "Nope. It's not my house. It's my mom's house."

"But you grew up there."

"No." He shook his head. He turned his back on me and started doing dishes. "I spent summers there."

"Summers that got in your blood," I said, remembering his poetry that evening on the school swings and putting the pieces together. "You moved here because this is *your* street."

"So?" He gave me an irritable look, back to being the grouch I'd met on that first day. "What's so weird about that? I loved it here as a kid. I wanted to live here forever."

"But . . ." I couldn't quite get my head around the enormity of this. "Why aren't you living in the house? Why did you sell it?"

Jake kept his back to me, his hands in the dishwater.

"Was that why you didn't want me to buy it, that first time we met? Because you wanted your family to keep it?"

"You're going to be late for work," he said bluntly.

"Can we finish this conversation later?" I asked nervously, unsettled by his stoniness. He couldn't just drop a bombshell like that and expect to just leave it there.

"Sure." He was curt.

I gathered my things and approached him warily. "Jake?"

"Yeah."

I put my hand on his arm, and he stopped scrubbing the roasting pan. "Thanks for telling me."

His greenish-blue eyes were churning when they met mine. "It wasn't easy selling it," he blurted.

I didn't know what to say. I had too many questions and I was too off-balance. So I rose on my toes and pressed a kiss to his mouth.

I felt some of his tension loosen. He closed his eyes and sagged against me. "It's a long story, Zoe. And it's not a nice one."

"I'm familiar with those kinds of stories," I promised, thinking of Tina. And I kissed him again. As I went down the outside stairs from the balcony, I saw him watching me through the kitchen window, a haunted look on his face.

I knew I should wait to talk to Jake, but I was churning with questions, and when I saw Elton, I just blurted out what I'd learned. He was out checking his house for storm damage when I did my walk of shame up the street, dodging the puddles and watching my breath form puffs of cloud in the cold air. I saw him suppress a smile when he saw where I came from.

"Good morning," he said in his usual gentlemanly way, his brown eyes twinkling. "You're up early."

"Jake just told me that this was his mom's house," I burst out. I hadn't meant to, but it was too much to hold inside of me.

"Indeed, it was," Elton agreed mildly. "And before that his grandmother's. And before that his great-grandmother's and her sister's. And before that their parents. That old house has been in the family a long time."

I frowned. That didn't feel good, to be the person who broke the chain.

Although *Jake* was the person who broke the chain, I corrected myself. Not me. If I hadn't bought it, someone else would have.

"And his mother's not dead?"

"He told you that, did he?" Elton's gaze drifted tenderly toward Jake's store. The pale wash of morning light caught the creases in the old man's cheeks when he smiled.

"He said she had the family curse." I bit my lip. "Like your Sylvie."

Elton nodded. "It's a pretty strong curse. Picks off a lot of apples on that tree."

I fell silent and we stood in the dripping street, listening to the erratic gusting of the wind and the cries of the loons.

"He said it was a power-of-attorney sale, not an estate sale," I let slip, unable to stop myself. "Because she's not dead . . ."

Elton sighed. "No, Jake's mother's not dead. She's in a nursing home in Camden, so she can be close to Marly."

I felt like he'd slapped me. "Wait, *what*? Marly's alive?"

"Alive and kicking and living in Camden."

"But . . . hold on." This wasn't sinking in. "Marly of Marly's place? *My* place?"

"That's the one."

His words replayed in my head. *She's in a nursing home in Camden, so she can be close to Marly.* "Elton?"

"Yes, my dear?" He was regarding me kindly, seeing the effect the news had on me.

"Why does Jake's mom need to be close to Marly?" I thought I knew the answer but I needed to hear him say it.

"Because she's Marly's daughter."

Of course. If this had been Marly's place *and* Jake's place . . . and Jake's mom was Marly's daughter. "Marly's Jake's grandmother."

The alarm went off on Elton's phone and he fumbled to pull it out of his pocket. "Oh lordy, I almost forgot to take my medication again."

I saw the time on his phone and yelped. I was going to be late for work. "Thanks, Elton," I said, as I backed away down my driveway. "I have to go."

"Have a good day, Zoe," he called. "You might want to turn your sweater around before you go to work. You've got it on inside out."

Flo sent me a dozen photos of her flower girl dress fitting, and another dozen photos of her lunch, which seemed to consist of a towering stack of pancakes and a waterfall of syrup. Then she demanded more proof-of-life photos of her cats.

Jake didn't message me once. The day dragged at work as I checked my phone compulsively. But no messages.

I had all the usual thoughts. Had I just been used? Had he fed me a line to get me in bed? Not even in bed, on the couch. But then I shook it off, remembering his haunted look at the window. I was living in his mom's house. The house he'd spent three months of the year in growing up, the summer house that made him fall in love with Oxeye.

I wondered which bedroom had been his: Flo's? Or the room with all the clothes in it? I remembered his familiarity with the house when he'd given us the tour, his attention to detail as he rebuilt the porch screens and turned the old laundry into a new room. He loved the house. So why hadn't he kept it?

Was it about money?

The thought made my stomach sink. I hated the idea that he

might have been forced to sell it. No wonder he'd seemed so hostile that first day.

In the afternoon, I went down rabbit holes online looking up the symptoms of early-onset dementia—which looked like it started a *lot* earlier than I'd realized. It began with losing the ability to handle money and pay bills, struggling to bathe, and some mild personality changes. It escalated to failing to recognize people, losing the ability to read and write, and withdrawing from the world. The final stage involved being unable to communicate, having no awareness of your surroundings, incontinence, and losing the ability to swallow. Patients who reached this stage made uncontrollable noises, had no interest in food, had seizures.

I thought of Jake's haunted look and my heart ached. How long had his mother lived in the house? How far gone had she been before they moved her to the nursing home?

Jake lived on the corner of her street for a reason, I thought suddenly. It wasn't just because he loved the town. He'd been caring for her. I remembered the scrubbed bathroom and the immaculate master bedroom we'd found on our tour. He had done that for her.

Hey, I texted Jake, deciding I couldn't wait for him to do it. But he didn't text back.

Driven by the memory of his face at the window, on the way home I stopped at the market and bought a bunch of hothouse roses and some supplies for dinner. As I turned in to Tinker Street, I saw that the hardware store and apartment above were dark. There was no sign of Jake or Hazel. I pulled over in front of his place and grabbed a pen from my handbag. I ripped a page from the back of my daily planner, scribbled a note on it—*Come to my place when you get this?*—and tucked it into the bunch of roses. Then I ran up the back stairs and left them propped against his kitchen door.

When I got home, the house was freezing, even with the heating on, and the cats were curled together in the laundry basket in

Flo's room, surrounded by all the clothes she hadn't put away before she left. I brought the cats downstairs, carrying them in the basket, and set them in front of the fireplace in the kitchen. The minute they smelled food they came leaping out of the basket, mewing like crazy. I took a million photos of them and sent them to Flo. Then I lit the fire and, as the hearth heated up, watched them sprawl in a higgledy-piggledy row in front of it, grooming themselves and each other.

I put the fire guard up, threw dinner on, and raced upstairs to shower, just in case Jake came by. My clothes were still strewn everywhere from the night before, when I couldn't decide what to wear, and I picked them up and crammed them into the chest of drawers. I'd sort it out tomorrow. I opted for my fleece yoga pants, a loose sweater, and a thick pair of ski socks, figuring tonight was about easing tension, not dressing to impress.

The casserole would keep warm for as long as it took. I was antsy as I waited, checking my phone but hearing only from Flo, who hearted all one million of the cat photos. One by one the cats jumped back in the basket and went back to sleep, enjoying the fire. I fidgeted for a while and then migrated to the dining room, ostensibly to kill some time sorting culch, but actually to spy on Tinker Street. From here I had a good view down the street to Jake's place.

But the hardware store and apartment above were still dark.

The weather had eased, and the clouds were breaking to reveal inky patches of moonless sky. Everything seemed hushed, like the whole street was exhaling after the storm.

I flipped through the paintings stacked behind the door. There were a lot of coastal landscapes, many of them brooding, some charcoals too, and a handful of bright still life oil paintings of summer flowers. I realized I might want to keep some of them. Including the map of Maine Jake had mentioned when he took us around on our initial tour. There was no *X* marking buried treasure, but it was a beautiful old map, and there was another one of Knox

County, which looked hand drawn and colored. I pulled it out and put it on the dining table, peering at it to find Oxeye. I hadn't realized there were so many islands out there in the bay. The map might look good in the hall. . . .

I heard a car turn the corner to the street and flew to the window, peering out. It was Jake's pickup. My heart pounding, I backed away from the window and turned off the light. I went into the parlor—to pretend like I'd been diligently sorting junk and not spying on his house all evening.

Distantly, I heard Hazel's high bark.

Music, I thought nervously. I should put music on, so I'd look extra casual. I didn't want him to feel any pressure. Or me to feel any pressure. I fetched our little portable speaker and threw on a relaxing playlist. I considered the parlor fireplace. I hadn't used it yet—should I bother? No. If he turned up, he wouldn't want to sit in here while I sorted his mother's junk.

His *mother's* junk. The realizations kept coming like aftershocks. I looked around the parlor. All those bags of pop beads and Happy Meal toys and all the other stuff had been hers. I looked around with fresh eyes. He'd spent his summer days in this room with its porthole windows and its egg-shaped chandelier. How weird must it be for him to come here now that I lived here?

Very weird, I assumed. And maybe quite painful.

I relived every time he'd been in the house, all the way back to that first day when he'd given us a tour. Him talking about the missing lampshades in the hall, the floorboards under the linoleum, the need for a heat pump. His stressed, pinched look, which I'd mistaken for grumpiness. The way he'd clutched the banister on the landing, looking like he wanted to run away. All those attempts to convince me I didn't want to take this place on . . .

What must he have been feeling?

I heard the crunch of boots on the street outside and Hazel's soft woof of excitement. I bit my lip, every muscle tensed as I strained to hear his footsteps. He was coming up the front steps instead of around the back. Why? Didn't he feel comfortable here with me anymore, now that I knew?

There was a gentle knock on the door.

I tried to act relaxed and walk casually, but really I sped to the door. I opened it, my heart skipping like I was a little kid and it was Christmas.

God, he looked good. He was in a thick cable-knit sweater and a beanie. His jaw was stubbled, which only made him look better. He stood there with his hands in his pockets, Hazel sitting at his feet, looking up at him with her adoring eyes.

"Hey," he said nervously, not quite able to meet my gaze.

"Hey." My breath plumed in front of me.

"I got your flowers." He risked a look at me.

I tried to radiate gladness to see him. "Thank you for dinner last night," I said lightly. "I wondered if I might repay the favor?" I saw him bite the inside of his lip. "No questions," I promised. "No talk of anything at all if you want. We can mime."

His dimple dented. "Mime, huh?"

"Yeah." I held the door wider.

He looked down at Hazel. "Uh, the cats?" He fidgeted. "I really can't leave her alone. And I don't like to leave her in the yard at night, it's so cold."

"She can come in, can't you, Hazel?" I stepped back into the hall. "I'll run the kittens up to Flo's room. They're okay up there, it's not too cold."

"Should we wait here till you get them up?" he asked.

Relief washed through me that he was staying.

"Um, here or the parlor? It's got to be at least a little warmer in there."

Gingerly he stepped over the threshold, Hazel trotting alongside, her tongue lolling. He took her into the parlor. I watched for his reaction to the room, trying to read every micro-expression. *Stop it,* I hissed at myself. I'd make him uncomfortable if I kept watching him like that.

"I'll be right back," I promised, dashing Mac and the Cheeses upstairs in their basket. I also ran up some kibble and water and freshened their litter tray, then washed my hands in the bathroom, spritzed on some perfume, and slicked on some lip gloss.

When I got back down, Jake was standing in the middle of the room. "You're making headway," he said gruffly. "You'll have this room ready to use by Christmas."

"I hope so." I laughed. "Because Suni and Wayne and the whole family are descending on me for the holidays. I have to set up some furniture. And buy a blow-up mattress or two."

"There are some folding cots in that other outbuilding if you want extra beds," he said. Then he bit his lip.

"No talking," I promised, holding up my hands. "Are you hungry? I've still only got the countertop oven so it's just a casserole. But it's hot."

I led him and Hazel out to the kitchen. She flopped in front of the fire, panting happily at being included. With only the crackling of the fire and the soft music curling through the house from the parlor to break the silence, we sat opposite each other, eating dinner and stealing looks at one another. Afterward, I made hot chocolate, and we turned our chairs to sit in front of the fire, watching the flames dance. Eventually, he reached out and took my hand in his, tracing my fingers.

"I haven't experienced quiet like this in years," I whispered. "Flo talks a mile a minute."

He smiled but didn't say anything. A little later, we did the dishes together, him washing and me drying, without saying a word. And when he went to leave, he pressed me against the wall and kissed me until I couldn't remember how to breathe. His hands cradled my head and his legs bracketed mine; I was cocooned in his embrace as he ravished my mouth with his. I didn't know kisses like this existed in real life. They'd always seemed the stuff of romance novels and old films. But here I was swooning, unable to stand without his support, and all because of a kiss.

By the time he pulled away, my lips were deliciously swollen and my whole body was languid with pleasure. He stroked my jaw with his thumb and then pressed a gentler kiss on my forehead. I knew he was saying goodnight, even though he didn't utter a word.

"Hey," I called as Jake trotted down the front steps with Hazel in tow.

He turned, raising a questioning eyebrow.

"What are you doing tomorrow?" I was still tingling from his kiss. "Seeing as how I don't have any kid to look after, I was wondering if I could buy you dinner? Maybe in Rockport or Camden?"

He broke into a half-smile. "Like a date?"

"Exactly like a date." I cleared my throat. "We can talk about the weather."

"We can talk about anything you want," he said, his voice husky. "Goodnight, Zoe."

The way he said my name made it sound like an endearment. "Goodnight, Jake."

Hazel barked.

"Goodnight, Hazel!" I laughed.

"Go inside, or you'll freeze," he said. "I'll see you tomorrow."

As he walked home, he looked back at me. More than once.

TWENTY-TWO

Flo got me a front-row seat to the school play.

"You're seriously not going to want to miss this," she'd promised me.

"I thought you said you didn't have any lines?"

"I don't," she said, with another one of those classic eye rolls. "You *know* I don't. What dog talks and sings?"

"Goofy."

"Well, I'm the Pluto kind of dog, not the Goofy kind of dog."

It was the first week of December and the icy coastal towns were festooned with lights. We hadn't had snow yet but there was plenty of ice and frost, which made driving a little alarming. I was glad when Jake offered to drive me to the play. He kissed me thoroughly when I slid into his pickup truck next to him.

"I like your Christmas display, by the way," I teased him, as we turned the corner onto Beach Road. He had a big plastic lobster on his balcony facing the road. It was lit up and he'd put a Santa hat on it.

"Thanks. And where are your lights?"

"I haven't untangled them yet."

He groaned. "Please don't tell me you're using Mom's old lights."

"Sure I am. I'm not made of money."

We'd skated around the topic of his mom the past couple of weeks. I tried not to ask too many questions, and he tried not to shut down and stonewall me. Mostly we avoided the topic. He seemed content to come help fix up the house, so long as he didn't have to drag up the past, so I let it lie. I figured he'd tell me when he was ready.

Our "dating," if that's what it was, seemed very slow moving. Since Flo had come home, he came for dinner a couple of times a week, and he was around doing jobs on the house as much as ever. There were a lot of stolen kisses, pressed up against walls behind doors, out of Flo's line of vision. And there were a lot of wandering hands and a lot of lusty looks. But not much else. Because Flo.

I'd only dated a few men in the past five years or so, and she'd hated it every single time. I was in no hurry to walk into that mess again, at least not before I'd enjoyed myself a little more. And I was pent up enough to jump Jake right here in the pickup. Except we had to get to the play.

"Have you ever seen the film version of *Annie*?" I asked him, as I played with the hair at the nape of his neck.

"Sure I have. I told you, I have a sister and a bunch of nieces."

"Flo and I watched it for our movie night last week. I'd never seen it."

He gave me an appalled look. "Didn't you have a childhood?"

I swallowed and forced a smile. I hadn't really had a childhood, I thought numbly. I'd had an old TV tuned to broadcast channels and a lot of reruns. I'd seen the old movies that ran all the time—*The Sound of Music, Grease, Jaws,* and *It's a Wonderful Life* at Christmastime—but not much else. Tina had taken me to the movies a couple of times to see Disney films but she'd always fallen asleep. I guessed my childhood would seem alien to Jake.

I kept quiet, not wanting him to look at me like I was from Mars.

He gave me a sideways look.

"If Flo's the dog, she doesn't get to do much," I said, swerving away from my childhood and back to the present. "Lainey will be onstage a lot, though."

"She sure will," he said dryly. "Which is precisely why my sister bought tickets for every member of the family."

I swallowed. I'd been nervous about meeting his sister, but it hadn't occurred to me I'd have to meet more family than that. "Wait," I said as something occurred to me. "*Every* member of the family?"

"Well, not Mom obviously," he said quickly.

"No, but . . ." I cleared my throat. "Marly?" My voice wavered. For some reason, Marly was a larger-than-life figure in my imagination, even though I now knew she hadn't been the one to fill my treasure house with culch.

Jake reached over and squeezed my knee. "Yes, Marly." He glanced at me. "Sorry, I should have told you. I didn't think . . ."

"No, I mean, why should you? Uh. Does she, um . . . know about me?"

"About you? Or about you and me?"

I wasn't sure how much there was to know about him and me, since we weren't actually a couple yet. We were just kissing like horny teenagers and hiding it from my kid.

"Ah, both, I guess," I said weakly.

"Yes, she knows about you, that you're living in the house. No, she doesn't know about you and me. Nor does my sister." He cleared his throat. "If you want me to tell them, I can. . . ."

But what would he tell them?

"Uh, no. I mean, we said we'd take it slow."

"*Emotionally* slow," he reminded me with a half-smile, although we'd slowed down on pretty much everything since Flo came home.

"I don't think we should tell anyone until Flo knows. . . ."

"Fair." He removed his hand from my knee. And he must have caught the hurt look on my face, because he said, "Just 'cause of the ice. There's enough black ice that I need to keep both hands on the wheel. If it weren't for the ice, I'd never take my hand off you."

I flushed. It was impossible, wanting him this much and not being able to have him. The thought of sitting near him in the dark while we watched the play gave me goosebumps. I hoped our seats were on opposite sides of the room.

The school was brightly lit, and a stream of cars was rolling into the parking lot. My heart was skittering like a scared rabbit as Jake slid into a space in a dark corner. I was charged with nerves at the thought of seeing Marly. His grandmother. Pixie stick herself.

Jake checked his watch. "Want to kill five minutes before we have to go in? I can take your mind off things."

I did, but it was a mistake. By the time he'd kissed me senseless and run his hands all over me, I was electric with lust. And so was he.

"I'll meet you after to take you home," he said, kissing me on the tip of my nose. "You go in. I might wait here for a minute. I'm not decent for company yet," he added wryly, pulling his jacket over his lap.

"I think you're more than decent," I teased him.

"Get out of here, woman, or we're not getting into the play at all, and you'll hate me when you miss your kid playing the dog."

I laughed and dropped down from the high pickup.

"Watch out for black ice on the paths," he called after me as I closed the door.

I did watch out, having learned my lesson the hard way a week ago. I still had the bruise on my ass from that one. I picked my way carefully to the theater, fishing my little paper ticket out of my pocket. The place seemed packed to the rafters. An instrumental version of "Tomorrow" was looping on repeat over the PA as I navigated the crowd to my seat, which was smack-bang in the middle of the front row. I guess Flo really didn't want me to miss her performance.

I couldn't help but turn in my seat and scan the crowd, looking for Jake so I could get a glimpse of his family. And Marly. But I couldn't see him. And then the school principal was onstage, doing a housekeeping speech, and I had to keep my eyes front.

The overture started. There was no school orchestra; the music was provided by a young teacher on an upright piano. He played with enormous energy but not much finesse.

My phone buzzed. It was Suni. *Don't forget to take photos!* They hadn't been able to drive up for the play, because Alison's ex had reared his head again and they were busy keeping her calm and safe.

I won't, I promised.

My phone buzzed again. It was a photo of the back of my head. Surreptitiously I turned to find Jake two rows behind me. He winked at me. I tried to steal a look at who he was with, but it was dark and there were people in front of them. Jake pointed at the stage, and I whipped back around just in time for the curtain to rise.

And, oh my God, was I glad I was in the front row. Mostly so Jake and his family couldn't see my face. Because Lainey Mullins couldn't sing. And I don't mean she dropped a note or was pitchy. She really couldn't sing. She came out in her Ronald McDonald wig, full of confidence like one of those train wrecks in the *America's Got Talent* auditions, and belted her little lungs out, only rarely hitting the right note.

Who on earth had cast her? And who had let her continue after rehearsals? It was mortifying to watch. The whole auditorium braced every time she opened her mouth. You could feel the tension in the room. There were a few nervous titters and some kids whispering and giggling, but you had to give it to Lainey, she was all in up there.

Flo was in a big shaggy brown dog suit with a giant headpiece.

You couldn't even tell it was her as she mugged about. I snapped some photos for Suni, catching Flo in some adorable gamboling. . . . If it *was* Flo. How would I even know?

The performance was painfully long. By the time they got to the final medley I was grinding my teeth. As Lainey and the tall boy playing Daddy Warbucks threw their hands out to receive applause, there was a long moment of silence. Then Flo started pounding her fluffy paws together. I heard a muffled "Bravo!" come from under her dog head. Taking the hint, a smattering of applause rose from the audience, and then people got into the spirit of supporting their children and there were cheers and an attempt at a standing ovation.

Lainey Mullins was beaming from ear to ear. And so was Flo when she pulled off her dog's head and her braids came tumbling down. She was flushed and sweaty, and very, very happy.

"I told you I was playing the long game," she whispered when she skipped out from backstage and I swept her off her feet into a hug.

I laughed. "Oh, Flo, you're evil."

"No, I just figured I'd let her do my work for me." She grabbed my cheeks with both hands. "*Wasn't she awful?*" she whispered.

"Well, *you* were a great dog. I got some photos to send to your dad and Suni and Wayne."

"They're serving refreshments in the cafeteria now," Flo said. "Let's go. I want to watch Lainey meeting her public." She dragged me along after her.

"Don't forget she's Jake's niece," I warned her. "Don't go relishing this too much."

"It's our secret," she promised. "But seriously, this is the greatest night of my life."

But she came up short when we got to the cafeteria and found Lainey surrounded by a whole army of admirers. She was holding an enormous bunch of lilies—which must have cost a fortune since they were out of season—and chattering animatedly to a collection of family and friends. Everyone was beaming at her.

Flo frowned. She was about to get a lesson in how life wasn't fair, I thought, with a feeling of dread in my belly, as I saw the principal going to congratulate Lainey roundly.

"I don't understand." Flo looked up at me. "How come they're all acting like she was good?"

"I guess because she's a kid," I said, putting my arm around her and giving her a squeeze. "And she's *their* kid."

"She's not Mrs. Viney's kid! And look at those girls from my class. They all laughed when she called me Fido, and now they're fawning on her after *that*?" Flo looked ready to pull her hair out. "She was *terrible.*"

"Yes, she was," I said fervently.

"Oh, this sucks. Let's get out of here."

I bit my lip. "Um, we can't."

She glared at me. "This isn't the time to tell me to be a good sport. I was the first one to clap."

"No, I mean we can't because I got a ride with Jake. He's going to drop us home after."

Flo groaned. "Oh *God.* That means we'll have to talk to her."

"Not necessarily. Why don't we grab a soda and a cupcake and go hide somewhere and I'll just tell him to text me when he's done?"

"Flo!" A short kid with a bob haircut and glasses came bounding over. "You were great. You were the only thing that didn't suck."

Flo snorted.

"Seriously, Brody took a video of it and was going to make a supercut of all her best notes, but then his mom confiscated his phone and said that was bullying. She has no idea." The kid shot Lainey a dark look.

"Well, it probably is bullying," I said carefully. "Even if *she's* a bully it doesn't mean it's not bullying."

Flo rolled her eyes. "Ash, this is my mom."

"Hi." Ash considered me. "I take your point. But then again, she did just stand up there and do that in public. And she'd probably *like* the supercut."

"And no one would laugh at *her*," Flo said, throwing up her hands.

I wondered what the hell a good parent would do here. "You don't really want people to laugh at her," I said, feeling like I was about to walk the plank as they turned disbelieving and slightly hostile eyes on me. "You just want her to understand how it feels, so she stops doing it to other people."

"No. I want revenge," Flo said.

"But that will make you as bad as she is."

Flo flung her hand in Lainey's direction. "That doesn't look so bad!"

"Flo?" Jake's voice cut through the babble, and I turned bright red, hoping he hadn't heard us being rude about his niece. He was holding a bunch of candy-colored roses wrapped with a bright yellow ribbon. "You were the best dog I've ever seen. Better even than Hazel." He held out the roses and Flo's eyes widened.

"They're for me?"

"If you were the one in the dog costume, then yeah." He passed them to her. "Congratulations, you're a natural."

"A natural dog?" She wrinkled her nose, even as she hugged the bouquet tighter.

"A natural performer. You were genuinely funny. Particularly in the scene where you followed Annie back to the orphanage."

"Well, I copied Hazel a lot. I watched how she trips over her feet when she follows you around. What did you think of the play overall?" Flo asked, sounding a bit bullish.

"Well . . ." Jake scratched at his stubble.

"Yes?" Flo and Ash were hanging on his every word.

"Frankly?" He took a breath. "It was pretty hard to sit through."

Flo exhaled hard. "Right!"

"There were moments I wished I had earplugs."

Flo sagged in relief, throwing Jake a big smile. "I started to think no one had noticed. Come on, Ash, let's get a soda."

"Where did you pull those flowers from?" I asked him, astonished, but also thrilled by the way he'd punctured Flo's bad mood.

"I had them in the back of the truck under the cover. One for her and one for Lainey."

I looked over at Lainey, who was glowing. "You're a good uncle," I told him.

"I am. I deserve a medal for sitting through that and then lying to her face."

"Surely she knows," I said, bewildered. "And if she doesn't, then someone really needs to tell her."

"Her sisters will," he said, sighing. "Imogen filmed it and is bound to make a supercut."

"I think there's a bit of that going on tonight."

"She'll survive. I hope."

"So," I said, with studied casualness, "do you want to point out your family?"

"Sure. Just over there, behind Lainey, that woman with the blond ponytail? The one telling off the teenager—probably for making a supercut to humiliate her little sister—that's my sister Liv."

The woman in question was tall and broad-shouldered, in a blazer and jeans. She was hissing furiously at a girl I assumed was her daughter.

"The one being told off is Imogen. Maddy is off somewhere with her friends. She snuck out of the performance halfway through and never came back. And there," he said, gesturing to a knot of men in intense conversation, "is my brother-in-law Hayden. He looks like he's talking football, which is his religion."

"And Marly?" I asked, dying of curiosity, scanning the group of people around Lainey.

"And Marly is . . ." he said, scanning the crowd, "coming right this way."

My heart leapt to my mouth. It was like meeting a ghost. Or a figment of your imagination.

Jake's grandmother Marly wasn't at all what I was expecting. She was tall and elegant, clad in tailored slacks and a soft wool sweater, both in caramel tones. She had silvery white hair chopped into a stylish pixie cut and very sharply observant hazel eyes. Elton had told me she was in her eighties, but she looked fighting fit. And nothing like the sad cat lady with the broken heart that I'd spent months imagining.

"So, Jake," she said, kissing him on the cheek. "This is the woman who bought the house." She turned those sharply observant hazel eyes on me.

"It is," Jake agreed. "Zoe, this is my grandmother, Marilyn. But most people call her Marly. And Grandma, this is Zoe Copeland."

"Hi," I stuttered. She was *nothing* like the Marly of my imagination. And she looked *nothing* like a "pixie stick." My stomach twisted. I'd made so many assumptions. This poised woman with her expensive haircut and bounty of grandchildren and great-grandchildren didn't resemble the tragic figure I'd conjured at all. I'd spent so much time fixating on the sad character I'd invented that it was hard to believe this Marly was real.

"And how are you finding it, Zoe?" Marly asked me smoothly. "Little old Oxeye?"

"I love it," I gushed. I couldn't stop staring at her.

Her greenish hazel eyes twinkled.

"Until recently I thought you'd lived in the house," I told her. "I imagined . . ." My throat grew tight. I'd imagined her life was like my childhood, I realized.

"I can't bear to think what you imagined," Marly said, and I noticed she reached for Jake and pressed her hand unobtrusively against his arm. To offer comfort.

Jake's mother was her daughter, I thought faintly. The house on Tinker Street had been *her* house. The reality of it was stark. Jake and Marly thought of her whenever I mentioned the house. Once again, I tried to picture his mother and I couldn't. Marly had been the woman who'd stolen my imagination. How had Jake's mom ended up surrounded by all that culch? Had she filled the house with treasures to remind her of her life when her memory started to fade? Had she squirreled away parts of her childhood, pop beads and old books and tin toys, to try to keep her life wrapped around her, when she could no longer remember who had given her the beads or read her the books?

"Jake tells me you've been restoring the old place," Marly said softly. I think she could tell by my pained silence where my thoughts had gone. "I'm glad. It needs some love."

Jake was leaning into Marly as though drawing comfort from her. And she was leaning into him, receiving comfort in return. I felt a deep and very old pain. And an envy so sharp it cut me like a knife. What must it feel like to have family like that?

"It *deserves* love," I told Marly through my ever-tightening throat. And I meant it with all my heart. That house had so much treasure in it, a wealth of lives lived in its embrace; it *did* deserve love.

And maybe so did I.

"Mom, I'm having a second 7Up and you'll just have to deal with it, because I have had a *night*." Flo barreled up, her roses still hugged tight, interrupting the charged moment.

"Nice try." I took the can of soda off her.

"And who's this?" Marly asked, although I could tell by the way she glanced sideways at Jake that she already knew.

"This is Florence. My daughter."

"Flo played Sandy the dog in the play," Jake told his grandmother.

Marly looked impressed.

"Flo, this is Jake's grandmother," I told her. I cleared my throat. "Marly."

"Hi." Flo didn't get the reference.

"She used to own our house," I said carefully, bracing myself. I never knew what Flo might say next.

"*Our* house?" She looked up at Marly. "All that junk was *yours*?"

"No, the house was mine," Marly said, sounding amused, "the junk was all Jake's mom's."

"Wait. *What?*" Flo turned to me and Jake, outraged. "Your *mom*? Why don't I know about this?"

He shrugged. "I didn't want you to."

Flo took her 7Up can back. "I think I'm going to need this."

"It's delightful meeting you both. I'd love to talk more but the kids are coming back to my house for coffee and cake," Marly said, suppressing a smile. "I'd best be going so I can get the coffee on."

"Maybe you can come and see the house when it's done?" I blurted.

Her expression clouded and became unreadable. "Maybe." And then she was gone, off into the tangle of family.

"Did I say something wrong?" I felt a beat of panic.

"Nah. She's just got a complicated relationship with the house," Jake said ruefully.

"Don't we all." Flo stepped out of reach as I tried to take the soda can off her. "Let it go, Mom. I've earned it."

TWENTY-THREE

"I thought we were going to buy a new oven," Flo said as she watched me approach the old kitchen range like I was approaching a sleeping grizzly bear.

I *had* planned to buy a new oven, until I saw the prices. Fixing up the basics of our house had been pricey, and I was short of cash—especially with Christmas coming. It had been Doris who suggested I get over my fear of the existing kitchen range and save the money.

"What do you need a new one for, you've got a great one already. You got any idea what people pay for wood-burning stoves like those?" she'd said last time she'd popped by.

I had no idea what people paid, but I looked it up. Some of them were well over ten thousand dollars. At first, I considered selling it—I could do a lot with that money—but then I remembered Jake's comment about houses losing their identity when they were modernized too much. The range was part of the house, and in some way, I felt selling it would be like ripping the heart out of the house. I'd grown attached to the big sleeping dragon of a thing.

"I don't trust anything that doesn't have dials," Flo told me now as I inspected the range. It was a gusty, rainy Saturday and the rain was lashing at the tall kitchen windows.

"People have cooked on these for hundreds of years," I said reassuringly, trying to soothe myself more than her. "How hard can it be?"

"Oh my God, Mom. People used to go to the toilet in pots they kept under their beds. I really don't think we should look to the past for solutions. The black-and-white times were *nasty*."

I ignored that. "I watched some YouTube videos. I don't think it's that hard. Look, this here's the firebox." I pointed. "You make the fire in there. Easy."

"Is it easy?" Flo groaned. "Let's just microwave things."

"We can do this," I told her firmly. "I believe in us." I showed her where the ash drawer was and the baking oven. "Just imagine the cakes we can bake."

She perked up at that. "Can cake be the first thing we bake?"

"Sure." Anything to get her on board. "And we'll make the best Christmas turkey ever."

"Followed by more cake."

I rolled my eyes. But at least she was involved now.

"What's this?" she asked, yanking on a handle between the cooktop and the firebox.

"I think that's the chimney bypass?" I bit my lip. "It pumps the heat around . . . or you can shut the heat off, cooling the oven down. Maybe we should watch another video. . . ." I was feeling out of my depth.

Flo fetched my laptop and we watched a couple of homemade instructional videos for antique wood oven ranges. Then Flo moved on to videos about how to bake cakes in one and left me to play with the range.

I fetched well-seasoned hardwood from outside and started a fire in the firebox.

"Hey!" Flo suddenly yelped. "Did you make sure the pipe thing was clean? This lady said she set fire to her kitchen by not cleaning her pipe thing."

My heart stopped. Then I remembered that Jake had checked it when he'd done the chimneys. "Just in case," he'd said, winking at me. I'd scoffed, sure there was no way I'd ever be using the ancient thing.

"It's fine." I breathed out shakily, glad to see the flue was working and the kitchen wasn't filling with smoke. "Shall we start by using the stovetop?" I suggested nervously. "We could boil some water?"

"No, look, this video says pancakes are the best thing to start with." Flo was gleeful.

"Seriously?" I was dubious, but she showed me the video. Sure enough, the guy on the screen showed how pancakes were perfect to teach you how to play around with the bypass to control the temperature. "Okay then, let's do this."

Together we whipped up the batter, and I gave Flo a long lecture about how hot the stove was and how to be safe around it. She rolled her eyes at me a lot, but I could tell she was listening.

Our first pancakes were a total disaster. It was around our third batch of batter that we got the hang of it. I'd never felt such a sense of triumph as I did regarding the perfect stack of fluffy golden pancakes at the end of the afternoon. Flo was grinning ear to ear as she high-fived me. She was grinning even more as she poured syrup all over the pancakes and scarfed them down.

"I can't wait to tell Doris we did it!" I said, feeling giddy. I'd mastered the range! All by myself. Well, with Flo's help, but mostly by myself. I felt indescribably proud. We'd had a lot of help with the house so far, but this we'd done all by ourselves.

"Don't tell her," Florence urged, high on sugar. "Let's not tell anyone. Let's just ask everyone around to dinner and serve them the best meal they've ever had and act all casual, like, 'Oh, this? Yes, we just whipped it up on our *black-and-white-times stove*.'"

I laughed. But then I considered it. "You know what? Yes!"

Flo's eyes widened. "What? Really?"

"Yes, let's have a dinner party! And we won't tell them until afterward that we cooked dinner on the range."

She was excited. "What should we cook?"

"Something easy." I giggled. "I don't want to serve them charred food."

We ate pancakes for dinner and searched for recipes online. And a week later, after a lot of practice and a bunch of both burned and half-raw attempts, Flo and I had mastered roasting a chicken and baking a simple chocolate cake.

We invited all our neighbors, set the dining table with our newly polished silver cutlery, and set out the mismatched wineglasses. The house smelled gloriously of roasting chicken and Flo had iced our cake with about three inches of frosting.

And there was nothing better in the world than the laughter and applause from our neighbors, or Jake's warm, proud gaze, when we showed them where we'd cooked our masterpieces. I don't know that I'd ever felt so good in my life.

TWENTY-FOUR

December crept in, icy and bright with frost. The approaching holidays seemed extra magical in our new house. We gathered sprigs of holly and mistletoe from our garden, and practiced baking gingerbread in our range. We even got our Christmas tree from our own patch of woods. Jake showed us how to pay the tree registration fee (who even knew there was such a thing?), and we headed out on a bright Saturday morning, to the accompaniment of Alan's bagpipes. Jake wasn't a fan, but I quite liked the mournful wailing of the pipes through the shivery morning air. It made me feel like I was in *Outlander.* Hazel loved it too, maybe a little too much, barking like a maniac at every note.

There had been a light dusting of snow over the past two days, but not enough to qualify as *actual snow,* in Flo's opinion. Thin white powder frosted the spines of the branches and clung to dips in the earth, but otherwise everything was still drab brown and green.

"I thought there was supposed to be a lot of snow in Maine,"

Flo complained as we tramped through the woods to the stand of balsam firs at the far edge of our property.

"When it comes, there'll be so much of it, you'll wish it away," Jake promised her.

"There better be. And it better come by Christmas." Flo slapped her hand on the trunk of a stout fir. "How about this one?"

"That is never going to fit in our house," I told her firmly.

"This is probably more your speed." Jake pointed to a fat little tree.

"That's not even as tall as you are," Flo complained, pouting at him.

"No, but it's the right size for us to carry home. Try and imagine it decorated." He stepped back and considered its shape. "It's got a straight trunk and nice symmetrical boughs."

"I don't mind a wonky tree," Flo protested. "That's how you know it's real and not fake."

"No, the *smell* is how you know it's real and not fake."

"They have fragrance sprays for that now."

Jake looked disgruntled.

Flo threw him a bone. "Okay, we can take this one, but can I have a try with the ax?"

"I didn't bring an ax. I brought a reciprocating saw." He held up the power tool. "And no, you can't have a try with it."

Flo clamped her hands over her ears and complained that a power tool didn't seem very Christmassy. But she was just being Flo. And Jake seemed to enjoy bickering with her. They kept it up the whole walk home, as we carried the tree awkwardly between us. The sharp resin fragrance of the cut tree was like being drenched in Christmas. It gave me a giddy feeling.

Tina had loved Christmas but could never afford a tree. She bought a little tinsel one from a dollar store one year but lost it when we moved. Another year she broke a branch off a street tree, stuck it in an empty bottle, and strung cheap battery-operated lights on it. They looked like little colored cobwebs, and I'd loved it. But I'd also stared enviously at the trees in the front windows of people's houses, watching the lights twinkle. One time Tina was heading out to work for the night and caught me standing on our stoop, staring in the front window of Mrs. Trezona's, where a plastic tree draped in fat, sinewy ropes of tinsel blinked with a whole star field of lights.

"You like that tree?" my mother had said, joining me on the stoop. Something about carrying the perfect Christmas tree home through the snow with my kid, the air perfumed with balsam fir, made the memory so vivid I felt like I'd stepped back in time.

"It's okay," I told Tina, out there on the front stoop in the cold. I didn't want my mom to feel bad that we didn't have a Christmas tree.

"I can beat that tree," she told me, grabbing my hand. "Come on." Tina dragged me downtown, walking so fast I had to trot to keep up. She was in her work clothes, which consisted of a pair of very short denim cut-offs and tall boots. She had a fuzzy little coat on, but she must have been freezing—I could see the skin of her legs turning blue. The sound of her teeth chattering clashed with jewelry jangling as we walked.

"There. How's that for a Christmas tree?" she said as we rounded a corner.

I'd never seen anything so beautiful in my whole life. The tree that dominated the square in the city was as tall as a small building and it blazed with light, the flashing golden bulbs cascading from top to bottom. It was topped by a shining star and, as I looked at it, I could have very well believed in magic. Tina smiled at my awe, and then she bought me a hot dog and we sat on a low wall in front of one of the city skyscrapers, watching the Christmas tree lights flash in the raw winter evening.

"You good to catch a bus home by yourself?" Tina asked, eventually standing. "I've got to earn us some money or we won't be eating anything this Christmas." She saw me to the right bus and watched me get on. I cleared the fog off the window so I could wave to her as the bus pulled away, but she was already walking off. It had started to snow lightly, in thin sleety pellets, and she had her hands in her pockets and her head down. Behind her the Christmas tree blazed and twinkled, but she wasn't looking at it anymore. Or at me.

"Mom, lift your end up, you're dropping it." The sound of Flo's voice broke me out of memory and brought me back to the chilly woods. I obeyed, lifting the tip of the tree higher. Flo and I always had a tree—the smallest one available at the lot near our apartment—and every year as we put it up, I thought of that tree in Pittsburgh that Tina had taken me to. This was the first year we would have a premium tree, and it was fresh-cut from our own land.

The tree seemed a lot bigger once we got it inside. I'd bought a stand from Jake's hardware store, and he screwed the tree into place in the parlor, by the reglazed front windows. The parlor looked like a different room. I'd worked my ass off to get it cleared in time for Christmas, finding homes for everything I could through online platforms, notices in the local papers, and calls to antique stores and vintage dealers. I only kept the things I loved: a couple of beautiful old soft sofas, and the wing-back armchairs by the fire. The apple-blossom Tiffany lamp took pride of place on a walnut side table and made my heart sing every time I turned it on.

We tethered Hazel to an armchair so she wouldn't go hunting the cats and Jake and I sat untangling Christmas lights while Flo fished through the record collection she'd kept, looking for Christmas music. She had the vintage record player set up on the floor, and winter sun flooded through my new windows, pooling around her on the floorboards. By the time we'd run through Bing Crosby, Nat King Cole, and Dean Martin, we had a tree that made my heart turn somersaults of happiness. Star fields of golden light flickered in the boughs, and the vintage glass baubles caught the light in their colored shells, spangling merrily. Our kitschy little angel perched on top of the tree, her crooked halo rakish.

"My mother bought that," Jake said, as he watched me fiddle with her so she'd stand up straight. "At a flea market."

I wanted desperately to hear more about his mother—I still didn't even know her name—but I didn't want to spook him. He hadn't spoken about her much since the night of the storm. Luckily, I had Flo there to pepper him with questions for me.

"What's a flea market?"

The problem was Flo didn't always ask the right questions.

"It's a market where people sell secondhand stuff."

"She needed more stuff?"

I tensed, but Jake laughed. "No, she did *not* need more stuff." He shrugged. "She has a kind of OCD. From before the dementia, I mean. She compulsively collects and buys and hoards. Things make her feel better; she likes to be surrounded by her stuff." He sighed. "It's hard for her in the home. We tried to pack her room with as much stuff as we could, but it's not the same. And the home won't let her have that much anyway, because they have to keep the room clean obviously."

"She actually lived here, even when it got so full you couldn't get in the rooms?" Flo asked. She was sitting cross-legged by the fire, playing with Hazel, who'd rolled over for a belly scratch.

"She did." Jake sat down heavily on one of the sofas. He looked exhausted by the topic. "She kept mostly to the big bedroom, though, in the last couple of years. That was the only room I managed to keep clear for her."

"That must have been hard," I said softly.

He met my gaze and I saw a complicated shimmer of pain in his sea-glass eyes. "It was." His voice was thick with emotion. "It was really hard."

"How come you didn't just get rid of all the stuff?" Flo asked, curious.

Jake let out a sigh that made him sound a million years old. "I wish it was that simple, kid."

"Why isn't it that simple?"

"Flo, maybe that's enough," I said anxiously, remembering how fast he'd shut down the night after the storm and how slow he'd been to open up again.

"No, it's okay," he said, giving me a shy sideways look. "I don't mind."

"She has that weird thing about public conversations and private conversations," Flo reminded him.

He nodded. "Well, some things aren't private so much as painful, I guess. Everyone around here knows about my mom. They were gentle about it, but they always knew she wasn't doing well."

"Like the way everyone knows Lainey can't sing but is gentle about it?"

Jake laughed. "Yeah. Like that."

Like how I knew Tina might die every time she went to work, but I never asked her to stop. Like how I knew she was chasing highs for secret subterranean reasons of her own, but I never asked her about it. I was gentle with her. Always afraid she, or we, might break. But in the Nar-Anon family meetings I eavesdropped on, I'd learned there were words for that kind of gentleness. Enabling. Co-dependency.

"Don't ever be gentle with me," Flo instructed us imperiously. "If I'm making a mess of things, I want to know about it."

"Me too," Jake said fervently.

"Me three." I sat down next to him on the couch and surreptitiously took his hand, on the side Flo couldn't see. I squeezed it.

"Is it weird for you to be here?" Flo asked him, cocking her head. "Because it's not your mom's place anymore."

"No." He looked around the room. "To be honest, it's nice to see it come back to life." He tightened his fingers around mine. "It's like the place kind of disappeared under all the junk. Just like Mom disappeared. And I lost sight of what it used to be. What *she* used to be." He had to pause to collect himself. "She was a big personality, my mom. Easy to anger, easy to cry, easy to throw her arms around you. She just kind of let it all hang out. But over time, it was like her personality changed. She seemed to get quieter, more nervous, until she was like a mouse hiding in its burrow." He seemed to be struggling with tears. I squeezed his hand tighter and he exhaled, staring up at the ceiling, trying to get a hold of himself. "I miss my mom, you know?"

"I know," I whispered.

Hazel whined and pulled away from Flo to come sit on Jake's feet. She looked up at him, worried.

"When Mom went into the nursing home," Jake continued, "my sister and I talked it over, whether to keep the house or not. Marly said we could make our own decision because when she'd gifted it to Mom, she'd gifted it to all of us—me and my sister as well. But my sister already lives in Rockport and doesn't need it."

"And you?"

"Well, I would have had to buy my sister's share of the house off her," he said carefully. "And I looked at the state of it and all the culch and I didn't want to throw money at it. And, really, I just didn't have the heart for it. It was too sad. But I didn't want some developer to have it. Or people with too much money and no sense of what's valuable about a place like this, you know?"

Flo nodded. She'd also crept closer and was comforting Hazel as Hazel comforted Jake. "We have the heart for it."

"You seem to." He reached down to pull at Hazel's ears. "Besides, I like my place. I like seeing the ocean."

"We can see the ocean."

"Sure. But I'm closer."

I turned to find him staring at me, his marble-glass blue-green eyes calmer.

"Jake?" Flo asked. He tore his eyes away from mine.

"Yeah?"

"You should come have Christmas with us. You're here all the time anyway." She gave me a sly look.

"Yes, you'd be very welcome," I said, trying to act naturally.

Jake flushed, looking both pleased and surprised. "Well, that's a lovely offer. I'm going to spend Christmas Eve with my mother and Marly, and I promised to have lunch at my sister's Christmas Day. But I'd love to come by after, if that's okay?"

"That's great," said Flo brightly. "You can help with the dishes."

"Flo!" I shot her a dark look.

"Joking!"

"You sure that's okay?" Jake asked me, his fingers tightening on mine.

"It's better than okay, it's perfect." I gave Flo another look. "And no dishwashing will be required."

It started snowing the week of Christmas and didn't stop, heavy snow with slow, fat flakes. Our street looked like something out of a fairy tale, the balsam forest heavy with drifts, and the lazy flakes drifting in veils over the cliffs and ocean. We'd strung lights up on our porch and they made the long icicles hanging from the gutters shine. We still didn't have any curtains, so the outdoor lights cast their twinkles into the parlor too, melting into the golden shimmer of our Christmas tree and the orange glow of our roaring fire.

The house was barely recognizable. It hadn't been painted and still had smudgy walls, scuffed floors, and peeling linoleum, but there were new windows and gutters, toasty heating, and no visible culch. I'd set Flo up a folding cot in my room and added another one for Ali. We rearranged Flo's room so Suni and Wayne could move in for the week between Christmas and New Year's.

I washed the windows and scrubbed the kitchen and cleaned the old floorboards. Jake helped me hang some of the artwork around the house, following me as I indecisively moved the pictures around until I was sure where they should go. I chose some of the moody landscapes of Maine's coast and the maps for the hall, and a mix of botanical watercolors, oil paintings of ships at sea, and lush still life paintings of flowers and fruit for the other rooms. By the time I was done, I was feeling house-proud and satisfied. And I couldn't wait for my foster family to see what I'd achieved.

"As soon as you give it a lick of paint, this place will be as good as new," Jake marveled as he took it all in.

"Oh God, I have to decide on colors," I groaned. I had a little sample book of colors and had been walking around the house holding the cards up to the walls and trying to imagine what they'd look like. "It's too big a decision—if I get it wrong, I'm stuck with it."

Jake shook his head and laughed and pulled me into a hug. Flo was busy icing cookies in the kitchen and we could hear her singing along to Frank Sinatra, cheerfully belting, "Let it snow, let it snow, let it snow!"

"Just pick one," Jake said as he leaned in to kiss me. His lips were warm and soft, and he tasted of vanilla and spice. "And if you hate the color, you can always paint over it."

"I can, can't I? Because it's *my* house." I wrapped my arms around his neck and kissed him back. "I can do whatever I want."

"That's right," he breathed, pressing a kiss to my neck, "you can"—*kiss*—"do"—*kiss*—"anything you want." He lifted me off my feet. "And I hope you do it soon because, woman, you're driving me crazy." His mouth took mine, his tongue sliding into me. I moaned and threaded my fingers through his hair.

"What is *happening* here?"

Jake dropped me sharply and we both spun, turning red. Flo was holding the kitchen door open and staring at us open-mouthed. She was wearing a pair of fluffy reindeer antlers that we'd found among Jake's mom's decorations and was holding a knife that was dripping red icing all over my clean floorboards.

"Were you just *kissing*?"

Neither of us could think what to say. We glanced at each other, shamefaced.

"Oh, this is *so* good! Wait until I tell Suni!" She disappeared back into the kitchen. Then her antlered head popped back out again. "Keep kissing. It took you long enough." A few seconds later I heard her muffled voice through the door, speaking in excited tones. She hadn't wasted a hot minute calling Suni, it seemed.

"I guess maybe we didn't need to hide it from her," Jake said mildly. "She seems okay with it."

"I guess not. And yeah, I guess she does." I couldn't hide a goofy smile.

"So," he drawled.

"So." I bit my lip.

He grinned and yanked me into his arms. "Who am I to disobey your daughter?" And he kissed me like he was never going to stop. He held me hard against him and teased me with his tongue. "Maybe while your family's in town," he said, his breathing shallow, "you could come over to my place one night. . . ."

"Oh God, yes." I wrapped myself around him like a vine, feeling like my Christmas wishes were all coming true.

The snow was still flying in fairytale swirls when the Overbecks streamed into Oxeye on the morning of Christmas Eve. Suni and Wayne pulled up first with Alison in tow, and my foster brother Lance and his wife Tasha came half an hour later. Jake had just finished shoveling our driveway and was there for introductions.

"This place is *gorgeous,*" Tash exclaimed when we met them on the street. She was the opposite of Lance. He'd always been cool, a skater punk type, whereas Tash was an enthusiastic and very girly nerd. She was wearing a pink parka with a beanie that had two fluffy pom-poms like ears. She bounded across the snow, excited to see our place. Proudly, Flo and I showed her and Lance around, grinning as they *ooh*ed and *ahh*ed over the period features.

"You should have seen this place before they cleaned it up," Ali told them, as she carried her bag into my bedroom. "Then you'd be *really* impressed."

I'd never hosted anyone before—how could I in our old postage-stamp-sized apartment?—and I discovered that I loved it. I loved making them all rounds of coffee and hot chocolate, taking them for snowy walks through our woods, showing them the little horseshoe beach, which was currently deep in snow and rimmed with ice.

"You got your snow on the beach, Flo-bug!" Wayne exclaimed, spinning her around. They both started singing the Taylor Swift song.

As I watched them, I felt a wave of perfect happiness flood me.

"Are you and Jake the only people in town?" Tash asked, astonished by all the shuttered summer houses. The only Christmas lights on the street were ours and Jake's.

"No." I laughed. "But, in truth, there aren't *that* many more of us." I ran through the list of the year-round inhabitants, most of whom had gone to visit family for Christmas. Oxeye's windswept clifftop was an icy place to spend the season, and most of them headed for sunnier climes if they could.

But I couldn't think of anywhere I'd rather be. I liked the starkness of the cold, and the drama of the cliffs and the bay in the winter. I loved the snowy forests and the festoons of icicles, like nature was throwing up its own tinsel for the holidays. I loved the absolute hush. There were no panicked shoppers rushing around, no traffic, let alone traffic jams, no sense of stress and busyness. It was like time stopped at the town limits.

It was the most perfect Christmas I'd ever had. The house was full and chaotic and happy. I gave the old kitchen range a workout as I cooked enormous quantities of food for them; we played the board games Flo and I had saved from the culch; and we listened to Flo's cheesy Christmas music as we sat by the fire and fell into remembering old times.

"You should have seen this kid the first Christmas after she came to us," Wayne told Jake on Christmas afternoon, when he'd finally returned to join us. Jake was pink from the cold and happily sitting on the floor by the fire with Hazel in his lap and Flo feeding her the dog treats she'd bought the puppy as a Christmas present. Jake was curious about my past, I could see.

Wayne wrapped his arm around me and squeezed. "She was so smitten with the tree, she'd sit in the dark for hours, just watching the lights blink."

I shook my head, embarrassed. "You're making it sound weird. I didn't just sit in the dark; usually I had a lamp on and was reading a book."

"I remember you used to ask before you opened the refrigerator." Lance laughed. "Even after you'd been there for years. Like you were a perpetual houseguest."

It was true, I'd always felt like a visitor. They might have welcomed me in, but I never quite felt at home—I never allowed myself to. Because they weren't my family; they were borrowed. And I was always waiting for the other shoe to drop, for the rug to be pulled out from under me.

"She was just polite," Suni scolded him.

I could see Jake's gaze flicking between them all, absorbing everything.

"Mom was a foster kid," Flo told him matter-of-factly. "It's like being an orphan, only your parents aren't dead."

I'd told her the truth about my father—that I didn't know who he was—and she thought my mother had abandoned me. Which she kind of had.

Jake's gaze flew back to me, and I gave him a weak smile. My stomach was churning because now I was thinking of Tina. Of Christmases at the Overbecks', when I'd scanned the presents Christmas morning, wondering if there was one there from my mom.

"We took her in when she was thirteen," Wayne told him, "and she was so wonderful, we never wanted to let her go." Wayne gave me another squeeze and then went off to the kitchen to find more wine.

"Suni and Wayne took in a few kids, not just me," I told Jake. I felt painfully exposed. Mostly because I knew he was reading my every expression. And because I'd told him none of this.

I heard a gasping sound and saw Suni had started to cry.

"Oh, Mom," Alison said, scooting over and giving her a hug.

"Sorry, I just . . ." Suni shrugged helplessly as the tears fell in earnest. "I just got to thinking about Bethany."

I winced. "I'm sorry, Suni, I didn't think."

"Bethany was another one of the foster kids," Lance told Jake. "It's our first Christmas since she died."

"Oh hell, I'm sorry," Jake blurted. "That must be awful." I noticed he held Hazel a little closer.

"It is," Suni sniffed. I fetched her some tissues, and she gave my hand a pat. "But much less awful because we're here with our other lovely kids for Christmas."

I hugged her fiercely. I still hadn't really dealt with Bethany's death. I'd pushed it down deep. Just like I did with Tina. As I comforted Suni, I acknowledged that I had a lot more junk to sort through than I'd realized.

"You know what would help this situation?" Flo interrupted. "A game of charades."

"I don't think now's the time," I said quickly.

"Now is *exactly* the time," Flo insisted. "What else are you going to do, sit around and cry?"

"The kid has a point," Lance said.

Suni gave a breathless hiccup. "Charades, huh?"

And it turned out charades was exactly what we needed. As the snow flew outside, and Wayne came back with a towering stack of leftover turkey sandwiches and another bottle of wine, we took turns standing in front of the tree, madly trying to think of ways to act out *Infinity War* or "My Funny Valentine" or *The Cat in the Hat*.

Jake and I were on the same team, and I sat on the floor between his legs, my back against his chest, his arms around me. Hazel had migrated to Flo's lap, her leash still looped around an armchair because the cats kept wandering in and out. The fire was warm, everyone was laughing, and I was almost perfectly happy.

Which was why I had no defenses up when the knock came at the front door. I assumed it must be Alan and Roger come to join the festivities. Sometimes they popped in when they saw the lights on, and I knew they were driving back from their day at Roger's mother's in Bangor.

But it wasn't Roger and Alan.

The windows in the door were completely fogged over, so I had no advance warning. I opened the door to the swirling snowy night and my heart stopped.

"Surprise, Angel Face!" Tina cried, launching herself at me and covering me in kisses.

TWENTY-FIVE

I couldn't believe my eyes.

The Tina I knew had been rail thin, her riot of hair framing a hollowed face; this Tina had a round face and straightened hair dyed blond. She wore a leopard-print beanie and a puffer coat with a faux-fur trim. She hugged me so tight I couldn't breathe, then pulled away and took a good look at me.

"Angel," she said, putting her hands on my cheeks. She wasn't wearing mittens, and her hands were ice-cold.

"Mom." I was in shock. "What . . . how?"

Tina laughed, the same husky laugh I remembered from my childhood. "I told you she'd be surprised," she called over her shoulder, her words appearing as dragon breath in the night air.

My stomach sank when I saw she had someone with her. It was a beefy man, in his fifties or sixties, with a salt-and-pepper goatee. He wore a sheepskin coat and work boots and he was smoking a cigarette, flicking ash into the snowdrift next to the stairs. The Christmas lights threw candy colors across his face.

"Angel, this is Tate. I told you about him in my letters—my special friend from Hazelton. And Tate, this is my angel baby. Zoe."

"Heya Zoe," Tate said gruffly.

I was sweating, even though the December air was arctic. "How . . . I mean . . . *how*?" My mind was racing so fast I couldn't grab hold of a thought. *Tina*. Here. How?

"I got paroled," she said gleefully. "Good behavior!"

"But . . . why didn't you tell me?" And then it hit. "Wait, if you're on parole, you're not allowed to leave the state."

Tina flapped a hand at me. "It's Christmas," she said, laughing again. "Who's going to hold it against me, wanting to see my baby girl for Christmas?"

"Uh, the parole board?"

"She always was a worrier," Tina told Tate.

He stubbed his cigarette out on my porch rail and tossed it into the snow. "Is she going to ask us in? I'm freezing my nuts off out here."

I didn't want to ask them in. My stomach was in a cold hard knot. And then I heard a small voice behind me.

"Mom?"

Oh God. *Flo*.

It was like watching a car crash in slow motion. Flo stepped out into the hall, carrying one of her lanky kittens, her head cocked. "Mom? Who's at the door?"

"*Mom?*" Tina all but exploded. "Did she call you *Mom*?"

Flo looked back and forth between me and Tina, unsettled. "Mom? Who's that?"

"Oh my God, Angel, don't tell me I'm a grandma!" Tina grabbed at Tate's arm. "Tate! I'm a *grandma*!"

My head was swimming. I felt like I might faint, even though I'd never fainted before in my life.

"Mom?" Flo sounded a little panicked. She crept closer to me. "Mom, what's she talking about?"

The commotion had drawn people from the parlor. Suni and Jake appeared first, the others close behind.

"It's okay, honey," I said, drawing Flo close.

"You had a *baby*?" Tina said, looking at me with big, wondering eyes. And then the penny dropped. "And you never *told* me?"

"How did you know where I live?" I asked shakily. I'd never told her that either. Her letters were always delivered to Suni and Wayne's house.

"Tate's got a friend who works at Social Security," Tina said. She was fascinated by Flo.

"But that's illegal!" Suni exclaimed. "They're not allowed to give out private information!"

Tina scoffed. "No one is going to call the cops on a mother trying to find her long-lost daughter."

"Still freezing my nuts off out here," Tate grumbled.

"He's right," said Tina. "We're freezing out here. Don't be rude, Angel—let us in." Tina crossed the threshold, pulling Tate in her wake. "We've been driving for more than twelve hours to get here, and in bad weather to boot."

Jake joined me and Flo at the door. I didn't close it. I felt panicked at the thought of closing it. "Are you okay?" he murmured. "What's happening?"

"No," I said, my teeth chattering, more from the shock than the cold. "I'm not okay."

My memories of Tina were colliding with the actual Tina who stood here before me in the flesh. I saw flashes of her dancing in our apartment, singing into a wooden spoon like it was a microphone, stopping halfway through doing her makeup to swipe some lipstick on me, curling up in bed like a cat while I read to her. But here in front of me was a wrinkled older woman with the energy of a prowling animal. And *Tate.* A prison guard who had helped my mom break parole and illegally ripped my details from a database. I felt my two lives—past and present—colliding. It was like watching a documentary where a black hole swallowed a star. My life was hitting an event horizon.

"Mom." Flo pulled my head down to look at her. "She said she's my grandma."

"I am, precious," Tina exclaimed. "I'm your Grandma Tina." She bent over so she could be eye to eye with Flo. "Oh my goodness, this can't be *real.* And what's your name, baby angel?"

Flo's nose wrinkled.

"This is Florence," I said, still shivering.

Jake gently closed the door and put his arm around me.

"Florence?" Now Tina's nose wrinkled. "Why *Florence*?"

"Because I liked it," I said tightly.

"Sounds like an old British woman."

"Any chance I can use your restroom?" Tate asked, bored with the whole scene.

I didn't want him in my house.

"I'll show you where it is," Jake rumbled. I saw him exchange glances with Wayne and Lance as he led Tate to the bathroom.

"Did your mommy tell you about me?" Tina asked Flo, smiling.

The smile dropped when Flo shook her head. Tina stood up abruptly and fixed me with a wounded glare. "I don't know about her, she doesn't know about me—what the hell, Angel?"

"Mom?" Flo looked up at me, and for the first time in a very long time I saw her look a bit scared. My heart pinched painfully.

"Okay," I said. "Stop. Let's just stop." I tried to gather my wits. This was what happened with Tina. Chaos. I had to find some order. "Look, Tina—"

"Tina? Since when am I not Mom?"

"Mom," I corrected myself. "I didn't tell Flo about you because . . ." I couldn't say it. Or maybe it was just there were too many things to say. "Because she was young, and I didn't know how to explain it so that she'd understand."

"Explain what?" Flo asked, sounding more subdued than normal.

"Explain that your grandma was in prison," Tina told her, flinging her hands up dramatically. "That she was a *junkie.* Your mom is ashamed of me."

Flo was still looking up at me, her big dark eyes full of questions. I squeezed her, hoping she'd understand that I'd answer them later.

"I didn't know how to have that conversation with a little kid," I said, keeping my voice even. "It wasn't that I was ashamed." Although I was.

"Listen." Suni stepped into the fray, trying a placating smile. "It's late, and it's Christmas—"

"And who's this?" Tina asked, eyes narrowing.

"You know who this is," I said, exasperated. "Suni used to bring me to my visits, remember? She's my foster mother."

Tina turned cold. "I'm your mother, Angel." She was brittle with hurt.

I felt the old acid disloyalty I used to feel when I was younger and caught myself enjoying Suni's affection. I knew Tina got jealous. Not jealous enough to clean herself up and come get me, but jealous enough to make me feel awful about liking Suni.

Jake and Tate emerged from the back of the house, providing a welcome distraction. "I was just talking to Tate," Jake said, ushering the man ahead of him, in the direction of the front door. "I've got a cousin who runs a motel just up by Rockport—only ten minutes up the road. I can pull some strings and get you a free room for the night. It's a real nice place with a view of the ocean and they serve a mean breakfast, all included with the room. As you can see, we've got kind of a full house here, nowhere comfortable to sleep for a couple who've been on the road for more than twelve hours."

Somehow, he managed to hustle them out with a steady stream of chatter.

"You know what?" he said. "You really ought to see Camden while you're here, and I've got another cousin who runs a beautiful little bar, cozy, also with ocean views. You guys could have lunch there with Zoe tomorrow and talk things out. I'll get my pickup and you can follow me to the motel, how's that sound?"

He placated Tina with all his friendly talk and his promises of time with me tomorrow.

"I just wanted to give you a Christmas surprise, Angel," Tina told me petulantly, as she was ushered out to Tate's car.

"You certainly did that," I admitted.

"Well, so did you." Her gaze locked on Flo. She bent over again. "And I'll see you tomorrow, baby angel. Your Grandma Tina can't wait to get to know you!"

"Well, you sure have some explaining to do," Flo declared as soon as I'd closed the door and put the security chain on.

"All right, everyone else to bed," Suni declared, clapping her hands. "Let's give these two some privacy." She took the kitten out of Flo's arms. "I'll settle these little ones." She kissed Flo on the forehead, then she gave me a sympathetic look and kissed me too.

"Jake left Hazel behind," I said numbly, as I heard her whine in the parlor.

"He'll come back for her, I guess, after he deals with . . . my grandmother." Flo fixed me with a disbelieving stare. "I mean, what the fuck, Mom?"

"Florence! Language!"

"She said I looked like an old English lady!"

"No," I corrected her, as a slightly hysterical giggle escaped me. "She said your name sounded like the name of an old English lady."

Hazel whined again.

"A junkie is a drug addict," Flo said as we drifted into the parlor to soothe the puppy. Hazel strained on her leash, her dark eyes begging us to bring Jake back to her. Flo sat in the armchair and pulled the dog into her lap.

"Don't say 'junkie.'" I sighed, sinking down to sit on the floor at her feet, facing the fire, which was starting to die down to coals. "She has a disease called addiction." The tree lights winked on and off. "It's not her fault." I felt a spurt of anger as I said the words. Part of me wanted to force Tina to take the blame. I wanted to rage at her and curse her and shame her and vent decades of poisonous anger. I wrestled with myself to find compassion, reminding myself I wanted Flo to learn kindness and understanding, not bitterness and judgment.

"Your mom was a drug addict," Flo marveled. "Like on *Law and Order.*"

"Yes."

"And she was in prison?"

"Yes." I felt tears pricking.

"You can crash out now if you need to. I think this warrants it." I felt her hand land on my head. She gave me a couple of pats. "Is that why you were with Suni and Wayne when you were a kid? Because your mom was in prison?"

I told her an abbreviated version, omitting the details that I knew she was too young for. Even though I lived with them when I was her age. Younger. And for a shocking moment as I looked at her I saw myself at her age, desperately needing a mother's protection.

Flo's pats turned to strokes. She ran her fingers through my hair.

"Mom?"

"Yes, honey?"

"Is she dangerous? Because she kind of scared me."

"I don't think she means to be," I said, my throat swollen. It was hard to get the words out. "But yes. And she scares me too."

Flo slid off the armchair to the floor next to me, bringing Hazel with her. "Is she still a drug addict?"

"I don't think you ever stop being a drug addict. You're just using or not using, but you're always an addict. Like I said, it's an illness. You can manage it but you can't cure it."

"Is she using, then?"

I put my arm around her and rested my cheek on her head. "I don't know, honey."

But the signs sure weren't good.

We sat there, having slow circling conversations, falling into silence broken only by the sound of the coals hissing in the grate and Hazel snoring, until my phone buzzed.

"It's Jake," I told Flo, when she stiffened.

"Oh." She relaxed.

"Hey," he said, when I picked up. "I'm outside. I didn't want to knock in case people were asleep."

I kissed Flo and disentangled myself, padding to the front door to let him in. The snow had thickened to hazy white sheets. He had snowflakes in his hair.

"Hey," he said, as he stepped inside.

"Hey." I searched his face, wondering what he was thinking.

He reached out and brushed my hair away from my face. "How are you doing?"

"How do you think she's doing?" Flo called from the parlor. "Her junkie mom busted out of prison and tracked her down and now she's having to explain to me why she's lied to me my whole life!"

"Flo," I hissed, "people are trying to sleep upstairs."

"Oh, sorry," she hissed back.

I met Jake's gaze and had an urge to giggle. He pressed his lips together, trying not to smile.

"I mean, she's not wrong," I whispered. "Except for the busting out of prison bit. She only busted out of her parole."

He snorted.

"So," I said helplessly, "you've got your sad mess. This is *my* sad mess."

"'Mess' seems too low-key for this situation," Flo stage-whispered from the parlor.

"What do you want to do?" he whispered.

I bit my lip. "I don't know." My stomach was all knotted up.

He stroked my face and leaned down and kissed me.

"Is this really the time for that?" Flo sighed.

"Time for bed," I told her. "We can talk about my history of lying to you tomorrow."

Jake and I went into the parlor. Hazel saw Jake and went into paroxysms of joy, wriggling and lurching on her leash. Jake went and collected her. She exploded with happiness, licking his neck madly.

"Do all adults have this many secrets?" Flo asked as she headed up the stairs to bed.

"Not all of them." I sighed. "Just the ones in this house."

TWENTY-SIX

Oxeye, Maine, 1960

It took twenty-two porcelain cats before Marly decided she could see Freddie de Marche in person again. He'd sent her postcards and packages regularly over the past few years. She tacked each postcard to her corkboard, so she could see them from her bed.

For the cat lady, the card had read, when the first cat had arrived. *From your friend F.*

She'd snorted. He was such a smart-ass. She wasn't *actually* going to be a cat lady because he didn't love her. In fact, she'd started dating Terry Davis the spring after Sylvie's wedding, when he'd asked her to the prom. And he'd pinned her by New Year's. He was no Freddie, but he was sweet and funny and a really good kisser. And he made her last years of high school less lonely, especially with everything that was happening with her mother.

There had been rounds and rounds of doctors' appointments and then the bewildering diagnosis of *senility.* Although the doctors argued a lot. Some called it "pre-senility" because Mom wasn't that old. In the end, the diagnosis didn't really matter as there was nothing that could be done. By the time Marly was halfway into senior year, Mom had to be hospitalized, because she'd started to wander. And once she'd nearly burned the house down trying to heat soup. She walked the house at night, talking, hallucinating people who weren't there. She often called out to the boys, thinking they were still young children, ordering them to drink their milk or pack up their toys. Once she scared Marly badly by standing over her, singing a lullaby, thinking Marly was a baby who couldn't sleep.

The hospital always made Marly cry. It was a bleak and sterile place that smelled of antiseptic. Mom shared a room with a couple of other women, both a lot older than her, and all of them had to be sedated. They sat in their chairs, or in their beds, placated by chemicals, their eyes vacant.

Marly had chosen to go to Wellesley when the time came for college, because it was close to home and Mom was only a thirty-minute bus ride away. She went regularly and sat there for the full visiting hours, even when her mother didn't seem to know who she was.

Her romance with Terry didn't survive their move to college. He'd chosen Stanford and neither of them were interested in a long-distance relationship. That hadn't been love, anyway, she'd thought after she'd wept a few tears and picked herself up again. For a while she dated a friend of her brother Virge's. His name was Acton, which she never quite accepted. Acton wasn't a name that inspired passion. And neither did Acton the man, who preferred football games and frat parties to romance.

As she got older, Marly developed some sympathy for Freddie de Marche, and she often felt that maybe she owed him an apology for not responding to a single letter. And for that scene on the beach. Acton had a seventeen-year-old brother and he seemed *very* young. If he up and declared his love for her, Marly wouldn't know what to say. He was a *child.* She tried to imagine that day on the beach from Freddie's perspective. Honestly, he'd been quite kind.

Sometimes she shuddered to think what might have happened to her, if she'd propositioned a guy other than Freddie de Marche. Now that she'd been to college and learned a thing or two about men, she had a pretty good idea of the kinds of things that could have happened to her, alone on a beach, telling an adult man she loved him.

But Freddie had always been a stand-up guy.

Even now, he was a stand-up guy. As soon as he'd learned about her mother from Elton and Sylvie, he'd shifted from postcards to writing Marly long, distracting, chummy letters, telling her about his leave in foreign countries. It turned out that Freddie de Marche loved the army.

You know, short stuff, I think this was exactly what I needed. The structure, the comradeship, the adventure. It sure beats contract law.

Marly often felt a pang as she read his letters or received another exotic postcard. Her own life felt narrow and constrained, hemmed in by that thirty-minute bus ride to her mother. Aunt Betty and Sylvie were good about visiting Mom, and Dad went twice a week on Wednesday evenings and Sunday afternoons, but still the thought of Mom there all alone haunted Marly. The thought of Dad home alone haunted her too. He ate TV dinners on a tray in front of the television at night. It made her sad.

Sometimes, in the dead of night, when she lay awake in her dorm room, staring at the collection of little cats on the windowsill or the postcards on the corkboard, she thought maybe it would be best if Mom would just slip away. But Mom was young, and her body was healthy. It was only her mind that was wasting away.

"Your mother would be so proud of you," Aunt Betty said at Marly's college graduation. She'd come along with Dad and had wept the whole time. Not really because she was proud of Marly, more because of the Mom-shaped hole in their lives. After the ceremony, they'd taken Marly out to lunch at a fancy restaurant and Uncle Don and Paul had joined them. Bobby had been away at graduate school in Connecticut, while Virgil was in Pensacola meeting his girlfriend's parents. They'd both sent her telegrams to congratulate her, and Paul brought her a bunch of chrysanthemums from all three of them when he arrived at the restaurant. Her brothers were ginger with her these days, as though she might break like Mom had.

"We're *all* proud of you," Dad rumbled, briefly covering Marly's hand with his and squeezing it. He didn't meet her eye. Then he blindsided her with a gift so ridiculous she didn't know what to say.

It was the house in Oxeye.

"Sylvie and Elton bought the place next door," Aunt Betty said, "and Templeton has a summer place in Camden, so Cilla will have a place there too, after the wedding." She cleared her throat. "But I don't have the heart to go back there," she said, her face locking up as she tried not to cry.

"What about the boys?" Marly said helplessly, looking at Paul.

"We don't want it, Marls," Paul told her.

"I'll leave them the city house," Dad said gruffly. "You can have this."

"We want you to have it now," Aunt Betty said, "so you can enjoy it . . ."

While you can. The unfinished words hung in the air. Because, it turned out, Mom wasn't the only person in the family to have suffered early senility. Marly's granny's mother had too, and so had two of her brothers and one of her sisters.

It's like Russian roulette, she wrote to Freddie de Marche when she finally gathered the courage to write him back. *You don't know whose chamber has the bullet and whose doesn't. The way they all looked at me made me think they were sure it's going to be me. Maybe because I look like Mom? And they might be right. Sometimes I think I might have signs of it, when I lose my keys, or can't think of the right word. Anyway, Daddy told me to go and take the summer at the house, that he and Aunty Bet can keep an eye on Mom. He says he'll visit her every second day. But I don't know.*

When I think of it, I'm crushed with guilt. There's so much guilt, Freddie. When I think of how snappy I used to be with her. Oh, I wish I could have the time back to do it again. I'd be so much nicer. But then I think I should be nice to everyone now because I might be thinking this about them tomorrow. Yet when I try it, I run into the same old problem. Ordinary life just gets in the way of being nice to people. Sometimes you just do the best you can and you're still snappy. Well, I am. So, the long and the short of it is I'm running away to Oxeye for the summer, to my own little summer house. I'm sure I'll be desperately lonely.

Marly arrived at Oxeye in late June, driving in during a sun shower, when thick bars of hazy light fell like streamers from the clouds to the ocean. She hadn't been back to the summer place since Mom had been hospitalized and she felt a rising tide of nostalgia as she slid past the spit and the white shimmer of Saint-Cyr in the woods.

The house was all shut up, the curtains drawn and the front porch furniture taken in. Marly let herself in around the back, inhaling the dark musty air. She'd known on some level that going back would be hard, but she hadn't been expecting to cry the moment she stepped over the threshold. But cry she did, like a baby.

There were memories everywhere. She could practically hear the old wireless radio warbling and Aunt Betty mixing up a jug of "vacation cheer," the spoon clinking against the glass wall of the jug as she gave it a hearty stir. Monopoly games on the porch and reading on the swing; dinners at the long table in the front room; lazing in the parlor way past her usual bedtime. Mom drinking coffee in the morning sun on the front porch, idly thumbing through a screen magazine; Mom laughing with Sylvie as they set the table for dinner; Mom stopping by Marly's room to say goodnight . . .

The first week was the hardest. She pulled all the dustcloths off the furniture and got everything in order, just as Aunt Bet and Mom did every year. She tidied the yard. She slept in her old room, under the oak tree, just because it was routine. But then, after a week, she decided it was silly not taking the master bedroom, given this was her house now, and she moved all her stuff in.

By July she was restless. She wrote a lot of letters, to friends, to her dad and her brothers, and to Freddie. And then, in the middle of the month, a telegram came.

Home on leave. Fancy a visit? x F

The moment Marly saw Freddie de Marche she decided she'd never loved him. He was standing on her front porch, holding a bunch of blue flag iris and grinning ear to ear. He was suntanned and fit, his hair buzzed short, and even though he was in navy shorts and a white knit shirt, he stood ramrod straight like he was in uniform.

"Well, hey there, pixie stick," he drawled, pulling off his sunglasses, his pale eyes sparkling like the sun glinting off the ocean.

Oh. Marly had a revelation as the feelings hit her. The blast of heat in her cheeks, the slow throb in her belly, the itchy restless longing. This was *lust.* She didn't love Freddie de Marche. She lusted after him. Now that she was older and had more experience, she could recognize it for what it was, although she'd not felt lust like this with any other boy. As Freddie gave her a crushing hug, Marly was aware of the contours of his body against hers and she made a soft breathless noise.

"Belated congratulations on the college degree," he said cheerfully, passing her the irises. "Wish I could have seen you in that mortarboard."

"I looked great. You missed out."

He laughed and followed her into the house, carrying his bag.

Marly's heart was skidding in her chest. Maybe she hadn't

thought this through, she thought as she led him to her old bedroom. The thought of him staying didn't seem like such a good idea now. She'd convinced herself that they were just pals, that she'd matured, that he meant nothing. But now that he was here in the flesh, she was burning up.

"You brought all the cats here," Freddie said, having noticed the porcelain cats tucked into curious spots all over the house.

"I did," she said primly. "A crazy cat lady house needs cats."

He grinned at her with his crooked lips. "You're never going to be a crazy cat lady, short stuff."

"I don't know if you've noticed, but I'm not so short anymore."

"I noticed." And something new glimmered in his blue gaze, something that made her tingle. Freddie de Marche had noticed she'd grown up. And maybe he was burning up a little too.

Freddie stayed with her for two weeks. Two of the best weeks of Marly's entire life. They walked on the beach, swam in the rolling waves, read books, and talked about nothing and everything. The thing about Freddie, she thought, was that when she was with him, she had his full attention. He gave her the sense that there was nowhere else he'd rather be and no one he'd rather be with. Marly, so used to being left in the margins, found it intoxicating.

But she didn't want to be intoxicated anymore, she thought helplessly. Freddie had made his feelings about her perfectly clear. And although he was stealing looks at her in her bathing suit now, Marly knew Freddie well, and knew he was only seeing the bits in the bathing suit, and not her whole self. He still called her half-pint, and short stuff, and pixie stick. For Freddie, she would always be a kid.

And Marly didn't want that.

And yet he drove her *crazy*. She also stole looks at *him* in his bathing suit, with his golden, army-fit body. His arms and legs were defined with muscles, his chest and stomach hypnotizing. Sometimes she had the strongest urge to touch him. The feelings she was having *had* to be carnal sins. At night she lay in her bed in the front bedroom, listening to the creak of his bedsprings as he rolled over, and she felt like she had a fever. There were times she gripped the brass bars of her bed to stop herself getting up and going in to him, the urge was so strong.

"You seeing anyone?" he asked her as they lazed on the sand one afternoon. It was the first time he'd ever asked about her love life.

"I was," she said. "We broke up just before graduation." Marly had ended it because she'd realized there was nothing she wanted *less* than to be Mrs. Acton Barr.

"Ah, I'm sorry."

"Don't be. I'm not."

"Why? What'd he do to you?" Freddie darkened.

"Proposed to me." Marly giggled, stretching. She sensed Freddie's gaze dropping down her body as she did.

"What'd you do, break the poor guy's heart?"

Marly snorted. "He'll be fine. He was more interested in football than me anyway."

"I doubt that," Freddie said, and she heard the tightness in his voice.

He wanted her. She knew he did.

As she lay there in the sand, languid from the heat, Marly wondered what would happen if she rolled over and ran her hand down him. Over those shoulders, down that arm, across that lightly furred chest and those small brown nipples, down . . .

She bit her lip and pressed her forehead into her forearm. She tried to concentrate on the playful lapping of the waves on the shore and the high calls of the gulls. She thought of her mom in the hospital—Mom would never lie on this, or any, beach again. And there was a ticking clock in Marly's body too, which might or might not speed up.

Time was short. And she was only young once. And this might be the only time she'd ever be alone like this with Freddie de

Marche. He was going back to the army, which he'd decided to make his career, and he'd go from posting to posting, sending her postcards. While she'd be here. Alone.

As the day wore on, unspooling like an endless thread, Marly considered things from every angle, and then decided angles were overrated. She wanted him, he wanted her.

She made her move that evening. They were sitting on the front porch swing, watching the pink and gold sky fade to indigo over the wide sighing bay, the fireflies winking on and the sound of moody jazz washing over from one of the summer houses.

"I can't believe you actually like the army," Marly said, shaking her head in wonder. He'd been such a *fop* when she'd met him.

"I really do," he said with a smile. He had both hands behind his head and his feet stretched out in front of him. He was a happier version of himself, relaxed in his own skin. Marly was jealous—she envied him that he'd found a place to belong. And there was still a sting inside her that he didn't want to belong with *her*.

And then he'd turned his head. They'd only been inches apart and she'd felt like he was staring straight into her soul.

While you can.

The words echoed in her head.

Spend time at the summer house *while you can.*

See Freddie de Marche *while you can.*

Kiss him *while you can.*

So she kissed him. Years of pent-up longing were delivered in that kiss. Longing that had once been childish and naïve transformed in that moment to something much, much more. Marly grabbed his shirt in her fist and kissed him with her whole body. She seduced his mouth open with her tongue, bending him back over the arm of the swing. Her bare legs tangled with his and his thigh wedged between hers. She moaned and kissed him even more thoroughly, running her hand down the length of him as she teased him with her mouth.

"Wait." Freddie pulled back. "No, I shouldn't, pixie—"

"In case you haven't noticed, I'm all grown up," she breathed. She pushed her breasts into his chest to underscore her point. She was sprawled across him, his shirt bunched up in her fist. His stomach was bared, his skin hot against her. She ignored his protest and kissed him again. He tasted so much better than she'd imagined he would, his mouth sweet and hoppy from his beer. His crooked lips were soft under hers and she felt his breath catch as she touched her tongue to his. She rubbed herself against him, feeling his arousal. Freddie de Marche wanted her.

Freddie kept his hands in the air as she kissed him, as though scared to touch her. She was having none of it. She took his hands and put them on her body.

"Oh no." Freddie pushed her away. He wiped his mouth and stared at her with wide eyes that were both starry and a little afraid. "Oh no, this isn't right, honey."

Honey. He hadn't called her pixie stick.

Marly sat back and considered him. "Why not?" she asked bluntly.

"Well, because you're . . . and I'm . . ."

"What?" She lifted an eyebrow.

"It's just not right."

"Okay." She pressed a kiss to her own finger and then pressed the finger to his lips. "Okay, Freddie de Marche. I'll wait till you come to me." She had no intention of waiting long. She rose from the swing in long sinewy movements, knowing she looked good in her white shorts and the blue shirt tied at the waist. She saw his eyes drop to her exposed midriff. Marly strolled to the door. As the screen door swung behind her she heard him swear and she smiled.

But the damn fool man didn't come.

Freddie de Marche had no idea what he was up against. Marly hadn't lived through all those years of longing without learning a thing or two. She'd imagined plenty of ways to seduce him and she was sure she could put them to good use until one of them worked. She went upstairs and changed into her pajamas. Not the usual ones, but the light cotton ones that were so fine they were almost-but-not-quite transparent. The set consisted of very brief shorts that skimmed the bottom of her ass, and a button-up short-sleeve shirt that clung to her. She unbuttoned the top three buttons, to give him an idea of where to start.

He called up the stairs to ask if she wanted supper, sounding nervous.

"I've lost my appetite," she called back, checking herself in the mirror. The white cotton was seriously indecent, she thought with satisfaction.

There was silence, and then the sound of his bare feet on the stairs. There was a gentle knock at her door. "Marly, I think we need to talk."

She opened the door just a sliver, so he could only see her face. "We do?"

He looked worried. "I'm sorry," he said softly. "I know it must hurt to be rejected twice. I just need you to know you mean a lot to me. I really care about you. And it doesn't feel good hurting you."

"I'm not hurt," she told him calmly, although inside she felt anything but calm. Raging desire was clashing with simple rage. The look on his face brought back humiliating memories of that day on the beach after Sylvie's wedding.

Well, she wasn't that naïve kid anymore. She wasn't a child throwing herself at an inappropriate crush. She was Marly, and he was Freddie, and this was *this.* Lust. And lust could be slaked and satisfied. And *then* she could move on.

"You're not hurt?" He seemed surprised.

"No." And then she opened the door wider, leaning against it like a starlet in one of her mom's movie magazines.

She saw his eyes widen, his cheeks flush, heard his breath grow shallow. Freddie's gaze ran over her slowly, lingering on all the places she wanted it to.

"Marly," he said in a strangled voice.

"Yes?" she said, stepping back so he could come in.

He pressed his lips together. He seemed to be warring with himself out there on the landing. He was shaking his head, but he couldn't keep his eyes off her.

She did a slow turn, so he could look his fill, and gave him a cheeky wink over her shoulder. "Grown-up enough for you?"

And that was the end of him.

"I'll do the right thing," the idiot said, straight afterward. They were tangled in the sheets, and she was sprawled half on top of him. She still had the button-up pajama shirt on, but it was completely unbuttoned.

"The *right* thing?" Marly had propped herself up. "What do you mean, the *right* thing?"

"We can tell our parents before I ship."

"Tell our parents what?" She frowned at him.

"I'm a good guy," he said fiercely. "I'm not the type to use a girl and leave her."

"Yes, you are," she said, confused. What had gotten into him? Marly sat up. "Wait. What do you think happened here?"

"I . . . despoiled you," he said grimly.

Marly couldn't help it. She laughed. "Oh Freddie, get over yourself." She slid out of bed and grabbed her shorts. She was aware his gaze was trailing her every move.

"I mean it, pixie stick, consider yourself engaged."

"How romantic," she said dryly, rolling her eyes.

"Jesus, Marly. What else is a guy to do when he takes a girl's virginity like that?" Freddie was sitting up against the headboard. He was beating himself up something fierce.

"Oh Freddie, you're not the first," she scoffed, annoyed.

That got him to shut up. For a minute anyway.

"What do you mean, I'm not the first?" He hauled a sheet around himself and followed her to the bathroom, where she grabbed her toothbrush and started scrubbing.

He stood there the whole time she brushed, waiting for an answer.

She spat. "You're not the first," she said matter-of-factly. "Or even the second. And frankly I'm a little insulted you thought I came across as virginal." She reached out and pinched his nipple.

He yelped. "Hold on. Back up. How many *have* there been?"

"That's none of your business."

"I think you just made it my business."

"No, I think I just made it *not* your business when I told you that you don't have to marry me out of some misguided sense of honor." She headed downstairs.

He followed, dragging his sheet with him. "You seduced me," he accused.

"Yes," she agreed.

He didn't know what to say to that. He sputtered a bit.

She reached the kitchen and put the coffee on, giving him time to have his sputter.

"Well," he finally demanded, when he was articulate again, "why?"

"What do you mean why?"

"I mean *why*? If you don't want to get married."

She turned and considered him. He really was gorgeous there, with her sheet wrapped around his waist. "Why, Freddie?" She approached him and put her hands against his chest. She could feel his heart cannonballing against his ribs. "Because I wanted to. Because when I look at you, I get hot."

His gaze grew hazy, but Marly wasn't done yet.

"Because I like the way you look," she said, running her hands down him. "And I like the way you taste." She inched closer until her lips were a hair's breadth from his. "And I think, if you can just get over thinking of me as a little kid, you'll realize how ridiculous you're being." She could hear his breath hitching. "Freddie, I don't want anything from you. No marriage proposals. No declarations of love. The kid I was at seventeen thought she wanted all that and you told her she'd grow out of it. Well, she did. *I* did. Now all I want is to enjoy the next few days." She hadn't buttoned her pajama top, and she let it slide open as she stepped back. He made a soft, uncontrolled noise. "What do you say, Freddie? Shall we enjoy the next few days?"

He didn't say anything. He was too busy kissing her.

TWENTY-SEVEN

I was at a loss, reeling from the chaos Tina brought. She and Tate settled into the motel just outside Rockport and didn't look ready to leave anytime soon. I'd met Tina for lunch at Jake's cousin's bar the day after Christmas. I hadn't taken Flo. I wasn't letting Tina see my daughter unless she was clean.

The lunch was difficult to get through. I hadn't been around Tina in a long time, and I'd forgotten how it felt. Tina sucked up all the oxygen in the room—it was hard to get a word in edgewise. She rattled off disjointed stories about the drive to Maine in the snow (they could have been killed, the roads were so bad), about some friend of her cellmate's who was going to fix her up with a job (what kind of job, she didn't seem to know), and she talked endlessly about meeting Tate (who was some kind of knight in shining armor, according to Tina). The only question she asked me was why the hell I'd kept her baby angel granddaughter secret from her. She wasn't curious about why I was living in Maine, or what I did for a job, or who Jake was to me. She didn't tell me she missed me and she didn't offer me a single apology. The more she talked, the more I felt like I couldn't breathe.

By the time I left, I was wrecked. Tina, meanwhile, was energized and ordering a tequila sunrise from the bartender.

As I drove away, I knew that Tina didn't belong in my life anymore. And I most certainly did not belong in hers.

And I didn't like Tate. He was cold and weird, and I was more than a little scared of him. He had a way of looking at me, flat-eyed and without a hint of kindness, that unsettled me. There was also the fact that he'd stolen my address and aided and abetted my mother in violating her parole.

I barely slept for the next couple of days, my stomach hurt, and I was constantly falling down holes into my past, lurching back in time and reliving Tina's overdoses and the times guys hit her or followed her home, banging at the door and scaring the wits out of both of us.

"Mom?" Flo approached me one afternoon as I hid in the garden. I'd told everyone I'd gone to gather wood for the fire, but actually I just wanted to be alone. My house was very full, and so was my head. I was sitting on the chopping block behind the outbuilding, watching a light dusting of snow settle on the bare crab apples.

"There you are!" Flo said, exasperated, when she spied me.

"Hey, watch out, it's slippery," I warned her, as she navigated the icy path.

"What are you doing?" Flo asked. Her cheeks were blazing red in the cold air.

"Just watching the snow." I forced a smile.

She reached me and put a heavy hand on my shoulder. She adopted a very adult, knowing expression. "Mom. Do you think you might be depressed?"

I gave her a shocked look.

"I read about it online," she told me. She cocked her head.

"Have you got trouble sleeping? Can't stop thinking about your problems? Lost your appetite?"

I couldn't help but laugh at her gravity. And the fact that she sounded like an infomercial. "That's not depression, bug. That's having Tina in my life." I grabbed her and pulled her into a hug. "Thanks for worrying about me, but you don't need to. I'm okay."

Flo pulled away and put her mittened hand over my mouth to stop me from talking. "No, you're not. Mom. It's *okay.* The world won't fall apart if you have feelings."

I was speechless.

"You always act like things are fine when they're not," Flo told me, and I could see she was upset. "It's weird how together you act when things go wrong. It's okay to throw a tantrum sometimes. I mean"—she sighed—"you have a junkie mom who just turned up with her prison guard boyfriend." She lowered her voice. "And you know what? I think maybe he ought to be in prison himself."

I exhaled shakily. "Yeah. Me too."

"And you just got caught *lying to your kid.* That's got to be hard too."

"I didn't lie to you." I sighed. "We've been through this. I was . . . protecting you. You don't understand."

"So, tell me." Flo pushed me gently sideways and plonked herself down next to me on the chopping block.

I didn't want to do this right now. I just wanted to be alone. But Flo took my gloved hand in her mittened grasp and leaned into me, waiting. I looked skyward, feeling tears prickle.

"*Tell* me," she prodded.

All these years, I'd tried to protect her by *not* telling her. And now Tina had forced my hand.

"It was really hard," I whispered, feeling my voice break. "It was hard having Tina for a mom. And . . ." I struggled to speak. "It's really hard having her back now."

I felt Flo squeeze my hand.

"It's like my past is never over." Oh God, I hated crying in front of Flo. I never wanted her to feel like she had to take care of me, like she had to be the grown-up in the room. I swiped the tears away, feeling the cold leather of my glove against my cheek. "There are all these trapdoors taking me back down to where I started, like in snakes and ladders."

"You mean snakes, then. Not trapdoors." She patted me.

I laughed, my breath a white bloom in the air. "I'm just sad. And angry . . ."

"Fair."

"And . . ." I cleared my throat. "Yeah, maybe I'm a little depressed." I glanced at her. "I never wanted you to worry about me the way I worry about Tina," I said helplessly. "I hate that you googled 'depression.'" I felt like a failure. All I'd wanted was for her to have a carefree childhood. "I wanted you to feel safe. I wanted to protect you from all the shit in my life."

"Oh my God, Mom. You can't control *everything*. Maybe sometimes it's okay not to feel safe. Like when you're *not* safe. Like when the crazy grandma you didn't know you had turns up with her crazy boyfriend. Maybe then feeling unsafe is totally appropriate!"

I was crying in earnest now. There were so many big, scary feelings writhing inside me. I felt like they might split me right open. "I don't want you to feel as scared as I did." I gasped for breath. "As I do."

Flo took that in. We sat there in the swirling snow, each wordlessly grappling with our feelings. The sound of my crying seemed loud in the white garden.

"It's scary when you cry," Flo admitted in a small voice. "But you know, sometimes it's scarier when you don't. Sometimes it's like you have all these secret feelings and I know you're feeling them, but I don't know what they are, and that's scarier. Because what if they're about me?"

"What?" That froze me to the core.

"Well . . ." She shrugged. "Maybe I upset you. Maybe you kind of hate me for ruining your life."

"Flo!" I was horrified.

"I'm not stupid," she told me flatly. "I know you didn't dream about working the phones at the medical center or sleeping in a twin bed next to your kid in a tiny apartment. Or"—she gestured at the white landscape in front of us—"moving to the middle of nowhere because it was the only place you could afford. Because of me."

"*Not* because of you. Because of the economy." I felt a surge of panic. She'd been feeling all this? "Bug, you're the best thing in my life. The best thing that ever happened to me."

She snorted. "Sure. Having to drop out of college and raise a kid was the best thing that ever happened to you." She let go of my hand and held her mitten out to catch snowflakes. "I saw how Dad was living in Seattle. He and Alyssa have a fancy condo overlooking Puget Sound. They're cashed up. You could live like that too if it wasn't for me."

"I don't *want* to live like that," I said, astonished. "And this isn't the middle of nowhere. This is *home.* It's all I ever dreamed of." Which was true. "But, Flo, even if we'd never found the house, it wouldn't matter. Because I have you. You're my treasure, bug."

She seemed unsure.

I pulled her close. "You are. We're family. And I needed you so much. When you came into my life, it was like someone turned the lights on in a dark room. I don't regret anything, baby. And I'm sorry if I scared you by keeping Tina secret from you. It's just that my feelings are so big and so messy—I don't even know how to explain them to myself, let alone to you."

"Really?"

"Really." I kissed her forehead. "This is hard, but I'm okay. I promise you."

"You don't have to be," she protested. "I don't need you to be okay all the time. I just . . ." She shrugged. "I don't know. I guess I just need you to not hide in the garden and not tell me what's happening."

"Deal." I kept my arms around her for a moment, feeling her exhale a shuddery, relieved breath. "I love you, Flo."

"Well, duh. I know *that.*"

After Tina had been in town for a few days, hassling me the whole time to let her see Flo, Jake called me at work. At first my heart leapt into my mouth at the thought that Tina had turned up at the house while I wasn't there so she could talk to Flo. But it wasn't that.

"Look, it's probably not my business," he started. Then he changed his mind. "No, screw that, you're totally my business."

"What is it?" I was poisonous with stress, imagining all the ways that Tina could hurt Flo. My time with Tina this week had shown me nothing was different. If anything, now that I was an adult, she scared me even more. "What's she done?"

"Your mom has had her DO NOT DISTURB sign up at the motel since she got here, so my cousin said the cleaners haven't been in. Your mother and Tate have barely left the room. The only time she leaves is when you meet her."

I closed my eyes, dreading what he'd say next, even though I half expected it.

Jake sighed. "Well, today Tate set the smoke alarms off with his cigarette, and when the motel staff went in, they found glass pipes and a bag of crystal meth."

I was unsurprised. I had the old sucking feeling in my gut.

"My cousin didn't call the cops."

"Oh." I felt oddly disappointed.

"Do you want me to tell him to call them?" There was a long pause. "Or not?"

I didn't know what to tell him.

That evening after work I volunteered to stay back with Dr. Nock for the Nar-Anon family group. Instead of slipping out the back and hiding out of sight until they were done, I took a seat in the circle of chairs. I saw Dr. Nock giving me a sideways look, but I kept my gaze on the floor. The day Flo had come to sit with me in the snowy garden, I'd decided it was time to get some help. I owed her that. I owed *me* that.

I had seen my mother stoned, high, tweaking, overdosing, dying. When I thought of her, there was a wild cry inside of me. But there was also a deep exhaustion. I couldn't manage her. And I didn't want to. Not just because I didn't want her in Flo's life, but because I didn't want her in mine.

I was so *tired* of carrying it all around inside of me, a freak show no one knew about. The weight of it was too much. I wanted to put it down.

I didn't intend to speak in that first meeting. But even though I didn't intend to speak, when it came time to introduce myself, I started talking and couldn't stop. The entire hot mess of my childhood came pouring out of me. The circle was silent and attentive, everyone still as stone, and their quiet presence made me spill secrets I'd never told anyone.

"The last time they took me away from her, it wasn't just because she'd overdosed." Numbly I was aware that I was crying. "It was because I'd written a composition for class. We had to write something about our vacation, so I did. I told them all about my vacation, with Tina passed out and me trying to stretch a box of macaroni and cheese so it could feed me for three days."

They stayed quiet, their watchful, gentle gazes on me.

"I guess it was maybe a cry for help. . . ." I cleared my throat. "Or maybe I wanted to punish her. I wasn't thinking. . . . I mean, I didn't think. I didn't realize they'd report her and then it would be my fault she was back in prison." The guilt was overwhelming. It was a sick, sweaty, crawling feeling. A nastiness I'd carried for years.

I used to lie awake at night, knowing it was my fault Tina was in a cell. I knew how lonely she was in prison, how much she suffered through withdrawal, how much pain she was in. And it was because of me.

"You feel it was your fault?" Dr. Nock asked in his measured way.

I was shivering. "It *was* my fault." And something Flo had said in the garden had thrown a light on subterranean thoughts I hadn't realized I was even having. "*All* of it was my fault. She didn't know how to look after me. She was drowning. Because of me she had to work the streets. Because of me she had to escape with the drugs. Because of me . . ." My voice cracked.

"Why do you feel you need to take responsibility for her choices?" Iris, the elegant woman to my left, asked.

"She didn't mean to get pregnant," I said, feeling desperate. "I was an accident. I derailed her life."

"That's not your fault," Iris told me gently. "And she chose to keep you."

"I turned her in," I reminded her. "I sent her to prison. That wasn't her choice."

"But if you didn't turn her in, what choice would you have been making?" It was the teenage boy I'd heard at the first meeting. "You would have been helping her slowly destroy her life and yours."

Dr. Nock passed me a box of tissues.

"You didn't deserve to be in that position," the tired guy across the circle told me. "It was a bad hand. And how is a kid supposed to make those decisions?"

"How would you feel if it was your daughter forced into making that decision?" Iris asked. "What would you tell her to do?"

The thought of Flo trapped in a cold walk-up apartment with Tina made me dissolve. Smart, funny, vulnerable Flo. She would be so scared and so alone. And I would tell her to do whatever she had to do to survive, no matter what it took. I couldn't breathe or see through the tears.

"Sometimes it's hard to give ourselves the understanding and compassion we give so readily to others," Dr. Nock told me softly.

At the end of the meeting, Dr. Nock gave me the literature. And then he passed me Sweet Serenity Bear. I held the Care Bear close, oddly comforted by its stuffed weight in my arms. Dr. Nock was reassuringly himself, not looking at me any differently than he had before I'd sat in that circle. "The steps aren't just for addicts, Zoe. Children of addicts often have addiction behaviors of their own, just without the substance abuse. Or," he added wryly, "sometimes with the substance abuse." He walked me to my car. "I'm glad you felt comfortable enough to join the circle." Dr. Nock held the door for me as I got in, still shivering. "I hope you decide to come again. You don't have to be alone." As I drove off, he patted the side of the door, as he always did.

I didn't want to go home. I *couldn't* go home. I was too raw, too exposed. I messaged Suni and she told me to stay out as long as I needed.

Call us if you need us, she messaged.

She knew I was going to see Tina.

We're always here for you.

I loved Suni fiercely in that moment. She'd been there for me in ways my mother never had. She'd even been a grandmother to my kid. She *was* a grandmother to my kid.

Why had I taught Flo to call them by their names and not Gran and Pop, or something that reflected their actual relationship? Why had I kept Suni and Wayne at a distance?

Because I was scared it was temporary, I thought feverishly as I pulled into the motel parking lot. Snow was falling in thick white curtains and I sat there in the flashing light of the motel VACANCY sign, my hands gripped tight on the wheel. I shivered, but not from the cold.

You don't have to be alone, Dr. Nock's calm voice sounded in my head.

I *wasn't* alone. I had Flo. And Suni and Wayne and Ali and Lance and Tash. And Jake . . .

I didn't know what I was going to say to Tina, but I knew I had to see her. Because whether I spoke to her or not, I was making a choice. Shakily, I made my way to her door. I knocked. My hands were sweating as I waited for her to answer. I knocked again.

"Mom?" I called.

There was no answer. I tried calling her. It went to voicemail. But Tate's car was in the parking lot, so I knew they were here. I had a familiar poisonous feeling in my belly. I was just about to head to the front office to ask for a key when I heard mumbling from inside and the door swung open. The smell of cooked meth rolled over me.

"Angel!" Tina was vibrating with energy, her pupils enormous. She started talking a mile a minute when she saw me. "You caught me off guard. I haven't cleaned up—"

"Where's Tate?" I interrupted nervously, peering over her shoulder.

"Out," she said, rubbing her face. "He's out."

"Out where? The car's here."

"He went in Dave's car."

"Dave? Who's Dave?" But I knew. Dave would be some random dealer. How did they find these guys? Tina seemed to be able to score anywhere, anytime, even in a town where she knew no one.

She was so pepped up on meth she didn't even notice the icy December cold. She was bare-armed in a tank top but she wasn't even shivering. As I watched her, grinning, high as a kite, I knew exactly what I wanted to say.

"You can't see my kid," I blurted. "Not unless you're clean." I straightened my shoulders. "And you can't see me either."

"Jesus, Angel, it's just a little holiday hit. Where's your Christmas spirit?"

She wasn't the mom I wanted. She wasn't the mom I deserved. And she wasn't the mom she deserved to be.

"I loved you," I said, my voice cracking. Distantly, I was aware I was using past tense. "I missed you so much." She blinked but didn't seem to be listening to me. "But I've got my own life now and I've got responsibilities. I can't do this." I took a breath. "I don't *want* to do this."

"Do what?" She rubbed her face again. "Honestly, Zoe, you're always so dramatic."

"I need you to go."

She gave me a sharp, feral look at that. "You *need* me *to go*?"

My stomach clenched but I stood my ground.

"You've got some nerve, asking your own mother—who you haven't seen for *years,* who you haven't once visited, who you kept a whole *kid* from—to *go.*" She was bitter, even through her high. "You didn't send me so much as a goddamn postcard from this backwater hole," she said, her voice picking up pace until she was talking so fast the words all blurred together. "Who do you think you are cutting me out of your life? After all I went through for you!"

"I'm not discussing it," I said numbly. Each word she spoke was a direct hit to my heart. But if there was one thing I knew, it was that I didn't want Flo to go through a repeat of my childhood. I didn't want her knowing what meth smelled like, or how to recognize signs of using.

"We're not done talking." Tina followed me to my car, oblivious to the icy snow on the soles of her bare feet.

"You know what, Mom?" I said as I climbed into my car. "We are." I looked up at her. "We can talk if you ever get clean."

Even if she got clean, Tina would still be an addict. And for the rest of my life, I'd be the child of an addict. That was my issue to deal with, and it was time to deal with it. "I needed you to stop using a long time ago," I told her, my hand white-knuckled on the door of the car.

"Yeah, well, I needed you to stop judging me a long time ago." She scowled at me. The neon lights of the motel sign formed a corona around her in the sheeting snow. "Tate and I will come by for a visit with my grandkid tomorrow," she told me sharply. "You can't get between us like this."

But I could. And I would. A part of me would always want my mom, but I didn't want her near my daughter.

TWENTY-EIGHT

Boston, Massachusetts, 1962

Marly wanted her mom. That was her first feeling when the doctor confirmed she was pregnant. She wanted to cry on her mom's shoulder, feel her arms around her, and be told everything was going to be okay. But Mom barely even knew who Marly was anymore and there was no comfort to be had in that hospital room.

Marly doubted there'd be any comfort to be had from her father either. He was the old-fashioned sort, and this would shock him to the core. But what choice did Marly have? Dad would find out eventually, as her stomach swelled out like a balloon, and the first thing he'd ask is whose baby it was. She knew she couldn't tell him, though. How could she, when she wasn't even going to tell the baby's father?

Freddie de Marche had made a habit of spending his leave from the army in Oxeye, where he tumbled into bed with Marly as soon as he hit town. They'd been blurry, blissful weeks, out of ordinary time. Marly had been sure she could drink her fill of him and get him out of her system, but it didn't seem to work like that. Instead, she couldn't get him out of her head. She thought about him *all* the time. She *lived* for the weeks in Oxeye, counting down her year until she saw him again.

"Hey, pixie stick!" he'd holler, sweeping her off her feet and carrying her upstairs.

And then they'd reach the end of the interlude and Freddie would head off to wherever he was stationed, and Marly would . . . wait. Which she *hated.*

She drove him to the airport the last time he visited, feeling irritable and cheated. Freddie himself was cheerful, which only irritated her more.

"I was thinking maybe you could meet me in Paris sometime," he suggested, as he kissed her goodbye. Their goodbyes could take a while. There was a lot of kissing.

Marly had pushed him back, the heel of her hand on his chest. "I thought we were just a summer thing?" Only they weren't, were they? Because she was obsessed with him spring, fall, and winter too.

Goddamn him. Why didn't he feel it too?

Freddie had grinned at her. "We are a summer thing. But we can also be a thing at other times, can't we?" He kissed her again. "We can walk along the Seine, find a nice comfortable bed somewhere . . ." The kissing got serious. Too serious for the front seat of a car in an airport parking lot.

"You just want a sure thing while you're on vacation," she gasped.

"And what's wrong with that?" he teased. And then he was dashing off to his life, which only included her as a name and address on a postcard.

She was sitting by her mother's bedside one Sunday afternoon, reading through Freddie's latest letter, which was as chummy as ever, when she decided enough was enough.

Dear Freddie, she wrote, *I'm afraid I won't be able to host you at Oxeye next summer. I hope you'll understand. There comes a time when a girl has to trade flings for the real thing. Much love, M*

And then, in spectacular timing, one week later she discovered she was pregnant.

"Who?" Dad asked her when she finally screwed up the courage to tell him. He was turning red. Marly had expected him to explode, but he didn't. He just took a few deep breaths.

"Does it matter?" she said, knowing she was needling him. She wondered if she was trying to find the limits of this remarkable composure.

"Of course it matters."

To her horror, tears shone in her father's eyes. "Oh, Dad, don't!"

"Have you told him, whoever it is?"

"No."

"Are you going to tell him?"

She didn't answer. No. Yes. Maybe. She didn't want Freddie to be all honorable again. The last time was goddamn humiliating, but this would be a million times worse. She didn't want him proposing because he *should.* The idiot should propose to her because he loved her.

"Why not tell him?" Marly's father seemed flummoxed.

She lifted her chin. "You wouldn't understand."

"But he might do the right thing."

The right thing! As if marrying her was only right if she was compromised. It made her want to scream. Dad seemed to sense her rising temper and backed off.

"You know I'll always be there for you," he said gruffly, but he seemed extra deflated that night, as he sat over his TV dinner. Marly felt guilt worm through her. She'd made a miserable time in her father's life even more miserable. And there was no Mom to comfort either of them.

A postcard came from Paris when Marly was in the middle of vomitous morning sickness. Dad left it propped on her bed with the other mail, tactfully not interrupting her as she hurled. The postcard was the first thing Marly saw when she emerged from the bathroom, her mouth astringent with the Listerine she'd used to wash it out.

I was supposed to be here with a girl I know, but she stood me up. x F

Marly ran her finger over his words. Her heart hurt. How could he be halfway across the world when she needed him? Why hadn't he loved her the way she loved him?

Angry and hurting, Marly tucked the postcard inside her copy of *Forever Amber*. She'd been reading that book the night they met, she thought nostalgically. God, she wished she was rolling around in bed with him in Paris and not throwing up in Boston. But it was all the rolling around that got her in this mess in the first place. She slid the book back on her bookshelf.

"I told your mother." Her father's voice made her jump. He was hovering at the threshold of her bedroom nervously. She suspected by the way he was staring at the bookshelf that he'd read the postcard. Marly was glad Freddie never signed his full name.

"You told Mom what?"

"About the baby." Dad cleared his throat. He couldn't meet her eye. "I like to think she can still hear me, that there's still something of her in there." His voice sounded tight. "She loved you so much, Marly."

Marly was horrified to see his lip tremble.

"I know she'd never forgive me if I screwed this up," he said roughly. "I told her everything. I kept hoping she'd come to herself and tell me what to do. How to take care of you. Both of you." He glanced at Marly's stomach, which wasn't even showing yet.

"I can look after myself, Dad," Marly said, although she knew it probably wasn't true. How would she work and raise a kid all by herself?

"People will talk." He sounded wretched. "It's not easy when the baby's a . . ." He couldn't finish.

Marly bit her lip. "We can tell people I'm engaged. That would be bad, but not *as* bad."

"*Are* you engaged?" He looked her in the eye, and she could see he didn't hold much hope of a yes.

She shook her head. "But people don't have to know that."

"Well, where's the guy?" her father said. "Why isn't he marrying you, given the circumstances?"

"We'll tell people he's in the army."

His gaze went back to the book she'd hidden the postcard in and she saw his fist clench.

"You know I haven't told him, Dad. It's not his fault."

"And you haven't reconsidered telling him?" Dad asked gruffly.

Of course she had. She wasn't a total idiot. But her heart hurt at the thought of forcing his hand. If he married her like this, he'd resent them, her and the baby. She couldn't bear it.

"I'm telling people I'm engaged," Marly said firmly. "I don't want to cause too much scandal, especially for Virge's wedding. I'll go to Oxeye before I start showing. That way people won't even know . . ."

Dad gave her a look. Sylvie's summer house was right next door. How was Marly to keep it a secret from her?

"I just need time to think about what to do," Marly said desperately.

Dad nodded. His eyes were suspiciously shiny. "Your mother would want what's best for you," he said.

When he left, Marly sat on the floor and cried.

Marly settled into a lonely life at Oxeye, where she had too much time to think. And all she could think about was Freddie de Marche and her future without him. Sometimes it was all she could do not to pick up the phone and call his base.

I can't help thinking I made a mistake. Freddie's next letter came in the depths of winter, when Marly was fat with the baby and even fatter with misery. Dad had forwarded the letter on from Boston. *I heard you got engaged, pixie stick. E wrote and told me. I keep thinking about Maine. I'm an idiot, I guess. Anyway, I wish you nothing but the best with the guy who was smart enough not to be an idiot.*

God*damn* him. Why couldn't he rage and beg and do everything in his power to stop her wedding? Not that she was actually getting married. But he thought she was. Marly had cried a tempest over that letter. But then the next one came.

You can't blame a guy for being confused, he wrote in a scribbled hand. *I mean, you were a kid. And then you weren't a kid. We were friends. So how was I to know what the hell I was feeling?* The scribbling got so intense she almost couldn't make out the words. *How come you never told me for keeps was on the table?*

Marly looked down at her belly. That was about as for keeps as it got.

Meet me, he wrote. *I've booked a flight home. I'll be there on the 17th. Meet me in Oxeye?*

Oh God.

I haven't heard from you. But I wrote to E and he and Sylvie are happy for me to stay in their place. I'll be there. Come.

Marly was the size of a whale by then. There was no way she could hide it. She didn't know if she could bear the look on his face.

I've extended my leave to three weeks. Please come, Marly.

The 17th arrived and Marly balked. She couldn't handle him feeling like he had to marry her.

I'll wait.

TWENTY-NINE

By the time I left the motel, it was late. Suni and Wayne were looking after Flo and reassured me everything was fine when I messaged I'd be even later than planned. *Be safe,* Suni told me. I was in no shape to go home. I drove to Camden City Park, knowing I had to make a choice. The snow kept sheeting, obscuring the harbor. I sat there in my car at the side of the park, cocooned in the obliterating blankets of snow, and cried. I wasn't thinking of any one moment or any one heartbreak—it was all just an inchoate mass of misery. I felt a deep ache for me, but also for Tina. And for Flo. All the years of my childhood pressed in on me. My heart hurt.

And then I made the phone call. I was shaking so hard I misdialed the number on the first try. That old crawling, sweating feeling was back. The guilt, the shame, the raw terror. Last time I'd turned Tina in, it had been a side effect of writing a school paper. Although, if I was really honest with myself, I'd known exactly what I was doing. I knew I was opening the door on all our secrets. And I knew exactly what my teacher would do when she read about my vacation, abandoned by my junkie mother.

This time I wasn't even pretending that I didn't know the consequences of my actions. This time I called the police directly.

"She's at the motel in Rockport." I closed my eyes as I gave them the address, wanting to block out the world. My heart was lurching in my chest. It felt like I was having a heart attack. Tina would never forgive me for this. With this one call I was ending our relationship for good. Even though, in reality, our relationship had been severed a long time ago.

"We'll send someone to the motel now," the bluntly professional voice on the other end of the line told me. "If we find them using, we'll take them in," the officer said calmly, "but you'll need to come in to make a report if you want to follow up on the violation of your Social Security privacy."

When I hung up, I started sobbing in earnest. I put my forehead against the steering wheel and gave in to it. I felt like she'd died.

My phone buzzed and I tensed, sure it would be Tina and she'd be furious with me.

But it was Jake.

"Hey," he said when I answered.

"Hey."

"Are you crying?"

"Are you psychic?"

"No, you just sound like you've been crying."

"I'm still crying," I admitted.

"Where are you, honey?" he asked softly.

The "honey" made me cry harder.

"Hey," he said in a husky voice. "Hey, hey, hey. Is this because my cousin called the cops?"

I made an uncontrolled little wailing noise. "He did?"

"Yeah. God, sorry. I was calling to tell you—I'm sorry you found out before I could break it to you."

I dissolved. I hadn't needed to turn her in? Someone had already done it?

"Where are you, Zoe?"

I told him.

"Okay, don't go anywhere. I'm with my nieces, but as soon as I drop them home, I'll come get you."

"Jake," I blurted, panicked. "Can you stay on the phone?" I wiped at my face. "Please."

"I'm not going anywhere. You're not alone, okay?"

I let out a shuddering breath. "Okay." I sat there, crying into my phone, in the car at Camden Park, for what felt like forever. Jake made soft, soothing noises and kept calling me honey. I didn't know if I could have gotten through that moment without him.

Then there was a knock at my window. I jumped a mile.

A gloved hand wiped the snow off the glass and an unexpected face appeared.

It was Marly.

"It's your grandmother," I said numbly to Jake.

"Good. I messaged her." He sounded enormously relieved. "She lives just around the corner from the park. I didn't want you there alone. I'm still a ways away."

Marly was bundled up against the cold in a big woolen hat and a puffer coat. She waved at me, trotting around to the passenger side and letting herself in.

"Dear God, it's wicked cold." She slammed the door and stuck her gloved hands in front of the vents to heat them up. She brought the dry scent of the winter night in with her. "I hope you don't mind Jake texted me," she said, giving me a sideways glance. "Is that him?" She took the phone off me. "Hey, you," she said. "I'm here now. You drive safe. Don't go speeding and having an accident in your rush. She's just fine." She signed off and hung up.

I hastily tried to wipe my face. I felt naked and bruised and unable to speak.

"I live just around the corner," she told me, fishing a fresh tissue out of her pocket and handing it to me. "Jake thought you might want to wait for him at my place, out of the cold."

"Oh no," I blurted. "I couldn't." The last thing I wanted to do was dump my emotional mess on Jake's grandmother. On *Marly.* A woman who meant so much to me, even though I'd barely met her. I lived in her house. I'd read the postcards and letters addressed to her. I'd imagined her life so many times. Since meeting her at the school play I'd revised my imaginings from sad, lonely lady to glamorous woman, but she was still vivid to me. She seemed like the kind of woman who'd had a big life, with grand loves and heartbreaks. I still didn't know what had happened to Freddie de Marche, but judging by the last letters I'd read, it hadn't ended happily with him. I wondered what had happened next in her life and who she'd married. I wondered if I could learn the secret of how to love, and how to get over love when it broke your heart.

"Of course you can come to my house. I insist. What else are you going to do? Sit out here in a snowstorm and cry?"

"Yes," I whispered.

Marly frowned. "Come on, I'll give you directions."

Too wrung out to argue, I let her direct me away from the bay. Her house really was just around the corner. I turned in to a shoveled driveway in front of a small stone house with a shingled roof nestled in thick banks of new snow. Golden light fell through the windows and onto the drifts.

"Come on, we'll get you out of the cold and Jake will be along soon."

Marly seemed a lot warmer than the last time we'd met. Before I'd been intimidated by her, but now she was gentle with me, kind. When she opened the door to the house, a billow of heated air enveloped us. Her hazel gaze took in my mute misery, and she gently placed an arm around my shoulders to guide me inside.

She took me through to the back room, which was an open-plan extension. It had plate glass windows facing a snowy garden lit by floodlights. Right in the middle of the garden was a little fir tree, decked out in cobwebs of Christmas lights. There was a bookshelf across the entire back wall of the room; it held as many photographs as there were books.

"Let's get you a cup of something hot," Marly said. She pushed me down into a buttery leather couch. The copy of *Forever Amber* I'd found in the house sat on the table like a great fat brick, the postcards and letters wedged between the pages. I'd given it to Jake to pass on to her. I wondered if maybe that was the source of her new warmth to me as I picked up the book. The Paris postcard was poking out, the tip of the Eiffel Tower visible above the pages.

"Where on earth did you find those old things?" she asked me as she made me a cup of hot chocolate. "I haven't seen them for years."

I told her. I felt awkward perched on her couch, and the whole evening felt surreal.

Marly snorted. "My daughter told me she couldn't find those boxes anywhere. I bet she didn't even look."

"To be fair, it was hard to look, given the state of the place," I said weakly.

Marly reached for the book and fished out the postcards and letters. "Did you read them?" she asked me.

I nodded, shamefaced. "Sorry."

She waved my apology away. "I would have read them too." Her eyes twinkled. "Do you want to see a picture of him?"

"Who? Freddie?"

"Who else?" She rose and glided over to the bookshelf and fetched a silver framed photograph. "Sylvie always said he looked like Montgomery Clift." Marly shot me a sly look. "I bet you don't even know who Montgomery Clift is."

"He was in *From Here to Eternity,*" I said, still sounding stuffy from all my crying. The memory of watching the old movie in the cold walk-up apartment while I waited for Tina to come home almost set me off again.

Marly held out the picture frame. He did look like Montgomery Clift. The strong eyebrows, the piercing eyes, the slightly sulky mouth. Freddie de Marche was in a military uniform, looking very serious, but there was a twinkle in his gaze that reminded me of Jake.

Oh. The significance of what I was holding hit me. She wouldn't have a framed photo of him, unless . . .

I'll wait. That had been his last message to her that I'd read.

"*Did* he wait?" I asked Marly breathlessly.

"Of course he did. Stubborn man." Marly forced the hot drink on me. "Drink up and I'll get the albums, to give you some visuals to go with the letters." She came back with a cloth-covered photo album and flipped it open to the first page. "See the size of me?"

She was young and very pregnant in the photo; she had round cheeks and a cascade of dark hair. She was standing in front of the house on Tinker Street: my house. It looked so different. The yard was mostly lawn at the front, with a couple of sapling lilacs planted just in front of the whitewashed palings of the front porch. Marly had her hands splayed on either side of her huge belly. Standing next to her, his arm around her, beaming from ear to ear, was Freddie de Marche.

"He already had the ring," Marly told me, looking at the ring on the finger of the girl in the photograph. The same ring was still on her finger, I saw. "The idiot planned to propose to me. Even though he thought I was already engaged." She shook her head, still clearly pleased, all these years later. "And he didn't even know I was knocked up!" Marly turned the page and there were the wedding photos, Marly and her belly in a pink dress, with a cap and veil and a little bouquet of daisies, and Freddie in his uniform, still beaming from ear to ear.

"How did he take it when he found out you were pregnant?" I asked. I took a sip of the hot chocolate, and the sweetness flooded me. I felt better.

I remembered telling Tim I was pregnant. I'd taken the test in the bathroom at the mall, straight after buying it from the pharmacy.

I'd sat in the stall, watching the line form and knowing my whole life had changed in an instant. Telling Tim had been terrifying—mostly because I'd had a gut instinct how he'd take it. We'd been sitting on his bed, and he'd unconsciously leaned away from me as I spoke. He said all the right things, because he was always a nice guy, but there was a new haunted look in his eye. And he never quite looked at me the same way again. Although I don't suppose I ever looked at him the same way again either.

"Oh, it was exactly as I thought it would be." Marly rolled her eyes, looking for a moment like Lainey. "We fought. I said I wouldn't marry him in a million years. He said he'd ask me every day of his life till I said yes. I said go ahead. We fought some more. And then, well, you know what it's like, there's a moment where it all comes tumbling down around you. And then you stop fighting and start listening. And you say I love you and fall into bed and live happily ever after until the next fight." There was a wealth of bittersweet love in her voice.

Jake had never talked about Freddie, I realized. His grandfather. And he hadn't been at the school play. My stomach squeezed with sympathy as I watched Marly turn the pages of the photo album. What must it be like to lose the love of your life?

Soon after the wedding photos there were baby photos. A round-cheeked baby girl with bright blue eyes.

"Jake's mom," Marly said, her voice fragile with sadness. "Amber."

"You called her Amber?" That fact filled me with delight. I glanced at the book on the table, and the postcards dotted through it.

Marly gave me a sideways smile. "Nobody thinks I'm a romantic, but I have my moments. I was reading that book the night I met her father."

As Marly turned the pages of the photo album, I saw Jake's mom grow up. Playing in the garden at Tinker Street; making sandcastles on the little horseshoe beach with her dad; sitting on the swing on the back porch, surrounded by dolls and teddy bears;

laughing at a local carnival, holding a Kewpie doll in one hand and a candy apple in another. All those sun-splashed days by the coast, smiling and dimpled, in the summer house where she was conceived and born and loved.

My house had always been Marly's place in my head; I'd never really had a clear picture of Jake's mom as a person, even though I'd been clearing out her junk all these months. And developing feelings for her son. But seeing these photos of her as a kid made her seem real to me for the first time.

I could see why Amber had wanted to live on Tinker Street as her memories melted away. It was somewhere that had cocooned her with love. I felt a stab of pure jealousy as I traced her childhood through the album. I wished I could have grown up in that house too, with all that love.

The last photo in the album showed Amber at around Flo's age; she was holding a kitten like it was a baby and grinning gap-toothed at the camera. In the background Marly was standing on the black-and-white-checked linoleum I recognized from the kitchen, a vinyl record dangling from her hand. She was laughing.

"Freddie took that," Marly said softly. "I remember that day like it was yesterday. Just an ordinary day." She sighed and closed the album. "The best ones always are."

"Not all of them," I said, remembering the ordinary days with Tina. My childhood couldn't have been further from these photographs. I wondered when Freddie had died. Had it been while he was in the army? In Vietnam maybe? Had he left Marly a single mother? Had she had the same starkly lonely experience of parenthood that I'd had?

Marly considered me. She reached out and took my hand. "Jake told me not to pester you, but what do men know? A trouble shared is a trouble halved. So, do you want to tell me about it?" There was something so direct and disarming about her. She wasn't motherly exactly. It was more that she *saw* me. She looked me dead in the eye and didn't flinch.

"I think I just sent my mother back to prison." The words came out bluntly, brutally.

She still didn't flinch. "Is this a story that requires something stronger than hot chocolate?"

I started crying again, and for the second time that night my whole past flooded out of me, like a dam had collapsed under the pressure of it. I thought I had nothing more to unburden after the Nar-Anon family meeting, but it turned out I had a lot left to say.

And Marly was a good listener. "Mothers put you through the wringer, don't they?" she said eventually, sighing. "My mother broke my heart slowly, too, although in a different way." She gave me a kind, sad look. "Life comes with its share of grief."

"I don't want it," I said quietly, panic rising at the thought of these feelings lasting forever.

"Of course you do. If you want the good, you've got to take the bad."

I shook my head. "No. I don't. I don't want good or bad. I just want simple and ordinary. Boring."

Marly rolled her eyes again, reminding me even more strongly of Lainey. And of Flo. It was that preteen eye roll. "Even boring has pain attached to it," she told me. "No one gets away without hurting."

"But how do you survive it?" I wailed. "How did you cope, losing your mom and Amber and Freddie?"

She frowned at me.

"Life's just misery." I burst into tears again. "And it just keeps hurting. I don't want to lose people." The thought of raising Flo only to lose her made me feel wild with pain. And the thought of her one day losing me and being alone in the world hurt even worse.

"But you don't just lose them," she told me, exasperated, tapping the photo album. "You get to *have* them too."

I shook my head. "No. You get to borrow them. Look at your

daughter. Look at Freddie. All that love and then all you end up with is a house filled with junk."

"You've got everything backward." She was frowning in earnest now.

But before she could say anything more, we were interrupted by a commotion in the hall and we felt a blast of cold air billow through the house.

"Zoe?" Jake burst in and all but hauled me off his grandmother's couch and into his arms. "I'm so sorry, honey." He pressed his cold lips to my forehead, then my cheeks and my lips, as though he were trying to kiss my tears away. "I should have told him not to call the police until I'd talked to you again."

I closed my eyes and pressed my face to his chest. I didn't remember the last time I'd been held so tight. It filled me with a golden warmth so strong I could barely breathe. "It doesn't matter." Nothing mattered now that he was here. It was like his arms kept the world at bay.

What was happening to my mother was my fault, not his. If his cousin hadn't called the police, they still would have picked her up. Because of me.

"It *does* matter. *You* matter." He pressed a fierce kiss to my lips.

"What matters is you didn't take your boots off at the door," Marly scolded him, pushing him off her rug. "Let the poor girl breathe, and get your wet feet off my floor."

"I'm sorry I took so long to get here. The girls took forever to round up." He shot Marly an irritated look as she separated us.

"You can kiss her to death later. For now, I want you to drive us somewhere." Marly took me by the arm and pulled me with her toward the entryway.

"Drive somewhere? Where?" Jake was irritated as he followed after us.

"Hush up and come on."

I realized where we were going as we drove past the sign. The Sea View Care Home was on a hill overlooking the sprawl of Camden and the harbor. It was still decorated for Christmas and colored lights twinkled through the falling snow.

"This isn't a good idea," Jake protested. "She's exhausted. The last thing she needs is this."

"She's fine. I was there before supper and she looked fresh as a daisy."

"I meant Zoe, not Mom."

I agreed with him. I was in no state to meet his mother. I was crumpled and worn and running on empty.

"We're tired," he pleaded with his grandmother.

But Marly was determined. And she was intimidating when she was determined.

"Just be warned, Amber's not much of a talker anymore," she told me, as she jammed her hat on her head and left the car. "But there's something you need to see."

"What does she want me to see?" I whispered to Jake as he opened the passenger door and took my hand to help me out.

"Hell if I know," he admitted. He reached out to zip my jacket up to my chin. He had snowflakes clinging to his eyelashes.

"We don't have to do this right now if you don't want to," I told him.

Jake nodded. "I know. But, I mean . . ." He bit his lip and gave me a shy look. "I was planning to introduce you soon. If you wanted to . . ."

I did want to. Just maybe not after turning my mother in and crying my face off.

"Come on!" Marly insisted.

"It's up to you," Jake said quietly.

I glanced at Marly, who was giving us an impatient look, and sighed. "Well, I guess we're here now. . . ."

The care home was quiet except for the soft chatter of a TV and the hum of medical equipment. I felt like an intruder as we followed Marly across the foyer. She gave the nurse at reception a wave and led us down a corridor. As we reached the end, she turned and held her finger to her lips, gesturing for us to be quiet.

I felt Jake squeeze my hand as Marly silently eased open the door to the last room in the corridor. Buttery light spilled out and there was the soft rasp of a voice reading aloud. Marly gently pulled me forward, so I had a clear view through the crack in the door. She peered over my shoulder.

Jake's mom was sitting up in bed. She was surrounded by stuffed animals of all shapes and sizes. The yellow lamplight caught the planes of her face; she had a net of lines around her sea-glass-colored eyes and bracketing her mouth, and her long gray-streaked hair was braided. Her eyes shone as she smiled and listened to her visitor read to her.

My gaze settled on the man beside her bed, and I felt a shock zip through me.

Freddie de Marche.

He was older and his hair was thinner and his jaw softer, but it was clearly the man from the photographs. An old Montgomery Clift. His chair was pulled up close beside the bed, and he was reading softly. To his daughter.

"It's always the same books," Marly whispered behind me. "He must be bored to death, but he reads them just the same, because she loves them."

I couldn't believe it. Freddie de Marche had stepped out of the past and into my life. He wasn't dead. Marly wasn't a widow. All my assumptions of heartbreak and grief were wrong. Again.

I listened to the peaceful rasp of his voice and felt another shock. He was reading one of the *Anne of Green Gables* books.

"'Gilbert, darling, don't let's ever be afraid of things,'" he read. "'Let's be daring and adventurous and expectant. Let's dance to meet life and all it can bring to us, even if it brings scads of trouble and typhoid and twins!'"

It was from *Anne of Windy Poplars.* I'd read it so many times I almost knew it by heart. As I listened, I saw Freddie de Marche reach out a hand and pull a tissue from a box on the nightstand. Without breaking stride in his reading, he wiped his daughter's damp lips. She let him, as though she were a small girl.

"Nobody told me he was still alive." I was stunned.

"Nobody told you he was dead either," Marly whispered back. "You just assumed the worst."

Hearing the whispers, Freddie looked over to the doorway. He peered over his reading glasses, saw us there, and grinned. He had thick expressive eyebrows, just like his grandson. "Hey, Amber, sweetheart, it looks like Mom's here, and she's brought visitors." He pulled his glasses off and gestured to us.

Jake's mom looked over at us. She frowned, clearly not pleased that her book had been interrupted.

"Hi, Mom," I heard Jake say softly, as he ushered me into the room. He bent to kiss his mom, even though she seemed confused by his presence.

"But I want the book," she said.

"Keep reading," Marly told Freddie airily. "We were just in the neighborhood. We didn't mean to upset story time." She also dropped a kiss on Amber's cheek. "I just thought you might want to meet Jake's Zoe."

I flushed. Jake's mom gave me a confused looking-over.

"Zoe from Tinker Street?" Freddie rose from his chair, delighted. He oozed charm, just as I imagined he would from reading his letters. "The girl who found my postcards?" He winked at me. "And here I thought Marly had thrown them away."

"I *told* you I hadn't." She poked him. "They were just lost in the house."

"I want the book," Amber said, sounding distressed.

"You'd best get reading." Marly pushed Freddie back down into the chair. "Don't upset her. You can charm Zoe later. Jake will be bringing her to dinner later this week."

"I will?" Jake sounded disgruntled.

"You will if you know what's good for you."

I watched, struck, as Freddie kissed his wife goodbye. It was like seeing a character step out from a book, long after you thought the book had ended.

"Don't be too late," Marly murmured to him as she pulled away.

"I'll stay until she doesn't need me anymore." And then he put his reading glasses back on, picked up the book, and started reading aloud again. Amber settled, her gaze riveted on her father's face, hanging on his every word.

"He was always better with her than I was," Marly admitted as she closed the door behind us on the way out.

"You're too similar is all." Jake sighed. He seemed drained by the brief interaction with his mom.

Marly shot him a look. "I don't collect junk."

"Similar but not exactly the same," he amended. "You've both got sharp tongues."

Marly took pity on him and looped her arm through his. "It gets easier when you stop looking for your mom in her." She sighed. "And just accept her for who she is." She threw me a glance too. "Same goes for you. There's no point trying to turn the tides."

"Says the woman who's spent her whole life turning tides," Jake said dryly.

"He gets his sharp tongue from me," Marly told me.

We drove back to Marly and Freddie's house, and I slid out from Jake's car and into mine.

"I'll follow you home," he promised.

Marly bent over my open car door. "You come by any time," she told me. "And Zoe?"

"Yes?"

"Not all stories are tragedies, honey, even if they inevitably end." She patted me on the cheek with her cold glove. "Enjoy what you have, hmmm?" She glanced over at her grandson and then winked at me. She laughed when I blushed. "And you remember: That house of mine was happier than it was sad, and full of more love than it could hold. You keep it full, okay?" She leaned in closer. "You are very loved," she told me firmly. "Don't ever doubt it."

"How do you know?" I said in a small voice.

"I just do." She stared into me. "Sometimes people can't tell you, or show you, for reasons entirely out of their control. It took me a long time to learn that." She kissed me on the cheek. "Take care of my place, won't you? And take care of you. I'll see you for dinner next week."

She closed the door and waved me off. As I drove away, I saw her in the rearview mirror, standing on her porch, making sure we went safely into the snowy night.

THIRTY

Suni was waiting up for me when I got in. She was sitting on the sofa in the parlor, staring at the open fire, her lap full of sleeping kittens. She looked up when I came in, and I saw her face was pinched and drawn in the dancing lights of the Christmas tree.

"Everything okay?" she asked carefully.

And for the millionth time that night I burst into tears. I was amazed I had any tears left in me.

"Oh dear." She sent the sleepy kittens tumbling sideways onto the sofa as she rose to comfort me. "Jake told us his cousin turned Tina in." She took me in her arms. "Where is he? I thought he was bringing you home?"

"He followed me home but just went in to check on Hazel," I managed to sniff. "He was worried she'd have ripped the place apart while he was gone. I told him not to rush. I need some processing time."

Suni pulled away. "Okay. I'll head up—"

"No," I cut her off and pulled her back. "I didn't mean you." I swallowed. "In fact, I wanted to see you." I'd wanted to see her all night, I realized. It had been a shadowy need in the back of my mind ever since I'd left the Nar-Anon family meeting. It had grown when Tina had opened the door, reeking of meth, and then again when I'd seen Marly's photo album.

"Suni," I blurted. I had no grace. I wasn't articulate. I just had a burning need to say what I had to say. "All day I've wanted my mom. I've been so hurt and so scared and so lost. And I just wanted my mom so badly." The tears were streaming again. I was made of them.

"Oh, honey, I know," she said sympathetically. "You've always wanted her. I'm so sorry she hasn't been able to be the mom you needed."

She didn't understand me. I shook my head. "No. I mean, I wanted *you.*"

Her dark eyes widened.

"Suni, *you're* my mom. And when life gets too real, and I'm hurting bad, and scared, and I can't manage, *you're* the one I want." I pressed my lips together, trying not to break into ugly sobs before I could get the words out. "Tonight, I was looking at Jake's family photo album," I said, my throat tight, "and wishing so hard I'd had a childhood like his mom's. And then just now I came home and as soon as I saw the bare stalks of the lilacs I exhaled. Like all the tension went out of me. And I realized that coming home to lilacs feels like coming *home*. Because of *you.*" I drew an aching, shuddering breath. "Ever since that caseworker drove me up your drive, past all those flowering lilacs, they've meant home to me."

Now Suni was crying too.

"And I realized I *did* have a home and I *did* have love. It wasn't with the person I thought I wanted, or in the way that I wanted, but I had it. You were always there for me. You never forced love on me, never demanded it of me, you just gave me a place where I was safe when I needed it. And I needed it so badly."

"What's going on here?" Wayne appeared in the doorway in his sweatpants and Pirates T-shirt. He was alarmed by our ugly crying and the way we were clutching at each other. "What's happened?"

Suni shook her head. She was crying too hard to speak.

Now Wayne looked really worried.

"It's okay," I promised him, aware my swallowed sobs weren't reassuring. "I was just telling Suni how much you guys mean to me." I hugged him. Fiercely. "I mean, I was telling her that I love you, both of you."

"Well, we know that." He gave me a bewildered pat on the back. "We love you too."

Suni joined us, pressing a wet kiss to my cheek. "I love you as much as I love my own kids," she whispered, stroking my face. "I hope you know that."

"I do." I was still blubbering. "And I should have introduced you to Flo as her grandparents. You should be Gran and Pop or Granny and Granddad or whatever."

"We don't need names to be her grandparents," Wayne said, still sounding a touch baffled. "She's always been ours."

"Oh my God, who's dead?" Alison appeared at the bottom of the stairs, looking panicked.

"No one's dead, baby," Suni assured her. "We're just having an 'I love you' moment."

Alison looked like she didn't believe us.

"Come join us," I invited from inside Suni and Wayne's hugs. "I love you too."

"What's all the noise?" Flo leaned over the banister of the landing. "And why are you all hugging like someone died?"

"That's what I said," Alison called up to her. "It's weird to say 'I love you' like this, right? Unless someone died."

"You can pretend someone died if it makes it easier," Wayne rumbled. I pressed my wet face into his T-shirt to smother my giggle.

"How come you're crying?" Flo asked suspiciously as she trotted downstairs.

"Sometimes people cry when they're happy," I told her, hooking her into the group hug.

"Not me," she said firmly. She looked up at me, frowning. "You were gone a long time."

"Sorry. I had to say goodbye to my mom."

"She's gone?" Flo brightened. Tina really had made her uneasy.

"She's gone." I sighed, my breath hitching. I felt Suni's hand rubbing comforting circles on my back.

"Hey!" Lance's disgruntled voice sounded from the stairs. "How come I wasn't invited to this love-in?"

"You're always invited," Suni assured him, holding out her arm to beckon him. "Tash is welcome too if she's awake."

"We should get the kittens, like, if this is a whole family thing," Flo said.

"Or we could go make some hot chocolate and break out those cookies I bought," Wayne suggested.

"You guys go ahead," Suni told him. "I'm going to hug Zoe a little longer."

"You two are weird," Flo told us, wriggling out of my grasp and heading for the promise of cookies.

When Jake turned up, Suni and I were curled up on the sofa under a blanket and she was stroking my hair. Flo let him in.

"Maybe she'll tell you she loves you too," I heard her whisper as she pushed him toward the parlor.

He was blushing when he appeared in the doorway. "Hi," he said awkwardly. "I know it's late, but I saw the lights on and just wanted to come say goodnight."

"You know, Mom," Flo said, peering around him, "you should go stay at Jake's tonight and that way I can sleep in your bed instead of on the folding cot."

"Hey," Alison protested, on her way upstairs from the kitchen, "who says *you* get the big bed and not me?"

"It's my house," Flo told her blithely.

"I think Zoe might want to be in her own home tonight," Jake said quietly, meeting my eye. "She's had quite a day."

"Why don't I put Flo to bed and leave you two to talk," Suni said, pressing a kiss on my forehead as she rose from the couch. She pointed at her empty spot. "There you go, Jake, I kept it warm for you."

As soon as he lowered himself onto the sofa I leaned into him and his arms wrapped around me. Suni pulled the blanket up around us.

"Kiss your mom goodnight, Flo-bug."

Flo rolled her eyes. "She's had enough of that from you." But she kissed me, a big smacking kiss on the top of my head. "Night, Mom. Love you."

"Love you more," I promised her. I smiled as I listened to her and Suni chattering as they climbed the stairs.

I felt Jake's big hand stroking my hair. The room was quiet except for the pop of the log in the fire and the quiet murmur of Wayne and Lance talking in the kitchen.

"Marly was right," I said softly. "I assumed the worst. I thought Freddie must be dead. He wasn't at the play, and you never really talked about him."

I felt Jake shift beneath me. I could hear his heartbeat under my ear, steady as a drum.

"I guess maybe I've been primed to always assume the worst. But he *is* alive. And they look happy."

He frowned faintly. "Yeah, they are. I mean, except for being sad about Mom. He stayed with her so she wouldn't be alone during the play."

"You seem happy too. Even though you're sad about your mom."

"Well, one doesn't cancel out the other. You can feel both at once."

I nodded. "I guess I never realized it before." I bit my lip. "I thought the story of this house must be a sad one. Because it was old and full of junk. But it hasn't been a sad one, has it?"

"It's had sad parts," he said with a shrug. "Like every place." He looked tired.

I kissed him softly. "Jake?"

"Yeah?" He sighed into my kiss.

"Thank you."

"What for?"

"This. My home. I'm so glad you let me in."

He laughed. "Me too. I almost didn't."

"I remember." I kissed him again. "I need to warn you," I whispered against his lips, "I'm not an easy person to love."

"You're not?" He seemed surprised.

I shook my head. "I'm the kid of an addict, who spent most of her life in and out of foster care. I have every abandonment issue you can think of. I tend to push people away. . . ."

"I'm not feeling very pushed." He smiled, looking down at our bodies entwined.

"You might eventually."

He stroked my face. "You push all you need to, Zoe. I'm not going anywhere."

"You promise?"

"I promise."

"That's not an 'I love you'!" Flo scolded from the darkness of the stairs.

"We'll get there in our own time," I called out. "Go to bed."

THIRTY-ONE

Tina was charged with possession and parole violation and disappeared again into the correctional system. I knew eventually I'd get a letter from her, postmarked from one facility or another. She would go on, as she had always gone on, because that's what she did. Meanwhile, I'd keep attending Nar-Anon family meetings and trying to salve the hole in my heart that she'd left behind. Although at least I no longer felt that the hole would keep me from living my life. I could be sad about Tina but happy about everything else.

The rest of the winter was long and icy. The Overbecks all went home after New Year's, and Flo and I settled into the grind of January through March. But we learned that the upside of a long hard Maine winter is that when it melts and spring comes, you sure appreciate it. The snow turned muddy and gray and melted away and the birds came back to the yard. Green shoots spiked from the trees and the earth. The forest exhaled delicious green fragrances, and we threw all the windows open and let the sea breeze blow the winter mustiness away.

On the nights Jake didn't sleep over, he wandered up in the morning to have coffee on our porch with us, Hazel cheerfully lolling at his feet.

"I think we should have a housewarming party now that the house is free of culch," Flo said one April morning, as the skies turned blue and the daffodils bloomed. She was sprawled on the porch swing, admiring the view. "We can have it in the garden. I'll make the guest list. Basically, that's everyone in town, and Jake's family and our family. Suni, Wayne, Ali . . ." She ticked them off on her fingers.

Our family. The words filled me with a glow.

"I finished the sign," Jake told me, scratching behind Hazel's ears until she whined with pleasure.

I had decided that our house needed a name. Elton's house had a name. It was called "Sylvie by Sea," the name painted on a little sign to the left of the door. Given our house was its twin, it seemed wrong for it not to have one too.

Jake had made a little sign identical to Elton's and, after breakfast, the three of us circled the front door for the ceremonial hanging. Hazel tripped over her own feet in her haste to be part of the pack. The cats sat in the parlor window, watching us curiously.

"A bit to the left," I told Jake as he tried to position our sign. Jake moved the little wooden sign to the left.

"Up a bit," Flo ordered. He moved it up.

"There," he said.

"Yes," we agreed.

I put my arm around Flo as we watched him hammer it into place. We'd tossed around many names for the house. *Marly's Place* was winning for a while, although Flo pushed hard for *The Mac 'n' Cheese Shack.* But in the end, there was only one name that worked for me.

Jake hammered the nails in and stepped back. Carved into the wood in looping letters was our house's new name.

Forever Amber.

He nodded. "Good name," he said.

"You have to say that," Flo complained, "because she's your mom."

"No, I don't."

"Yes, you do. She's your *mom*."

They kept bickering as they went back into the house, the eggshell-blue door closing behind them. I sat on the top step of the porch and looked down the street toward the bay. The spring sky was sparkling blue, as though it had been freshly painted. Rays of light fell in golden shafts through the clouds, which cast shadows on the rippling sea, the waves distant brushstrokes of white foam. The light wind made the firs in the woods whisper and carried the smell of rising sap and unfurling spring. Along the path to the front porch daffodils nodded their bonneted heads in the teasing breeze. Soon the garden would be blooming, and summer would come with its summer people, their towels hung to dry like bunting on the front fences. I couldn't wait for the lilacs to froth and flower, their perfume welcoming me home.

Today was just an ordinary day. The kind that comes every day, one ordinary day in a long chain of ordinary days. But, I thought as I let the day bloom around me, ordinary days can change your life.

A pale silvery moon hung almost transparent in the blue morning sky, and I thought about how my mother had gifted it to me, long ago, when I was small and alone. And how I still had the moon, all these years later, as I sat on the stoop of my own house, staring at this beautiful world, even if I didn't have my mother, and hadn't had her for a long time.

I exhaled. It was good to be home.

ACKNOWLEDGMENTS

This book is dedicated to my beautiful, kind, strong, funny kids. Thank you for being your glorious selves. Never stop. I hope you keep groaning at my jokes and suffering through family dinners for decades to come, because you are my greatest joys.

The Treasure House is in many ways inspired by my experiences as a single mother. Parenting is hard, single parenting infinitely so. I was so lucky to have support in my journey. Thank you to my own parents, Jonny, Lynn, and Chelsea, and assorted extended family for keeping me afloat in turbulent years. Building a life and a home is hard, rewarding work, and this novel is a love letter to my experience.

Thank you to my wonderful agent Sarah Younger, who first sent me off looking at treasure house reels on TikTok, and who has always been inspiring and warm and an all-round superstar. Thank you to Anthea Bariamis and Lizzie Levot at Atria/Simon & Schuster Australia, Alicia Clancy at Ballantine/Bantam/Dell US, and Melanie Hayes at Simon & Schuster UK for the dream team edits. I can't tell you what a privilege it is to have such attentive, enthusiastic collaborators on edits. The four of you have made this an infinitely better book with your care and close reading. Special shout-out to Anthea for developing the concept and working with me from the beginning. Love you to bits!

I want to thank all the designers and the cover artist and copy editors and everyone who worked on the book. It takes a significant team to publish a book and I am grateful to each and every one of you. Thanks also to Amy Fletcher, Elissa Baillie, Gareth Woods-Jack, Ben Ball, and Dan Ruffino.

Thanks also to the writers in my life who talk books and craft and commiserate during the long slog. Special mentions to Lynn, my BFF; the Amy & Book Club crew (Abby, Justina, Payton, Harry, and Millie); Anne and Trish and Victoria and Bron and Pam; Alex and Rachel; and Jonny, always, who gets to hear me complain and brainstorm and complain some more.

I'd also like to thank Flinders University, my colleagues and my postgraduate students, who remind me of the joy of writing and research, and my undergraduate students. It's a great gift to get to live and breathe writing and I never take it for granted.

Last, but not least, thanks to all the readers. Story is how we understand being human and is more important now than ever. Thank you for reading and valuing storytelling.

This book was written in Tarntanya/Adelaide on Kaurna Country in South Australia. I'd like to pay my respects to the Kaurna people, elders past and present, and to recognize the Kaurna people's connection to land, sea, and sky, and to acknowledge the living culture of the Kaurna people today. This land always was and always will be Aboriginal land. I would also like to acknowledge the Penobscot Nation and the Wabanaki Confederacy and First Nations people of Maine, where *The Treasure House* is set. There are unbroken threads of language, culture, and connection to country, and I pay my respects to the people who connect those threads, past and present.

THE TREASURE HOUSE

A NOVEL

AMY MATTHEWS

Random House Book Club

Because Stories Are Better Shared™

A BOOK CLUB GUIDE

BOOK CLUB QUESTIONS

1. In *The Treasure House*, Zoe chooses a treasure house by the sea in Maine. If you could choose a treasure house, where would it be?

2. *The Treasure House* is a novel that explores the impacts of addiction. Do you think Zoe did the right thing when she turned her mother in? Why or why not?

3. Zoe assumes the treasure house has a tragic history but begins to see that many of her assumptions about life are negative. Are there any assumptions you make about people and places in your life? Is there another way of seeing them?

4. *Anne of Green Gables* is an important book for Zoe and for Jake's mother. Are there books that were important to you when you were young? What were they and why?

5. Flo tells Zoe that she doesn't need to protect Flo from her feelings. Are there moments in your life when you've hidden your feelings in order to "protect" others?

6. Zoe realizes that even though she's always felt alone, she actually had a family—with Suni and Wayne. Why do you think it took her so long to realize she belonged?

7. If you had to choose, would you rather spend a summer at Saint-Cyr with Freddie de Marche or a cozy winter in Oxeye with Jake Abernathy?

8. What role do you think Marly and Freddie's story played in changing Zoe's perspective on her own life?

© S. DUFF

AMY MATTHEWS is an award-winning author of books about complicated people and love. She is an associate professor of creative writing at Flinders University, a podcaster, and a book addict. Amy lives in Adelaide, South Australia, with her favorite people, both real and imagined. Her first novel, *Someone Else's Bucket List,* was a bestseller.

amymatthewsauthor.com
Instagram: @amymatthewsauthor

ABOUT THE TYPE

This book was set in Caslon, a typeface first designed in 1722 by William Caslon (1692–1766). Its widespread use by most English printers in the early eighteenth century soon supplanted the Dutch typefaces that had formerly prevailed. The roman is considered a "workhorse" typeface due to its pleasant, open appearance, while the italic is exceedingly decorative.